D0677140

RUTHERFORD
AT MANCHESTER

Lord Rutherford of Nelson
From the portrait by Sir Oswald Birley, by permission of the Royal Society

RUTHERFORD AT MANCHESTER

EDITED BY

J. B. BIRKS

W. A. BENJAMIN INC.
New York 1963

Originally published by
HEYWOOD & COMPANY LTD.
London 1962

Printed in Great Britain

CONTENTS

(contents *cont.*)

LIST OF PLATES

PREFACE

ERNEST RUTHERFORD, later Baron Rutherford of Nelson, the acknowledged founder of nuclear science, was Langworthy Professor of Physics at the Victoria University of Manchester from 1907 to 1919. The Rutherford Jubilee International Conference was held there in September 1961 to commemorate the scientific discoveries of Rutherford at Manchester and to mark the fiftieth anniversary of the Rutherford scattering law and the discovery of the atomic nucleus.

Four of Rutherford's former colleagues, Sir Ernest Marsden, Sir Charles Darwin, E. N. da C. Andrade, and Niels Bohr, spoke at the commemorative session of the Conference. In publishing their speeches in the present volume, it has been deemed appropriate to include other relevant material of biographical and historical interest.

The correspondence between Sir Arthur Schuster and Rutherford, which led to the latter's acceptance of the invitation to succeed Schuster in the Langworthy Chair, is published here for the first time. The Rutherford Memorial Lectures by H. R. Robinson, A. S. Russell and P. M. S. Blackett each pay their own personal tributes to the work of Rutherford at Manchester. That by Niels Bohr describes his personal friendship and association with Rutherford over the years. Nine of the important scientific papers published from 1909 to 1919 by Rutherford and his colleagues, Bohr, Geiger, Marsden, Moseley and Royds, are reprinted. Bibliographies are included of Rutherford's publications and of the other papers published from the Manchester Physical Laboratories from 1907 to 1919. The volume concludes with a song about one of Rutherford's 'jolly little beggars', an alpha ray.

The Rutherford Jubilee International Conference was sponsored by the International Union of Pure and Applied Physics, the Royal Society, the Institute of Physics and the Physical Society, and the Victoria University of Manchester. Acknowledgements are gratefully made to the following:

The Royal Society for permission to reproduce the portrait of Rutherford by Birley and a paper originally published in the *Proceedings of the Royal Society*.

The Institute of Physics and the Physical Society, and P. M. S. Blackett, N. Bohr, and A. S. Russell for permission to publish the Rutherford Memorial Lectures;

Sir Nevill Mott, editor of *The Philosophical Magazine* for permission to reproduce papers originally published in that journal;

and

Mrs R. S. Hutton for permission to publish the Schuster–Rutherford correspondence.

PUBLISHER'S NOTE

In the reprints of original papers which appear between pages 168 and 315, the style, layout, and spelling of the originals has been followed as closely as possible. The only alterations, apart from slight changes of arrangement made necessary by the format and typography of the present volume, are corrections of minor misprints.

Speeches at the Commemorative Session

RUTHERFORD AT MANCHESTER

By SIR ERNEST MARSDEN

FIRST, let me welcome to this Session so many visitors and in particular the personal friends and relatives of the late Lord Rutherford. We are indeed honoured by the presence of some of his own grandchildren. We join with them in gratitude for the memory of all the good that Rutherford did during his lifetime and for his rich legacy of inspiration to us all.

At the other sessions of our conference the speakers, perforce, have needed to express themselves in a strange new language using words like pions, leptons, spinors, and isospace, internationally accepted among us as part of the increasing common content of all our scientific languages and saving undue verbiage in our discussions. We are in this historical session to go back to the time when the words electron, alpha-particle, proton, neutron, gamma-rays, isotopes, were equally new and bewildering. They are now, however, words familiar to secondary school pupils and are even mentioned in the press and over the radio.

There is, however, an appropriateness both for our conference as a whole and for our session this afternoon. The time is ripe internationally for personal, across the table or bench, discussions and exchange of newer information on the inner details of the structure of the nucleus of the atom. This nucleus with its huge internal forces is at present perhaps the most important unit in our scientific world, and its energy we have already been able to tap in some slight degree in our nuclear power reactors. It certainly shares with that other kind of nucleus—the nucleus of the living cell—the position of being one of the two most important problems whose solution or further major understanding could be of more importance to mankind even at present, than all those nerve-worrying world problems that occupy the attention of our professional diplomats and whose considerations fill our newspapers and radio and nauseate us. Yet for us, as Mme Curie wrote to Rutherford in 1933 'In these troubled times scientific work is a relief from outside cares.'

There is a second reason and appropriateness for this conference and for its being held in Manchester. It was at this University that the first experimental evidence was obtained for the nuclear constitution of atoms, and it is just fifty years since Rutherford first put forward the idea and deduced some of the consequences of a nuclear atom. Moreover, Bohr and Moseley who in vital directions amplified Rutherford's suggestions were closely associated with Manchester. Further appropriateness arises from the fact that it was also at Manchester, almost a century earlier, that Dalton first produced experimental evidence that atoms of matter actually existed. Moreover, it was this University that nurtured J. J. Thomson and Arthur Schuster, who of British scientists contributed most to the experimental work leading to the idea first put forward by J. J. Thomson that there was likewise a unit or atom of electricity—the electron—and that this was, somehow, a constituent part of the structure of all atoms, although only one eighteen-hundredth the mass of the lightest atom known—that of hydrogen.

Thus fifty years ago there had grown up a feeling or conviction that there was a discreteness or unit conception at the basis of nature, that matter and electricity were not continuously divisible. Through chemical and electrochemical experiments we could get down to atoms; by intense electrical forces we could get down to electrons. Planck in Germany also produced strong evidence that energy also was quantized and this involved subtle rethinking in our mental pictures of 'time'.

It was at this stage that Rutherford came on the scene—destined to become the international spearhead in the attack on these problems of atomic structure. He arrived in England from New Zealand in 1895 at the age of 24 as the result of the award of a scholarship provided by the invested profits of the great Exhibition of 1851. He elected to work under J. J. Thomson at Cambridge. He had brought with him a problem of research of his own on which he had made good progress in New Zealand, considering that he had been unaided and had had to construct each item of apparatus himself, including even his electric batteries, which were made at his father's country house in Taranaki. The research related to a detector for wireless waves, and soon he held the then world record of reception at 2 miles; the detector was the precursor of that later used by Marconi. In the meantime Röntgen's discovery of X-rays towards the end of 1895 had burst on an astonished world, scientific and otherwise. Schuster in Manchester and J. J. Thomson in Cambridge quickly got on to the track. It is recorded that the latter, before tempting Rutherford to turn to the new subject, consulted Lord Kelvin as to the future of Rutherford's work in wireless and whether it was worth pursuing. The reply of the great man was that it might justify a capital expenditure of a £100,000 Company on its promotion, but no more. However, this kind of development was not to Rutherford's taste, and he joined J. J. Thomson, to the latter's delight, in an investigation of the conditions governing the remarkable conducting power for electricity imparted to a gas through which the Röntgen X-rays were arranged to pass. The work was carried out intensely and the main features were published by them in 1896. Thenceforward Rutherford worked on his own, or as senior partner with others, and he made the whole subject metrical and so real that he could personally almost envisage the ions which took part in the processes. 'Jolly little beggars' he called them as he made them dance to the tune of his applied alternating electric forces.

Then came the discovery of Becquerel in France that the metal uranium gave out rays which, like X-rays, could affect a photographic plate. Rutherford, with the new techniques and understanding gained from his work with X-rays, soon discovered that uranium rays produced the same kind of ions in a gas as did X-rays. At this stage, 1899, Rutherford obtained a position at McGill University, Montreal, and the new radioactive substances and their radiations became his life's work.

He soon discovered that uranium gave out two kinds of radiation which he named alpha and beta. Debierne added the third, the gamma-rays. At McGill, Rutherford was at the height of his mental and physical powers, and he used them with a vigour and orderliness which produced amazing advances that within a year or two gave him a position as the hub of work in this wonderful new subject. Apart from his own prodigious output of work, his published papers and his personality attracted a team of workers whose previous training had been as physicists, chemists or electrical engineers. Rutherford fitted in well with the free colonial atmosphere of Canada. He had Professor Cox, who unselfishly relieved him of much of the routine administration and teaching, and he had the tobacco millionaire Macdonald who had endowed the Professorship and who provided him with money to purchase radium and also a liquid air plant which made many of his best subsequent experiments possible. I would not have you think that money came easily—the museum of his apparatus at McGill shows an amazing degree of ingenuity and cheapness, including the use of tobacco tins. Macdonald himself lived on £250 per annum, and he could not understand that a professor needed more than £500 per annum. At McGill, Rutherford discovered thorium emanation and its subsequent radioactive products, which he at first termed the active deposit. He proved that the alpha-particle was positively charged, by contrast with the beta-particle which was a negatively charged electron. He deduced that the alpha-particle was most probably an atom of helium, a sensational finding since it involved the transmutation of the radioactive atoms emitting it. Rutherford measured the spontaneous heating of radium and equated it to the energy of the radiations emitted and self-absorbed. He made deductions as to the source of the earth's heat and the age of uranium-bearing minerals and these created a stir among geologists. The crowning achievement was the unravelling of the successive radioactive changes in the radium, thorium and actinium families. In this work Soddy, the chemist, collaborated. Rutherford published the theory in the Bakerian Lecture of the Royal Society for 1903, a work which is a classic.

Rutherford's rate of work was prodigious—his enthusiasm infectious. Of the many stories of this period the one I like is that related by R. S. Willows who visited his laboratory. Rutherford had electroscopes set up in several rooms on several floors and had samples with different previous exposures to thorium and radium emanation, whose activity he was observing from time to time, so as to obtain curves from which he could make deductions as to the radioactive products concerned. He could not spare time for a sit-down talk with Willows who had to follow him round up and down stairs from electroscope to electroscope—discussing matters en route.

But Rutherford appears to have had another visitor about that time, 1906, Professor Arthur Schuster of Manchester. Schuster was reasonably wealthy and was considering retirement, so that he could devote more time to theoretical studies, to international science, and to the Royal Society. He was a man of great moral strength and of scientific and administrative ability and above all devotion to the highest ideals of science. He wrote to Rutherford offering to resign his chair at Manchester if Rutherford would take his place and at the same time offered to finance personally a readership in Mathematical Physics, subsequently held by Sir Charles Darwin and later by Niels Bohr. Professor Schuster's daughter, Mrs R. S. Hutton, showed me last week the correspondence which passed between them. We do not have Schuster's first letter, but we have Rutherford's reply* of 26 September 1906—of which the following is an abstract:

'I need hardly tell you how much I appreciate the suggestion coming in the way it has. I fully recognise the spirit of self abnegation displayed by you in your letter,' and Professor Schuster's further letter a week later ended 'I can only conclude that your answer has considerably relieved my mind. I am so strongly attached to the place I did not bear to leave my position except to someone who will keep up its reputation and increase it. There is no one to whom I would leave it with greater freedom from anxiety than yourself.'

Thus Rutherford came to Manchester in September 1907

* Reprinted elsewhere in this volume.

and stayed for twelve years for perhaps the greatest period, almost certainly the happiest, of a particularly busy and happy life.

Rutherford lost no time in settling in and was carrying out experiments within a few weeks of his arrival. He liked the Manchester atmosphere of work and directness of its people and his new colleagues liked him from the beginning. He soon showed the research students that he was interested in us as human beings, although I found later that in a letter at the time to his mother in far-away New Zealand he had written that, compared with Canada and New Zealand, the Manchester students tended to look up to a Professor as somewhat of a god.

Schuster had left the laboratory well equipped with optical apparatus, and Rutherford used this with Royds in his first work which was to show definitely that the alpha-particle was an atom of helium. A small glass tube was blown so thin that, although gas-tight, it allowed the alpha-particles emitted from contained radium emanation to penetrate its walls. It was surrounded by a second glass tube highly evacuated. In this tube it was easy to show by spectrographic methods that helium accumulated with the passage of time as it got filled by the alpha-particles entering it and as they occluded from the outer tube walls in which they were temporarily embedded due to penetration as a result of their high velocity of impact. Later Rutherford and Royds measured the wavelengths in the spectrum of the new gas, radium emanation, and also did an experiment in which he may have found a puckish delight. Ramsay had rather patronized Rutherford in regard to his ability to separate small quantities of gaseous emanation from radium in solution. (This arose because some radium had been loaned to them from Vienna for their joint use.) Such an attitude of condescension or patronage was an unforgivable sin. Ramsay and Cameron had published an account of some experiments from which they had deduced that neon was produced by the action of radium emanation on water and incidentally also that copper was transformed into lithium. From a reading of his paper (*Phil. Mag.* Nov. 1908) it is evident to the initiated that Rutherford enjoyed proving that Ramsay's

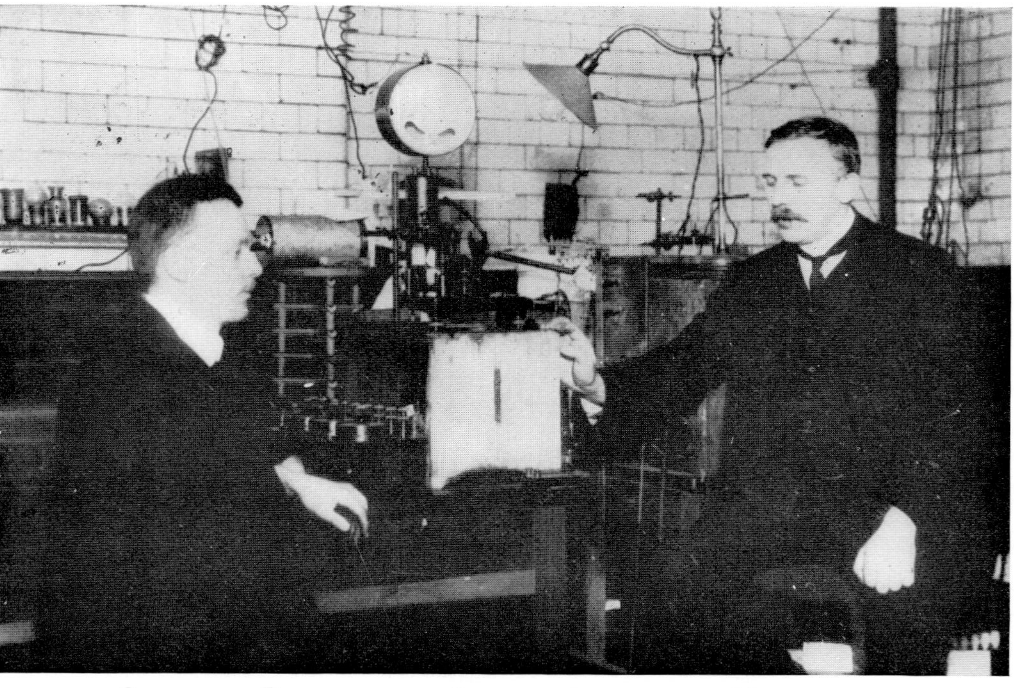

Geiger and Rutherford in Schuster Laboratory, Manchester

result arose from a small leak of air, with its accompanying neon, into the apparatus.

In the meantime Rutherford had planned a frontal attack on the atomic constants of mass and electricity, i.e. by counting alpha-particles one by one and also determining the electric charge they carried. From such measurements could be deduced a whole series of molecular data, including Avogadro's number of the molecules in a gram-molecule of any gas. He and Geiger constructed the first particle counter, later improved by Geiger and known as a Geiger counter. A thin wire or needle point charged to high voltage was inserted axially in a metal tube into which alpha-particles were allowed to enter (see Figure 1 from the original paper *P.R.S.* **81,** 1908, page 141). As each particle entered, the ionization produced was increased greatly by collision with air molecules at those high voltages and sufficed to cause a current to cross the gap and give an observable pulse on a connected electrometer. It was a beautifully designed and executed experiment and, considering the inexpensive standardizing gear available, it is remarkable that they obtained a value of '*e*', for example, within 2½ per cent of that obtained from the methods available over fifty years later. Their value was, however, 40 per cent higher than the value previously accepted. The consequences of this measurement were many in all branches of physics, but there were three rather special ones to us. Firstly, it made the classical physicists in England more sympathetic to Planck's quantum ideas since he had also deduced theoretically a value of '*e*' some 40 per cent greater than the old assumed value. Secondly parallel measurements indicated that the ordinary powdered zinc sulphide screen on glass was an efficient counter of alpha-particles, so that we could use such simple methods in future, where a few per cent accuracy was sufficient. Regener had already used thin continuous plates of diamond in this way, but all diamond material did not appear to discriminate sufficiently against scintillations produced also by beta-particles. The third consequence was one in which I became more personally concerned.

Although I had not yet graduated, such was the scheme of

training introduced by Schuster, that I was allowed to help Geiger in these experiments and in others made on scattering of alpha-particles when passing through thin foils of metal such as aluminium, silver, gold, platinum, etc. A narrow pencil of alpha-particles under such conditions became dispersed through one or two degrees and the amount of dispersion, as indicated by the most probable angle of scattering, varied as the square root of the thickness or probable number of atoms encountered and also roughly as the square root of the atomic weight of the metal used. One day Rutherford came into the room where we were counting the alpha-particles at the end of the $4\frac{1}{2}$ metre firing tube. We had been having trouble to obtain a constant figure and this was obviated by putting in the firing tube, at right angles to the axis, a series of washer-like openings, to stop particles scattered from the sides of the wall, by what we thought might be molecular-size protuberances. It almost appeared, however, as though they were reflected from the walls. We know now that such numbers would be small. Nevertheless, Rutherford had been thinking over the matter and he turned to me and said 'See if you can get some effect of alpha-particles directly reflected from a metal surface.' I do not think he expected any such result, but it was one of those 'hunches' that perhaps some effect might be observed, and that in any case that neighbouring territory of this Tom Tiddler's ground might be explored by reconnaissance. Rutherford was ever ready to meet the unexpected and exploit it, where favourable, but he also knew when to stop on such excursions. Naturally, I knew enough to appreciate that, even though a negative effect might be expected, yet if I missed any positive result it would be an unforgivable sin. Accordingly, I made quite sure of preparing as strong an α-source of radium emanation as I possibly could in a conical tube closed by an alpha-particle-transparent mica window—a technique which had been developed by Geiger. To my surprise, I was able to observe the effect looked for and I collected reflectors of metals from aluminium to platinum and made comparative measurements. I remember well reporting the result to Rutherford a week after, when I met him on the steps leading to his private room, and the joy with which I told him that the effect seemed to vary approximately as the 3/2 power of the atomic weight and not as the square root, which was the result obtained by Geiger in the work on compound scattering. Unfortunately I had to report an exception—silver. I had borrowed a coin of allegedly pure silver from a Russian scientist (Antonoff) working on electrochemical effects, and who said that Russian silver coinage was purer than ours, and at the time did not realize that he had by his own experiments contaminated the surface with polonium! A few weeks later Rutherford instructed that I should round off the experiment with Geiger in a form suitable for publication.

Rutherford thought over these remarkable results for many weeks. Such ponderings, related speculations and calculations were generally done in the quiet of his study at home, but out of it emerged his inspiration of the nuclear or planetary atom with its features of resemblance to a solar system in miniature, a brave conception in view of its reversal of the ideas current at the time, based on those of J. J. Thomson (1910) and Kelvin (1902) and in which the positive electricity of atoms was considered as dispersed in a relatively large sphere instead of being concentrated in a small nucleus. The solution was a direct answer to the problem he set himself to explain, i.e. the origin of the huge forces necessary to deflect the fast-moving alpha-particles, at the same time explaining why an alpha-particle could sometimes go straight through an atom or be scattered in a compound way by a number of encounters with electrons in the various atoms traversed.

Rutherford deduced the relation of the probability of this 'single' scattering through different angles and from atoms of different nuclear charge, and also the relation between the velocity of the incident alpha-particles and the amount of scattering. In addition he deduced from our results that the positive charge on the nucleus had a numerical value approximating to half the atomic weight.

The checking of these deductions was a large task. Geiger did preliminary tests which proved promising and I, who had in the meantime taken up a position in London, was invited back on a fellowship to join with Geiger in the larger task. Our test was stringent. For example in the results as regards angle, the agreement on all points for atoms of atomic weight greater than aluminium was sufficient to indicate the correctness of Rutherford's theory. However, although our results were relative we could not readily obtain an absolute result accurate enough for determination of the nuclear charge to less than 3 per cent. There were too many factors involved and the velocity was not known sufficiently accurately. Fortunately, within two years, as will be explained by Sir Charles Darwin, Moseley's experiments gave a more precise significance in the terms of the order of elements in the periodic table, to the effective number of positive charges in the nucleus of successive atoms, while Niels Bohr with a brilliant conception and use of considerations of quanta, provided an answer to the difficulty of explaining the production of line spectra from the atom model. In fact Bohr was able to deduce the wavelengths with astonishing accuracy and make further predictions which were verified by E. J. Evans in the Manchester laboratory.

The nuclear atom was thus an outstanding example of Rutherford's boldness in conception and simple directness of attack on the problem of explaining a definite but remarkable experimental result. It is true that Nagaoka had speculated on some such form of atom in 1904, a Saturnean atom with rings of rotating electrons, but there was little or no experimental support and the fact was only brought to Rutherford's notice by the elder Bragg in subsequent correspondence.

The acceptance of the nuclear atom meant that there were only ninety-two kinds of chemical elements in Nature between the lightest, hydrogen, and the then heaviest known, uranium, while there were obviously several kinds of radioactive atoms to fill any one particular place in the periodic or atomic-number table; for instance, the three radioactive emanations fell naturally and chemically into the same place, yet from a radioactive point of view they were different in half-life and energy of ejected particles. As long ago as 1903 Rutherford had ended his Bakerian lecture: 'The close similarity of the changes in radium, thorium and actinium, is very remarkable and indicates some peculiarity of constitution which still needs to be elucidated.' Such facts and the changed valency of 2 for instance, when an alpha-particle is ejected, were naturally common discussion in the Manchester laboratory. A. S. Russell, Fajans, Hevesy, and Bohr had all put forward ideas on the subject, but it was Soddy who was brave enough to be the eventual spokesman when he announced and invented the term isotopes, though no doubt he learned much through Russell, who had once been his pupil.

I now wish to lead up to the third great achievement of Rutherford at Manchester, apart from those important ones of his assistants and colleagues. I refer to the first observed case of deliberate artificial transmutation. Again I was lucky to have a small hand in it, but again the interpreter was Rutherford himself. The experiments of Geiger and myself related to the simple conditions of atomic nuclei massive enough that we could neglect conditions of recoil in close encounters with the much lighter alpha-particle. Darwin proceeded to calculate what would happen when an alpha-particle encounters lighter nuclei of atoms, for instance hydrogen, whose nucleus has only one quarter the mass of the alpha-particle. Elementary considerations of a head-on collision between an alpha-particle and the nucleus of a hydrogen atom showed that the latter would take up a velocity 1·6 times that of the incident alpha-particle and, presuming Bragg's law of absorption could be applied, it should have a range of four times that of the incident alpha-particle. Darwin worked out the case of oblique incidence also.

I determined to investigate this experimentally and results proved, in general, to be largely as anticipated, i.e. the 'H' particles resulting from collision had a range of nearly 100 cm. in hydrogen and the absorption in metal foils proved to be approximately as Bragg's Law. However, under certain conditions of absorption in air and at oblique emergence in particular and compared with Darwin's calculations, a serious anomaly showed itself. I spent much time and trouble in efforts to exclude any possibility of hydrogen contamination of the source, but without result. The 'H' particles gave a fairly distinctive point scintillation and one could, in air, observe them at well over 10 cm from the source which is a much greater distance than the range of alpha-particles from radium products. However, war broke out and the experiments were hurriedly written up for publication in a paper which ended 'There seems a strong suspicion that the H particles are emitted from the radioactive atoms themselves, though not with uniform velocity.'

Rutherford was excited at the possibility of his beloved radioactive atoms giving off a new kind of particle and on his return from Australia, where he had attended a British Association meeting, he wrote to me in New Zealand asking me if I 'minded' if he went on with the experiment as I had not the facilities. At the same time, without my prompting, he asked the Royal Society to provide me with some radium. However, I went to France in the Army to join all my other colleagues from the laboratory and during the next four years, with the assistance of the laboratory steward William Kay only, and in such intervals as he could spare from his war activities with R. W. Boyle and A. B. Wood, Rutherford repeated and extended my observations.

Although he agreed with the possibility that a few 'H' particles (which he later named protons at the suggestion of Darwin and F. Fowler, because he thought the name would remind people of Prout) did arise from the radioactive source, he found that the majority of the particles observed in some of my experiments arose in a very different and surprising manner, i.e. from actual disintegration of nitrogen in the air following the effects of intimate collisions of the alpha-particles with nitrogen nuclei, and with the production, as Blackett confirmed later in Cambridge, of a fast proton and probably the nucleus of an atom of an oxygen isotope. This was the first observed case of artificial transmutation of atoms. (In 1932, thirteen years later, Cockcroft and Walton made the next step by inducing transmutations using particles accelerated under electrical control.)

This was Rutherford's crowning achievement in Manchester. A little later, after much inner mental conflict in making the decision, he moved on to the chair of his old student laboratory, the Cavendish at Cambridge. There, with Chadwick and others, so much was done on the collisions of alpha-particles with light nuclei and information gradually built up on the peculiarities of force relationships in the neighbourhood of such nuclei and the consequent disintegrations produced. But that belongs to another chapter. I have concentrated on the work at Manchester relating more directly to the nucleus.

Those of us who were fortunate to work with Rutherford at either McGill, Manchester or Cambridge have had our standards of judgement, our mental measuring rod, set high for the rest of our lives. On important occasions of decision or action we search our memories and say to ourselves, 'What would Rutherford do?'

At this time and occasion, after fifty years, we can assess more in perspective the value of his work and influence, his scientific ideals, his standards of fairness to fellow workers. The verdict is clear and definite, and the words of the tribute of Sir James Jeans after Rutherford's death have additional significance as we have moved more and more into an age or period when team work in research is increasingly necessary and leadership more significant:

> 'Those of us who were honoured by his friendship know that his greatness as a scientist was matched by his greatness as a man. We remember, and always shall remember, with affection his big, energetic, exuberant personality, the simplicity, sincerity, and transparent honesty of his character, and, perhaps most of all, his genius for friendship and good comradeship.
>
> 'In his flair for the right line of approach to a problem, as well as in the simple directness of his methods of attack, he often reminds us of Faraday, but he had two great advantages which Faraday did not possess—first, exuberant bodily health and energy, and second, the opportunity and capacity to direct a band of enthusiastic co-workers. Great though Faraday's output of work was, it seems to me that to match Rutherford's work in quantity, as well as in quality,

> we must go back to Newton. In some respects he was more fortunate than Newton. Rutherford was ever the Happy warrior—happy in his work, happy in its outcome, and happy in its human contact.'

I would add to Jeans's description one, to me, important aspect. Rutherford was a shrewd judge of character and ability. He knew our shortcomings and weaknesses and yet although he corrected us and 'gingered' us up, as he called it, he never showed malice and other than kindness; he gently 'looked down' our faults. Therein we knew we were not despised. Moreover, as I know from personal experience on several occasions both to myself and others, he never neglected to act on the impulse to do little acts of kindness—which most others leave undone or despise. He had a kind and generous outlook on life.

During my experiences first as a Professor, then as head of a State Science organization and during the last four years back again at the laboratory bench, I have continuously had before me the question of efficiency in research measured not only in terms of money but in terms of the lives and potentialities of our young honours graduates. They are a country's greatest asset. When we read of Rutherford operating the Manchester laboratories on £450 per annum for apparatus and equipment and compare the advances made, we are made 'furiously to think'. Moreover, his inspiration was such that almost every one of his honours students was kept research-minded and contributed constructively to his country in later life.

We need to ask: what kind of training will produce more leaders even approaching his stature? What kind of organization will enable such leaders to work best, and cause others to work happily and effectively with them? Rutherford's success, apart from the application of his high degree of natural intelligence, lay in his good constitution, in his personal human characteristics of natural exuberant energy and enthusiasm, in his capacity to concentrate and to see an objective and proceed to it in the most direct way with the materials and equipment at hand and, above all, in the selflessness and force of character of his relations with colleagues and helpers. These qualities were all inculcated in his early home and environment, and these were the factors in his ability to gather round him willing collaborators working in harmony and with loyalty and happy affection, each zealous in the common cause of discovery.

I was honoured in meeting and knowing his father and mother who combined the best qualities of the early Victorian Scotsman and Englishwoman respectively. I now fully realize that Rutherford was right and not sentimental in his obvious devotion to his parents and his often-expressed appreciation of their influence, as exemplified by his cable to his mother on his elevation to the peerage 'Now Lord Rutherford, honour more yours than mine.' This was not sentimentality, it was heartfelt appreciation. I have never known of parents of higher character than were his parents, of more hardworking and honest qualities, of happier disposition, with less idiosyncracies. Thus, while Rutherford inherited a rich physical and mental endowment and was reared in a virgin country environment, which gave him a reserve of health and vigour for life, he was even more fortunate in the qualities and habits of work acquired from the example of his parents. He was surrounded by an atmosphere of no artificiality. He had his share of domestic chores, but he roamed the countryside in his play and was subtly guided in his education by a mother who shared with the early settlers of Nelson a realistic appreciation of what true education meant. It was his mother who taught her children by her home standards of language, reading, and discussion. It was she who sacrificed and arranged for extra tuition to supplement that of the isolated one-teacher country school. It was probably his father who gave him, when he was only eleven, to whet his appetite for knowledge, the book *Outlines of Physics* by Schuster's predecessor at Manchester, Professor Balfour Stewart, a book which stresses examples of simple experimentation.

Rutherford was also fortunate in his secondary school and particularly in his Maths and Physics teacher, Littlejohn. Classes were small and relations between teacher and pupil intimately friendly so that they roamed the countryside together. The same applied at his University College education, it was not mass organized, individuality was not discouraged.

Yet he was never more or less than normal in relations with fellow pupils, including participation in their outdoor sports.

Then later in his early days in Cambridge there were some few who said that Rutherford was not a cultured man. Some tend to say that of all scientists and engineers. I deny it. Whatever the subject of discussion he could contribute sensibly, constructively, brightly and usefully to it. It is true he did not, in the newly colonized New Zealand, have access to the classical exhibits of arts and paintings such as older countries can collect in their museums. He had no ostentation. He did not let his honours interfere with his friendly relations. When he was elevated to the Peerage he said to Niels Bohr—'Don't you Lord me,' and to A. H. Compton, 'Call me Rutherford—let others who do not know me call me Lord.'

I have not mentioned his International outlook, but while he was proud of his country and ancestry, I doubt whether any scientist was better known and respected internationally in his own lifetime. Witness his relations with Bohr, Arrhenius, Hahn, the Curies, Boltwood, Geiger, Kapitza. He showed no insularism—urged no priority of any discovery for his laboratory or countrymen. He was the life and soul of the Solvay Conferences and it is thanks to him that we have common terms relating to units in his subject.

When we consider the significance of this historical session relating to Rutherford's work and future progress in the knowledge of the nucleus he created, let us therefore also remember the things that helped to make him a great leader of us all and let us make some effort to strive for conditions, each in our own country, under which future Rutherfords may arise with the same international sympathy and understanding. For, with more leaders of his type, there would be far less danger of serious international differences.

MOSELEY AND THE ATOMIC NUMBERS OF THE ELEMENTS

By SIR CHARLES DARWIN

I INTEND to devote most of my time to recalling the work of Moseley and the classical series of experiments through which he established finally the exact significance of atomic number, but before doing so I may perhaps be permitted to spend a little time over the general situation in the Manchester Physics Laboratory in those days.

Both Moseley and I arrived in Manchester in the autumn of 1910. He had had the normal university courses of experimental physics, whereas I was a mathematician, and as such I had a somewhat different outlook on the problems of physics from that of the experimentalists. It is hard now to realize the state of puzzled mystery in which we lived in those days on account of the conflicts between the classical physics of Maxwell and Lorentz, and the quantum theory of Planck.

The classical theories aspired to explain to the last detail the behaviour of matter, and though of course everyone could recognize that there were a lot of things that we could not explain, it was hoped by many people that one by one these difficulties would yield to treatment without any revolutionary changes of doctrine. On the other hand at about the start of the century Planck had discovered the quantum, and at intervals after that the quantum had succeeded in invading more and more fields of physics with a high degree of success. We were thus faced with two bodies of doctrine, both of which had to be believed, and yet they seemed to be mutually contradictory.

It would hardly be interesting now to discuss such things, so I will only say that we could never feel absolute confidence in the results we worked out. In particular one might take a problem and, working with the classical theory, one might get what looked like a perfectly satisfactory answer for half of it, but then when the other half was examined, it might be that one would get not just a wrong answer but no answer at all. Should one then believe in one's explanation of the first half? This was, loosely speaking, the state of theoretical physics here when we were first visited by Niels Bohr. It was then that he started the quantum theory of spectra by deriving his formula for the hydrogen spectrum, but it would be out of place for me to comment on this great work here. However, I would like to record what a comfort he was to us all. It was of course only many years later that he developed the definite idea of complementarity, but even at that early time he seemed already to have a general feeling of the way the rival theories could live together, which after all they had got to do. Where most of us noticed mainly their apparent contradictions, he would notice how the two theories, so to speak, always avoided facing right up to each other, so that coexistence for them was possible.

* * * * *

I now turn to some of my recollections of the period when Rutherford actually discovered the nucleus. For a long time the alpha-particle had been his favourite, and much study in the laboratory had been devoted to its behaviour. In particular Geiger and Marsden had been for some time studying the deflections of the alpha-particles in passing through thin sheets of gold foil by counting the scintillations of the particles scattered in various directions. They got the exciting result that a few of them were scattered through quite wide angles. I remember two or three times at the laboratory teas hearing Rutherford say that there must be tremendous forces in the atom, and then he would leave it at that. But one of the great experiences of my life was that on one Sunday evening the Rutherfords had invited some of us to supper, and after supper the nuclear theory came out. The main principle was that the whole deflection must have been done in a single operation. At first he talked about it as *simple scattering*, and then he realized that this was ambiguous, and I can still recall the satisfaction in his voice when he hit on the name *single scattering*, since nobody could mistake what that meant.

He assumed a central charge in the atom—it was indeed a year or two before it was renamed the nucleus—repelling the alpha-particle according to the ordinary laws of electricity, so that it should travel in a hyperbola. He worked out the law of scattering, that is to say the number of particles that should be found at any angle of deflection. Rutherford was not a profound mathematician, and I would doubt if he had thought about the properties of the hyperbola since he had been at school, but he had remembered just exactly enough of them to serve his purpose, and he told us the trigonometrical formula that should give the number of alpha-particles deflected through any angle. Indeed, as far as I can remember, on that very evening he asked me to check over his work, which was of course perfectly correct.

I remember him also saying that there was nothing in the experiments to show whether the force was repulsive or attractive, though it was natural to suppose that all nuclei had a positive charge, so that it should be repulsive.

I also recollect that even on that first evening Rutherford was already speculating how small the nucleus might be. He had worked out the distance of closest approach of the alpha-particle, and he was hoping that some observations would conflict with his formula, so that he might say that the law of repulsion between the two charges altered when they got within a certain distance of one another. In this hope he was of course disappointed because the nuclei are all so small that, at any rate in those days, no alpha-particle could get near enough to show any departure from the behaviour of a point charge.

Now comes a little point I would like to mention, which illustrates Rutherford's generosity. In his work he had been thinking about the nucleus of a gold atom, which is much too heavy to be shifted by the alpha-particle. It occurred to me at the time that interesting things might happen if one studied the collision of the alpha-particle with a hydrogen atom, because then one might expect that it would knock the hydrogen nucleus forward at a higher speed than the alpha-particle itself had had before the collision. Rutherford was much interested, and said this had not occurred to him. It is this that makes me think that it could not have been many hours before our supper when he had actually first worked out his theory, because it was an obvious fact that nobody could have missed for long. Not long after this he came into my room at the laboratory and told me to write a paper about it. One has heard tales of some really great men who have had suggestions given to them by their juniors, and in thinking them over they have incorporated them in their own train of thought to such an extent that they forgot their original source. This point was really obvious, but even so Rutherford did not forget where it had come from and I am glad to have this opportunity of paying a tribute to his generosity.

* * * * *

I will now turn to the subject of Moseley. If any man could reasonably claim to have science in his blood it would be Henry Gwyn Jeffreys Moseley. His father and both his grandfathers had been Fellows of the Royal Society. His father had been the chief naturalist in the famous Challenger Expedition, and his father's father had been a mathematical physicist of note. His mother's father Gwyn Jeffreys was a well-known zoologist. In addition to his interest in physics Harry Moseley had inherited a keen interest in natural history. He was born in 1887, and his father died only two or three years later, so that he was brought up by his mother in Oxford where his father had been professor. He won a scholarship at Eton, and then at Trinity College, Oxford where he studied physics, and he graduated in 1910. It was a continuing surprise to me that he was only awarded Second Class Honours, since his knowledge of physics always seemed to me to be not only deep but also wide. In spite of the formidable antecedents of his ancestry and upbringing he was not in the least a formidable person to meet; in any mixed company he would have passed as an intelligent young man of quite a normal type.

Fired by enthusiasm, he applied to Rutherford to be allowed to work in his laboratory, and he was duly appointed to a minor post on the staff in October 1910. This post involved some teaching, but two years later he was given a research fellowship which set him free to devote all his time to his researches.

At first he was fitted into the normal run of experimental work of the laboratory, in particular doing useful and quite difficult work mainly on the beta-rays, but this work was similar to much of the other work going on in the laboratory. Then in 1912 we heard of the great discovery made by Max von Laue and his collaborators of the diffraction of X-rays by crystals, and we were shown a celebrated photograph with a pattern of spots coming from a fine beam of X-rays that had gone through a thin crystal. At that time the X-rays were still mysterious, as they were involved in all the contradictions of fundamental physics to which I have referred. On the one side they seemed to be electromagnetic waves of high frequency, but essentially just like ordinary light, but when a beam of the rays was sent through a gas so as to ionize it, the energy of the individual ionized electrons was so high that it seemed hard to believe that they could have been excited by the cumulative effect of waves. Consequently there were many people—indeed for a time Sir William Bragg was one of them—who thought that the X-rays were of the nature of particles, because that would make it much easier to understand these high energies. The new discovery was therefore most exciting, because it held the promise of clearing up these doubts.

In Manchester we were naturally much interested, and Moseley suggested to me that I might join him in work on the subject. I had had very little direct training in experimental work, but by good fortune I had spent a good deal of my time in the study of waves, a study that was not very much in fashion in those days. We thought we could make something of the subject, and we approached Rutherford. At first he was distinctly discouraging, because there was really hardly any practical experience of the X-rays at that time in Manchester, and he maintained that we would be heavily handicapped as compared with other laboratories where they were familiar subjects of study. However, we persuaded him to let us try. We were fired by our interest in a quite new unexplored field, and we had no idea where it would lead. We simply wanted to know what the X-rays really were.

Working with Moseley was one of the most strenuous

exercises I have ever undertaken. He was without exception the hardest worker I have ever known. Even before the time of our collaboration I used to go into his room sometimes to see what he was doing, and I would find him obviously in the last stages of exhaustion, having probably been up all night. When I told him he ought to be at home in bed, he would answer that when he was feeling well he wanted to be out walking in the country, and that it was only in this condition when he was tired out that he felt inclined for laboratory work.

There were two rules for his work. First: When you started to set up the apparatus for an experiment, you must not stop until it was set up. Second: When the apparatus was set up you must not stop work until the experiment was done. Obeying these rules implied a most irregular life, sometimes with all-night sessions, and indeed one of Moseley's expertises was the knowledge of where in Manchester one could get a meal at three in the morning. In spite of these irregular hours it was extraordinarily stimulating, because all the time we were discussing the implications of the current experiment either to fundamental theory, or else to the next experiment we should try. Here there arose dangers from yet another of Moseley's habits. He was always ready to take the whole apparatus to pieces and set it up again if he could see any possible improvement to be hoped for. Often he was quite right, but some of his proposals were really rather trivial, and I can remember occasions when I opposed him, suggesting that we had better give the current set-up a trial before spending a lot of time in changing it, and sometimes we found that the existing set-up gave all we needed.

I am not going to describe this work. Broadly speaking, by a varied series of experiments lasting over six or eight months we convinced ourselves that the X-rays obeyed the wave theory in the same way that light does. I ought to say that we were considerably helped by correspondence with the two Braggs. We adopted their method of reflecting the rays from the outer face of a crystal with a view to getting quantitative results. Most of our work was done with two fine crystals, each with a face about three inches square, one of rock-salt and the other

H. G. J. Moseley

of potassium ferrocyanide. We used ionization methods rather than photography to measure the reflected rays, and this was not an easy technique for the rather weak effects we were getting. The rays we studied came from the platinum anode of a Coolidge tube of rather irregular habits, and we deliberately worked with fine slits in order to get results which should be easy to interpret. There was one slightly unlucky consequence of this. Nobody at that time knew much about the X-ray spectrum, though it was clear that most of the radiation was like white light, as was demonstrated by the fact that we could get reflexions at any angle of setting. In fact, in addition to the white X-rays there is a spectrum of lines superposed, but by sheer chance we never happened at first to set our crystal so as to get any of them. However, we were lucky to have a visit from Sir William Bragg, who told us about the line spectrum, and this we could then easily verify. The line spectra were very convenient for disentangling the different orders of diffraction, which were rather inextricably superposed on one another in the white X-rays.

As I have said, we convinced ourselves from a considerable variety of experiments that the X-rays were like ordinary light but of much higher frequency. Also we acquired familiarity with the technique of X-rays which we had entirely lacked at the start. At the conclusion of this work we agreed to separate. I wanted to work out the mathematical theory, which called for new methods of calculation, even though in principle it was only a branch of ordinary physical optics. Moseley by now felt perfectly capable of working by himself at X-ray experiments, and he proposed to study the characteristic line spectra of the X-rays of a sequence of the chemical elements.

* * * * *

By that time there was a new stimulus giving great importance to the subject. This came from Bohr's work on the theory of spectra. For most of this time Bohr was working in Copenhagen, but there was good contact with him through visits and correspondence. He had extended his theory from hydrogen to heavier elements, again on the basis of the nuclear atom, and he had conjectured that the innermost electrons of these atoms should behave much like the one electron of hydrogen, and give a similar spectrum at a very much higher frequency; in fact the frequency ought to go up as the square of the nuclear charge. All this is now accepted as obvious, but I have recently seen again some of the letters that passed at that time, and all sorts of troubles had to be considered that have now been forgotten.

Moseley resolved to measure the wavelengths of the X-rays emitted by a sequence of elements, and he could now expect to give their absolute values, which had previously been uncertain by a factor of about 2 until Lawrence Bragg had worked out the crystal structure of rock-salt. Moseley took the sequence from calcium to zinc, which promised to have wavelengths in a range which would be convenient for measurement.

At first he used the ionization method of observation with which we were familiar, but he later abandoned it in favour of photography, which proved much easier for his purpose. I recall that practically every time I went into his room I saw a new set-up, and I cannot now distinguish between the various arrangements; but I do recall one, though whether it was the final one I am not sure. He had a closed cylinder of glass about a yard long and a foot in diameter. In it there was a railway truck on rails, which could be shifted to and fro by turning stopcocks at the two ends, each of which wound or unwound a wire with its other end coupled to the truck. On the truck there was a row of blocks of the elements he was examining, and in this way he could bring each of them in turn into position without losing his vacuum. Each in turn was thus brought opposite the cathode, and the X-rays excited in the anode then emerged from the vacuum through a thin screen so as to fall on the large crystal of potassium ferrocyanide which he used again in all this work. The rays reflected from the crystal fell on a photographic plate in a carefully measurable position.

The result was a set of photographs which has become a classic of the subject.* It showed that the wave frequencies from calcium to zinc were proportional to the numbers 20^2, 21^2 . . .

* See p. 262

30^2. It was this work which established beyond all dispute that the elements could be set out in numerical order according to their nuclear charges, and it therefore held the promise of a complete enumeration of all possible elements.

* * * * *

This work was completed at the end of 1913. At that time Moseley left Manchester, and returned to his home in Oxford, but I may perhaps be permitted to say a few words about the work he then carried out at the Clarendon Laboratory there. Its aim was to complete the enumeration of the elements, but there were new serious difficulties to be faced on account of the great range of the X-ray frequencies that had to be examined. The rays he had studied in Manchester were the K-radiations, but he reached a practical limit for these at silver, No. 47, because he could not get high enough voltages to go further. However, Bohr had also given a theory for the softer L-radiations, and so he used these in his study of the heavier elements. They set him new problems, for some of these rays were so soft that they could not pass through the air on the way to the crystal and the photographic plate. In some of this work he had to have the whole system evacuated and in the dark because the X-rays could not even penetrate the paper that should shield the photographic plate from the daylight. For this work he separated off the X-ray chamber by a thin sheet of goldbeaters' skin, and had much trouble because this sheet broke so often.

However, he overcame all these difficulties and by about May 1914, when I visited him in Oxford, he had made direct measurements of 38 elements, spread over the whole range of the periodic table. From this he could enumerate all the elements, and he could name the places of the missing ones, Nos. 43, 61 and 75. During this time he was visited by the French chemist Urbain who had devoted his life to the study of the rare-earth elements, and Urbain has recorded the fact that in two or three weeks he was given the answer to the problem on which he had spent many years, the question how many rare-earth elements there actually are.

Moseley had planned to go to the British Association meeting that was to be held that year in Australia in September. He duly set off with his mother, going by way of Canada. Then the war broke out. He attended the meetings in Melbourne and Sydney, and took an important part in the discussions there. But as soon as he had done this he returned home as fast as possible. He was offered scientific work in England of a type that would have been useful for the war effort, but he refused the offer. Instead he took a commission in the Royal Engineers as Signals Officer. In 1915 he was sent to the Dardanelles, and he took part in the Suvla Bay landing, where on 10 August 1915 in the course of duty he was shot through the head and died instantaneously.

The work he had already done at the age of twenty-seven has become one of the classics of physical science. It is no use for us to speculate what other things he might have accomplished if he had been spared to carry on his great work.

RUTHERFORD AT MANCHESTER, 1913–14

By E. N. da C. ANDRADE

IT is a great and unexpected honour to be invited to speak on Rutherford at Manchester. I understand that this is an occasion for personal reminiscences, so I trust that you will pardon me if at times I seem to be speaking much of matters in which I was personally involved. I spent only one year in Rutherford's laboratory, 1913 to 1914, but that was one of the most memorable years of my life and was also the culmination of a great period in Rutherford's career. The Manchester research school was then at the height of its activity, full of characters from all parts of the world working with joy under the energetic and inspiring influence of the great man. The coming of the war in August 1914 naturally broke up completely the family life, for such it was, of the laboratory. The majority of the laboratory workers were dispersed and Rutherford's attention was diverted to problems of national importance, as the term was. He became a member of the Inventions Board and concerned himself with, among other matters, the detection of submarines. But I am speaking of a period when few people in England took the prospect of war more seriously than the prospect of an invasion from Mars.

I had taken my doctorate at Heidelberg in 1911 and in 1913 was working at University College, London, when I was appointed John Harling Fellow in succession to Moseley—a distinction not so clear at the time as it is now. If I mention Heidelberg it is because the contrast between working under Lenard at Heidelberg and under Rutherford at Manchester could hardly have been more marked. Lenard, if not so epoch-making a figure as Rutherford, was a very great physicist, who carried out pioneering work on electron physics, including the discovery of the photoelectric release of electrons, the first measurements of ionization potential and the clear demonstration that swift particles could pass right through the atom, in the consideration of which finding he came near to the discovery of the true structure of the atom, just as in his work on phosphorescence he made a first approach to the modern theory of light emission. He was a genius who made fundamental discoveries and would seem qualified and fitted to found and direct a great school of physics, but he lacked Rutherford's human touch and power of inspiring others. He treated me with kindness and benignity, which I gratefully acknowledge. When I had taken my doctorate he offered me a post on his staff, but I felt that I should not be at ease in such a position, although I had close friends among those working in the laboratory, in particular Wilhelm Hausser, Walther Kossel, and Carl Ramsauer, who remained close friends of mine all their lives.

Twice a week, at fixed times, Lenard went round the research laboratory, followed ceremonially by his Assistant Professor August Becker and by Carl Ramsauer, who took a very active part in supervising the research work. In the course of such a tour of inspection, which was known in the laboratory as a *razzia* (an Italian word signifying 'raid', why adopted I know not) every research worker was visited and his work discussed, with everybody standing, briefly or at greater length according to the progress or problems that it presented. Very remote from this formality were Rutherford's daily rambles round the laboratory, in the course of which, if there was a difficult or interesting point to discuss, he would sit on a stool for some little time, throwing out incisive comments and suggestions. He talked to the research worker as to a friend and collaborator. Every day there was a meeting round the laboratory tea-table, at which Rutherford practically always presided in my days. Conversation ranged over a wide variety of topics, mainly, perhaps, concerned with physics, but including ordinary laboratory gossip, and here again, although there was no doubt as to who was the boss, everybody said what he liked without constraint.

The physics colloquium was also a contrast at the two

Universities. At the Heidelberg colloquium Lenard took the chair, very much like a master with his class. He had a habit, if any aspect of his work was being treated by the speaker, of interrupting with 'And who did that first?' The speaker would reply, with a slight bow, 'Herr Geheimrat, you did that first,' to which Lenard answered, 'Yes, I did that first.' On one occasion that I remember, however, to the speaker's 'Herr Geheimrat, you did that first,' Lenard replied 'No. J. J. Thomson did that first. He *really* did that first.' Lenard much resented that the first discovery that the electricity released by light consisted of electrons was often claimed for J. J. Thomson, whereas he actually had prior publication.

At the Manchester colloquium, which met on Friday afternoons, Rutherford was, as in all his relations with the research workers, the boisterous, enthusiastic, inspiring friend, undoubtedly the leader but in close community with the led, stimulating rather than commanding, 'gingering up', to use a favourite expression of his, his team. At the first meeting of the session he gave an account of work carried out in the laboratory in the past year. He was always full of fire and infectious enthusiasm when describing work into which he had put his heart and always generous in his acknowledgement of the work of others.

If I have compared work with Lenard with work with Rutherford it is not that I do not freely acknowledge Lenard's greatness; it is because I feel that some brought up in the Rutherford tradition, or rather some younger men reading accounts of the old Manchester days of 1907 to 1914, may think that the same kind of enthusiastic comradeship in research existed at that time in all laboratories where great discoverers were in control. No doubt something of the same spirit reigned in the Cavendish Laboratory at Cambridge when Rutherford carried out his early researches there under J. J. Thomson, but it was far from being common and Lenard's laboratory offers a great contrast. This is not a matter of nationality and, as I have said, I am very grateful to Lenard for his good will towards me and am far from wishing to disparage his achievement. Perhaps it would be well to let speak Carl Ramsauer, a true-born German, who was for some years on Lenard's staff and freely acknowledged his great qualities. Writing of Lenard's laboratory he said 'In fact there reigned in the Institute instead of a spontaneous rejoicing in the work a certain feeling of constraint'*, and further, giving in his contrast an exact description of the Rutherford atmosphere which I am trying to depict, 'The narrowmindedness of Lenard is also the reason why, in spite of his great qualities as an investigator, he did not succeed in founding a great research school of his own, for the foundation of such a school is not the constant control and guidance of his young collaborators by the master, but the awakening of their independent forces in the direction of his ideas.'† It was in this latter capacity that Rutherford excelled.

Needless to say, it was for me a joy to meet Rutherford in 1913, to hear that great voice becoming more and more enthusiastic as he spoke of what he was planning, the words almost falling over one another. There was, compared to Heidelberg, a great shortage of effective apparatus: according to Robinson the average annual grant for apparatus was, at the period in question, under £420 a year. Whereas at Heidelberg anybody who had proved himself could have the use of a Gaede rotary mercury vacuum pump if he needed it, with the necessary fore-pump, at Manchester, even in my time, much of the evacuation was done with a Toepler pump: there were one or two Gaede pumps, but they were jealously guarded. Improvization was the order of the day, and not a bad order either. When I had been a few weeks in the laboratory William Kay, the indispensable laboratory steward, everybody's friend, said to me 'Papa says you'll do', 'Papa' being the usual name for the head of our family among certain of the laboratory workers. I was naturally curious to know what had established me as a fit member of the fellowship and accordingly asked

* 'Tatsächlich, herrschte im Institut statt spontaner Arbeitsfreudigkeit ein gewisses Gefühl des Zwanges.'

† 'Die Engherzigkeit Lenards ist auch die Ursache, weswegen es ihm trotz seiner grossen Forschereigenschaften nicht gelungen ist, eine entsprechende eigene Schule zu begründen, denn die Grundlage einer solchen Schule ist nicht die ständige Gängelung und Leitung der jungen Mitarbeiter durch den Meister, sondern die Weckung ihrer selbständigen Kräfte in der Richtung seiner Ideen.'

Kay 'Do you know what made him say that?' 'He saw you making that plateholder out of cardboard and thought that you made a good job of it,' replied Kay. For our work on gamma-rays a plateholder made out of cardboard with a black paper front was as good as anything, and saved time and money. To 'get on with it' was Rutherford's great desire.

A word about Kay and 'Papa'. Some of us, including in particular Harold Robinson and E. J. Evans, had a great liking for the old-fashioned music hall, then well represented in Manchester. George Formby was a performer who was particularly popular and another was Harry Tate who had a celebrated sketch, called *Motoring*, about a motor car, something of a novelty still in those days, on which he was freely questioned by his son, who called him 'Papa' with a peculiar intonation used by the laboratory initiates. Incidentally, since these are reminiscences, I may perhaps recall that this sketch contained the only scientific joke that I ever, with a considerable experience, heard on the music hall stage. The son said, 'I know why your wheels won't go round, Papa.' 'Why, my boy, why?' 'Because they ought to be $2\pi r$ and yours are $4\pi r$.' This brought the house down, although I do not think that a large proportion of the audience knew what two pi R meant.

William Kay, the head laboratory steward, was an extraordinary man. Always, always busy, he was always good-tempered and willing to help. He was an excellent mechanic, an electrician who knew all about the electrical connections of the laboratory, a skilled photographer, and a great hand with apparatus of all kinds, who excelled in setting up the striking lecture experiments for Rutherford's first-year course. He made, in his spare time, a large number of drawings for Rutherford's *Radioactive Substances and their Radiations*. He and I speedily became friends, because he had been very successful as an amateur runner and I had done a certain amount of running, having, for instance, won the University College and Hospital half mile in 1907. My time for the half mile was nothing like as good as his, but running gave us a common interest which made him accept me from the start.

Another laboratory character was the German glassblower

Baumbach, an excellent craftsman who was responsible for, among other things, the alpha-ray tubes whose thin walls allowed the passage of the rays with but little decrease of velocity. When I had occasion to call on him shortly after the war broke out, he, who knew that I understood the language, broke out into a stream of fiery German prophecy as to what the German Army would do to Britain. I answered him in the kind of way he understood, telling him to keep his mouth shut or he would find himself in trouble. The next thing was that the Vice-Chancellor of the University sent for me and told me that Baumbach had complained that I had threatened him: it was very unworthy behaviour to threaten a poor defenceless German in our midst and he must ask me not to behave in this way! At the time this annoyed me, but nowadays I take such incidents as a matter of course. That I have not misrepresented Baumbach is demonstrated by what Niels Bohr has written, 'but the man's temper, not uncommon for artisans in his field, and which released itself in violent superpatriotic utterances, eventually led to his internment by the British authorities.' But he was a very good glassblower.

I venture to interpolate here that I won a bet with Rutherford, a fact which I record because I think it possible that I am the only man who ever did so. Our apparatus for the work on the wavelength of gamma-rays included a large magnet for deflecting the beta-particles out of the way. One day our plates began to be fogged systematically and we were very puzzled to account for this. Rutherford made a suggestion as to the cause of the trouble and I said—as one could to Rutherford—'No, I'm sure it's not that.' 'I bet you a shilling it is,' said Rutherford, and so the bet was concluded. Just after that I found the real cause of the trouble, which was not complex physics but simple meddling. All the electrical connections for heavy current were made in a room with the usual bars and plugs. Somebody had pulled out our plugs, probably by accident, and replaced them in the wrong bars, so that the direction of the field of our magnet was reversed, which, with our particular arrangement at the time, threw the beta-rays on to the plate. When I told Rutherford this he duly paid me the shilling, which I long treasured. It was lost when my London laboratory was destroyed in the late war.

An incident comes to my mind indicative of Rutherford's inborn conviction that the matter of prime importance was his work in the laboratory, which nothing must interrupt. There was in the laboratory a foreign lady—let us call her Natasha Bauer—doing research, for which she showed no outstanding aptitude. She was an ardent feminist and something of a man-hater: she would never ask a man to do anything for her. One day she had a bottle of SO_2, the closing mechanism of which had stuck so that she could not open it. Not wishing to seek aid from a man she took the bottle into a very small room and did something in the way of wedging the opener in the door, which effected a sudden rush of gas, with the result that she lost consciousness. Luckily a woman found her on the floor, and she was satisfactorily revived. Rutherford naturally heard of this—he heard of everything—and sent for her. It so happened that I was seated at the desk with him in his room on the first floor, discussing some point in connection with our work, when she arrived. 'What's this I hear, Miss Bauer?' he said as soon as she had shut the door, 'What's this I hear? You might have killed yourself!' to which she replied 'Well, if I had, nobody would have cared.' 'No, I daresay not, I daresay not' said Rutherford, 'but I've no time to attend inquests.' I believe that he was more than half in earnest, thinking of a morning wasted away from the laboratory, but from the lady's face this was not the reply she expected.

To attempt to give a picture of Rutherford's laboratory just before the First World War some reference to those working there is needed: 'Papa' and his family were one. Geiger was no longer there in my time, but his name echoed about freely: he was present in spirit. Chadwick, who had been working for two years under Rutherford on problems in radioactivity, had in 1913 gone to Germany to work with Geiger. Marsden was lecturer and research assistant. I need say nothing of his work, which is so well known to you, nor of his personality, for here he is. He was a responsible figure in the laboratory. In 1913 Moseley was just finishing his fundamental work on X-ray spectra, of which Darwin has spoken. He would undoubtedly have become a great leader in physics if he had not been killed at Gallipoli in the First World War. I am reminded of what Newton said of the early death of Roger Cotes—'If Mr Cotes had lived we might have known something.' Moseley was an outstanding character, not, perhaps, so hail-fellow-well-met as most of us. Typical is that he objected to other workers borrowing, perhaps permanently, his matches, so he bought a gross of boxes (which in those days cost him one shilling and sixpence) and made of them a heap on which he put a label worded to the effect 'Please take one of these boxes and leave my matches alone.' Charles Darwin had carried out with Moseley an experimental investigation on the reflexion of X-rays by crystals, an account of which appeared just before my time in the laboratory, but he was more interested in theoretical work and in 1914 published his classical papers on the mathematical theory of X-ray reflexion. Walter Makower, who had also been a John Harling Research Fellow, was mainly responsible for teaching the technicalities of the subject: he had published with Geiger in 1912 a book *Practical Measurements in Radioactivity* which was in the hands of everybody experimenting on the subject. As *Nature* said of it 'That it should come from the laboratory of Prof. Rutherford and have for its authors two such distinguished workers on radioactivity, practically ensures its general adoption in advanced physical laboratories.' He was much interested in the atmospheric investigations carried out at the kite-flying station installed on the moors above Glossop in Derbyshire, and Harold Robinson's first appearance in print was as a collaborator in a paper by Makower and two others on the electrical state of the upper atmosphere. Makower was a man of keen musical interest and I well remember a party at his house, or at the house of another Makower, at which there was excellent chamber music.

Harold Robinson, who later adopted the additional name of Roper and became H. R. Robinson, was perhaps my closest comrade in the laboratory and we remained on terms of intimate friendship until his death in 1955. We had common interests in books, sport, and the local music halls, as well as physics. He towered over Rutherford in physical height, being about six foot four inches, and was deliberate in movement and utterance, in contrast to Rutherford's excitable enthusiasm. It may seem strange to compare the great man with one of his students, but even in those days Rutherford seemed to have a particular liking for Robinson, while Rutherford was, as he always remained, Robinson's one hero. Their differences of temperament may have attracted them together, positive and negative. There is no need to say anything further about their relationship, since Robinson's lecture on *Rutherford: Life and Work to the Year* 1919, *with Personal Reminiscences of the Manchester Period*,* which was the first of the Physical Society's Rutherford lectures, gives a striking picture of the laboratory, enriched with many anecdotes illustrating the terms on which they stood in those days. Robinson, in spite of his deep-seated reverence for his hero, was completely outspoken with Rutherford as with everybody else. Throughout Rutherford's life, from the time that I am considering onwards, Robinson was probably as close to him as anybody.

Robinson's early work was all done in collaboration with Rutherford. After investigating the heating effects of radium and the emanation they worked together on the magnetic analysis of the beta-ray spectrum of Radium B and C, concerning which the first paper was published later in 1913. The magnetic analysis of X-ray electrons was Robinson's chief experimental interest throughout life. In 1914 he, like Darwin, Fajans and Makower, published a paper in conjunction with Moseley.

E. J. Evans was a skilled spectroscopist, a student of Alfred Fowler's, who in 1913–14 was carrying out precise measurements which showed that certain lines attributed to hydrogen were in fact due to ionized helium. Their wave numbers differed slightly from those to be anticipated for hydrogen, in a way that could be explained quantitatively, on Bohr's theory, as due to the finite mass of the nucleus. This offered support, valuable at the time, to the theory. Evans was a very efficient member of the teaching staff of the department. His research

* Reprinted in this volume.

lay somewhat outside the sphere of interest of Rutherford and of his school, but he was on the friendliest terms with many of us, especially with Robinson, whose affection for the local music halls and for shipping he shared. He stayed on the staff at Manchester after the 1914 war broke out and afterwards became Professor of Physics at Swansea, where he died in 1944.

J. M. Nuttall and A. B. Wood held graduate scholarships and both published papers with Rutherford which are well known. A familiar figure about the laboratory with whom I was on friendly terms was J. N. Pring, a one-time John Harling Fellow, who was Lecturer and Demonstrator in Electro-Chemistry. He was carrying out work concerned with the behaviour of hydrocarbons at high temperature and pressure, the pressure being maintained by heating petrol in a strong vessel and releasing the gas by a valve if the pressure became dangerously high. There was a vertical explosion-mat near the apparatus and I remember asking Pring why he did not sit behind it: he replied, with a laugh, that, if the vessel burst, the mat, and everything else, would go through the ceiling.

Among the foreigners working in the laboratory in my time were Stanislaw Loria and Bohdan de Szyszkowski, both from Russian Poland and both rather older and more experienced than many of us. I think that they had come to revel in the Rutherford atmosphere and to get in touch with the latest work in radioactivity. Loria was a most friendly and sympathetic soul who was, as K. Mendelssohn has written, a citizen of the world both in outlook and habits. He had already carried out, in Breslau, Berlin and Göttingen, significant work in physical optics on such matters as the Kerr effect and the dispersion of light in gases. Under Rutherford he worked on certain aspects of radioactive decay and on the volatilization of radioactive deposits. He published a paper on the branching of the thorium series from the Institut für Radiumforschung in Vienna in 1916, with frequent references to the work of Marsden and other Manchester workers. He was delighted to find that I knew something of the work of Witkowski, who had been his professor, and of Smoluchowski and Natanson, Polish physicists who were among his heroes. He was a man who could achieve a certain degree of mastery in whatever he undertook, and he afterwards became professor of theoretical physics, and later of experimental physics, at Lvov. He could discuss intelligently and with humour any subject that turned up—and a great variety of subjects turned up in the discussions in and around the laboratory in those days.

Szyszkowski was a man of some means, who liked to dine at the Midland Hotel, which was then under the distinguished management of Monsieur Colbert. The seven-and-sixpenny dinner there was about as good as anything in Europe and to it Szyszkowski invited me every now and then. We had many interests in common outside physics. He was a close friend of Arrhenius and we arranged to go together to Stockholm for a holiday in the second half of July 1914, where we saw much of Arrhenius, a most friendly and entertaining character who had spent a period at Manchester learning radioactive techniques. He entertained us with many an anecdote of scientists of European fame and with excellent drink. The outbreak of war caught us there. In due course I was able to get back to England and Szyszkowski returned to Russia. He had estates in Podolia, a former government of European Russia. I never heard from him after the war and am afraid that he disappeared in the revolution.

Another man from eastern Europe (Kiev) who was working in the laboratory was Stanislaw Kalandyk, a somewhat remote and melancholy character who always appeared to be pondering upon the ultimates of physics and upon time, death, and eternity, without attaining anything definite.

A very attractive character from the Continent was the Dutchman A. D. Fokker, closely related to the designer of the famous aeroplane. He was even taller than Robinson. He was a theoretical physicist and mathematician who wrote on, among other things, relativity. He, too, was attracted by Rutherford's fame and personality. From the Empire were D. C. H. Florance and R. W. Varder. Varder was a South African, who had taken his degree at the Cape: he was working on the absorption of beta-rays. He afterwards became professor at Rhodes University College, at Grahamstown. Florance, a specialist on the scattering of gamma rays, was from New Zealand, where he afterwards became professor.

There were others of note working in the laboratory, but those quoted will suffice to show the range of interest and character of the brotherhood, all united by the infectious enthusiasm of Rutherford, who knew so well how to produce results by a few directive words, apparently casual but probably the results of having the matter long in his thoughts.

Something must be said of Niels Bohr, who was only a visitor in the year of which I am speaking, but who had spent some months in Rutherford's laboratory before producing his revolutionary theory of light emission by the atom, and who, after the outbreak of war, succeeded Darwin as Schuster Reader. His name will ever be associated with the nuclear atom whose birth we are celebrating.

In 1911, when Rutherford first put forward his revolutionary conception, the nuclear atom aroused so little interest that even *Nature* did not comment on it. It is not always recalled that the structural scheme, as originally put forward by Rutherford, allowed the massive central particle to be either positively or negatively charged, since the angle through which an alpha-particle, aimed to pass near the charged nucleus (as it was later called), is deflected, is independent of the sign of the charge. As Marsden said, in his admirable summary published at the time, 'The author finds that an atom with a strong positive or negative central charge concentrated within a sphere of less than 3×10^{-12} cm radius, and surrounded by electricity of opposite sign distributed throughout the remainder of the volume of the atom of about 10^{-8} cm radius, satisfies all the known laws of scattering due to either α- or β-rays.' This is exactly what Rutherford showed. Even Rutherford himself, at the time, did not seem to regard his theory as of supreme significance. In his *Radioactive Substances and their Radiations*, which was published in 1913, there are only two references to it, both concerned with the scattering of alpha-particles. The latter one, near the end of the book, is indexed under 'Atom, structure of, to explain scattering,' which emphasizes that the

STAFF AND RESEARCH STUDENTS OF MANCHESTER UNIVERSITY PHYSICS DEPARTMENT, 1910

W. Eccles S. Kinoshita R. Rossi W. Kay G. N. Antonoff E. Marsden W. C. Lantsberry
F. W. Whaley H. C. Greenwood W. Wilson W. Borodowsky Miss M. White E. J. Evans H. Geiger T. Tuomikoski
S. Russ H. Stansfield H. Bateman Prof. Schuster Prof. Rutherford R. Beattie J. N. Pring W. Makower
R. E. Slade W. A. Harwood

scattering of alpha-particles, Rutherford's beloved playthings, was the chief thing in mind. This part of the book must have been written at the end of 1912: here, in contrast with the earlier references to the atom model, the concentrated charge at the centre is made positive and it is surrounded by a distribution of electrons 'throughout a spherical volume or in concentric rings in one plane'. This, then, was 1912.

In 1913, however, the nucleus had become a centre of attraction at Manchester and it was in this and the following year that its scope and fundamental importance were established, chiefly by Bohr's work. Bohr's first paper on the subject appeared in the *Philosophical Magazine* in July 1913, to be quickly followed by two subsequent papers, making up the classic trio in which his views were fully developed. The nuclear atom had suddenly come to its own, and just as the foundation of the Royal Society has been celebrated as occurring both in 1660 and 1662, so the year 1913 may be associated with 1911 in celebrating the establishment of the nuclear atom. The quantum theory was somewhat remote from Rutherford's inborn way of visualizing everything, a characteristic so important that I may, perhaps, be allowed to illustrate it by an anecdote. In the course of a discussion after a dinner at the Athenaeum at which I was present Eddington said something to the effect that electrons were very useful conceptions but might not have any real existence. Whereupon Rutherford got up and protested indignantly, 'Not exist, not exist—why I can see the little beggars there in front of me as plainly as I can see that spoon.' Alpha-particles and electrons he could see, but not quanta. He could not fail, however, to be impressed by the way in which Bohr's theory gave the correct value for atomic constants. At the British Association meeting in Melbourne in August 1914, the month of the outbreak of the war that closed an epoch, he opened a discussion on atomic structure with a speech in which he drew attention to the importance of Moseley's work and referred favourably, but without fully committing himself, to Bohr's theory of line spectra. Later, of course, he accepted the theory completely.

The fifty years that have elapsed since the birth of the

nuclear atom have seen marvellous advances in physics, but have not, perhaps, produced another Rutherford. I do not think that this is because there are no fundamental discoveries left to make: of the fundamentals of the solid and liquid state we know very little. I doubt even if it is because men of his calibre are no longer born. A condition for great discoveries is undisturbed leisure to think: Isaac Newton told one inquirer that he made his discoveries 'By always thinking unto them,' and on another occasion said 'I keep the subject constantly before me and wait till the first dawnings open little by little into the full light.' Such quiet respite to think Rutherford had, especially in the period at Manchester with which our minds have been occupied, a period so remote in spirit from the present day as to seem like another age. The physics research laboratory of Rutherford's Manchester days, with the professor in closest touch with all his research men, who, with little thought for their future living, were eagerly engaging themselves in obtaining results that seemed remote from any possible practical application, has passed, in the same way as the workshop where craftsmen took a pride in producing beautifully made objects has passed. Our universities have, inevitably and properly, become, in the mood of the age, factories for producing degrees and discoveries, which they do with great efficiency. It is only old men who regret the passing of the past, but it is well for us all to acknowledge the passing. '*Tempi passati sind vorüber,*' as they used to say in Vienna.

Rutherford at Manchester was free to do exactly as he liked, and physics was the consuming interest of his life. As far as I know, like Newton, he took no particular joy in music, poetry, the arts or the pleasures of the table. He 'kept the subject constantly before him': his life, his restless quest, was physics. He saw the atomic particles as clearly before him as your old cricketer, describing a match, will see the field before him. The radioactive elements were his children—some well-behaved, some troublesome, but he knew and loved them all. His favourite individual was, I think, the brisk little alpha-particle—and how he made it work!

His debt to Manchester he freely acknowledged, with an

unconcealed pride in his achievements there, as when, in 1931, towards the end of his life he said 'I owe a great debt to Manchester for the opportunities it gave me for carrying out my studies. I do not know whether the University is really aware that during the few years from 1911 onwards the whole foundation of the modern physical movement came from the physical department of Manchester University.' He knew what he had done and said so in his simple unsophisticated way. For simple and unsophisticated he was, but a supreme genius.

If I say that he was simple I have his support, for in a speech made and recorded in 1931 he said 'I am always a believer in simplicity, being a simple man myself.' I think, too, that he was a happy man and that the years spent at Manchester were the happiest time of his life. At any rate, years after, he wrote to Geiger, 'They were happy days in Manchester and we wrought better than we knew.' I think it was well for his peace of mind that he did not foresee the terrors, the threat to the human race, that would grow directly from the work of his school, for the nuclear bomb derives directly from the early experiments on the disruption of the nucleus, which in their turn derived from his Manchester work. Quite clearly he long believed that atomic energy could never be released on a large scale, for he said in 1933, only 28 years ago, 'These transformations of the atom are of extraordinary interest to scientists, but we cannot control atomic energy to an extent which would be of any value commercially, and I believe that we are not likely ever to be able to do so. A lot of nonsense has been talked about transmutation. Our interest in the matter is purely scientific, and the experiments which are being carried out will help to a better understanding of the structure of matter.' In 1936, the year before he died, he said 'While the over-all efficiency of the process rises with increase of energy of the bombarding particles, there seems to be little hope of gaining useful energy from the atoms by such methods. On the other hand, the recent discovery of the neutron and the proof of its extraordinary effectiveness in producing transformations at very low velocities opens up new possibilities, if only a method could be found for producing slow neutrons in quantity with little expenditure of energy. At the moment, however, the natural radioactive bodies are the only known sources for gaining energy from atomic nuclei, but this is on far too small a scale to be useful for technical purposes.' Thus he concluded his James Watt lecture. Even this, however, shows no foreboding of the nucleus as an agent of overwhelming destruction and disaster.

I have endeavoured with, I fear, but indifferent brushwork to set down a picture of Rutherford, with a background of his collaborators, at the time when I was working in Manchester. Others abler, more distinguished and more closely associated with Rutherford than myself have this afternoon told you in detail of aspects of the work inspired by him, with particular reference to Manchester. Those of you who did not know him will have gathered that not only was he an outstanding genius, who founded much of modern physics, but that he was also a great leader, who commanded the confidence and affection of all who worked with him and who, when the mood was on him, was a figure of inspiration. At Manchester the cares of office sat lightly on him and he revelled in the free exercise of his full creative powers. I am sure that I am speaking for my more eminent colleagues as well as for myself when I say that it has been a delight to be able to meet here and renew our memories of the great man and that the warmest thanks of all of us are due to our gracious hosts for having conceived the plan of these Jubilee ceremonies and for having so efficiently and delightfully put the plan into execution.

THE GENERAL SIGNIFICANCE OF THE DISCOVERY OF THE ATOMIC NUCLEUS

By NIELS BOHR

IT has been a pleasant and moving experience to listen to the talks of some of Rutherford's closest collaborators from the Manchester time, each of whom in his own way has described Rutherford's genius as a scientist and his great human personality. As one who had the good fortune, a few months after Rutherford's discovery of the nucleus of the atom, to join the group working here in Manchester under his inspiration, and during many subsequent years enjoyed his warm friendship, I am grateful to have been asked to add a few words on this occasion.

Having had the opportunity in a Rutherford Memorial Lecture* to dwell on some of my most treasured remembrances, I shall here only stress the point which formed the main theme for the Lecture. In completing to such an unsuspected degree our conception of the constitution of the atom, Rutherford's discovery from the very beginning presented physicists with the challenge to establish a comprehensive explanation of the experiences, accumulated through the centuries, about the physical and chemical properties of matter.

As we all know, the utilization for this purpose of the nuclear model of the atom was to rest essentially on the novel feature of natural philosophy introduced by the recognition of the universal quantum of action to which Planck was led in the first year of this century. Looking back on the development we might ask ourselves why the modern methods of quantum mechanics and electrodynamics, which now appear indispensable in dealing with atomic problems, were not already established at the time of Rutherford's discovery.

* Reprinted in this volume.

It is true that already a few years after Planck's pioneer work, the foundation for subsequent progress was laid by Einstein's ingenious analysis of the apparent paradoxes involved in the exchange of momentum and energy in elementary radiative processes, which had led him to the concept of the photon. The situation remained, however, so puzzling and strange that even a preliminary orientation as regards the mechanism responsible for the remarkable stability of atomic systems, on which all properties of matter ultimately depend, would hardly have been possible without such definite knowledge about the structure of the atom as that which Rutherford's great work gave us.

Indeed, the discovery of the atomic nucleus offered a decisive impetus at all stages of the ensuing development, by which it became gradually possible to achieve the incorporation of the quantum in a consistent generalization of the classical approach. As is well known, the realization of this great task demanded the co-operation of a whole generation of physicists from many parts of the world.

It has therefore been a most proper decision to connect the celebration of the fiftieth anniversary of Rutherford's epoch-making discovery with an international congress to discuss the present state of nuclear science. Great expectations are attached to this conference, and already from the first sessions we have got a strong impression of the spirit in which new knowledge and viewpoints have been exchanged between the participants.

We of the older generation have been vividly reminded of the atmosphere in Rutherford's own laboratory in the Manchester days, when we received such deep inspiration from his openmindedness as regards physical inquiry. Equally those of us who have benefited from Rutherford's unique gifts as a leader of scientific co-operation have had much occasion to remember his beliefs and hopes regarding the opportunities which science offers for promoting understanding and confidence between individuals from different nations.

PARTICIPANTS AT COMMEMORATIVE SESSION

(*left to right*) Sir James Chadwick, E. N. da C. Andrade, Sir Charles Darwin, N. Bohr, Sir Ernest Marsden

HONORARY DEGREE CEREMONY

Professor A. Bohr (Denmark) *Doctor of Science*	Professor G. Racah (Israel) *Doctor of Science*	Sir Ernest Marsden (New Zealand) *Doctor of Laws*	
Professor V. F. Weisskopf (U.S.A.) *Doctor of Science*	Professor H. Graham Cannon *Presenter*	Professor W. Mansfield Cooper *Vice-Chancellor*	Miss A. Ellis (England) *Master of Science*

Honorary Degree Ceremony

AT a ceremony held in the Whitworth Hall of the Victoria University of Manchester on 5 September 1961, the following honorary degrees were conferred by the Vice-Chancellor, Professor W. Mansfield Cooper.

Doctor of Laws (*LL.D.*)

Sir Ernest Marsden

Professor of Physics in Victoria University College, Wellington, New Zealand, from 1914 to 1922. Assistant Director of Education, New Zealand, from 1922 to 1927. Secretary of the Department of Scientific and Industrial Research, New Zealand, from 1927 to 1947. President of the Rutherford Jubilee International Conference.

Doctor of Science (*D.Sc.*)

Professor Viktor Frederick Weisskopf

Professor of Physics at the Massachusetts Institute of Technology and Director-General of the European Centre for Nuclear Research.

Professor Aage Bohr

Professor at the Institute of Theoretical Physics, Copenhagen.

Professor Giulio Racah

Professor of Theoretical Physics at the Hebrew University, Jerusalem.

Master of Science (*M.Sc.*)

Miss Annie Ellis

Formerly Senior Physics Mistress, Manchester High School for Girls, and part-time Demonstrator in the Department of Physics.

The honorary graduands were presented by Professor H. Graham Cannon.

The following were among the distinguished delegates at the degree ceremony and at the commemorative session.

Professor P. Huber, representing the International Union of Pure and Applied Physics.

Professor P. M. S. Blackett, representing the Royal Society.

Dr T. E. Allibone, representing the Institute of Physics and The Physical Society.

Sir Arthur Sims, representing Canterbury University, New Zealand.

Professor R. E. Bell, representing McGill University, Canada.

Professor O. R. Frisch, representing the Cavendish Laboratory, University of Cambridge.

Dr P. H. Fowler, representing the Rutherford family.

Professor E. N. da C. Andrade.

Professor N. Bohr.

Sir James Chadwick.

Sir Charles Darwin.

The Rutherford-Schuster Correspondence

MCGILL UNIVERSITY
MONTREAL

The Macdonald Physics Building Sept. 26 1906

Dear Professor Schuster,

I was very glad to receive your kind letter in reference to the Chair of Physics at Manchester, as it came at a time when I was seriously considering my future plans. I have had to decide during the past year between the attractions of McGill & Yale University and finally decided to remain here. My chief reason for this step was my hope to return ultimately to England to a position where I would not have to sacrifice laboratory facilities by so doing. The position at King's College seemed to me to involve the probability of the latter.

I very much appreciate your very kind and cordial letter and am inclined to consider very favourably the suggestion of becoming a candidate for the position you propose. The fine laboratory you have built up is a great attraction to me as well as the opportunity of more scientific intercourse than occurs here.

It may possibly save time if I briefly state my views on the suggestions made in your letter. I would be prepared to give five lectures a week but not more, as otherwise there would be a serious curtailment of time and energy for research. At the same time, I should like to feel that there was sufficient lecturing staff in the department to give over one or more of these lectures occasionally in order to substitute a course in some special subject in which I was interested. I have had a good deal of committee work here as I belong to two faculties. I would be quite prepared to do my duty in that respect, but would like to escape as far as possible from too much committee routine not involving my own or allied departments.

There is one point of importance on which I should be glad of further information, namely the state of the funds for the working of the department, including the amount for general teaching, research &c and how far the powers of decision in regard to expenditure are in the hands of the Director.

I need hardly tell you how much I appreciate the suggestion coming in the way it has: I fully recognise the spirit of self abnegation displayed by you in your letter. Nothing could give me greater pleasure than to have you a member of the department to add your strength in the branch—Mathematical Physics—in which I should most value assistance. It is hardly necessary for me to say that I should be only too delighted to have your assistance and advice and I am sure that, as far as I am personally concerned, you would never regret the arrangement.

I should be glad to hear when you expect a decision to be made. Should I be appointed, I presume that I would not have to take up my teaching duties until next October.

Classes here are now in full swing and I have settled down to another year of busy work. Kindly remember me to Mrs. Schuster.

Believe me,

Yours very sincerely,

E. RUTHERFORD

THE PHYSICAL LABORATORIES

The University
Manchester.
October 7 1906

Dear Prof. Rutherford,

I was very glad to receive your letter yesterday and can I think give you satisfactory answers to the questions which you very naturally ask. The Council are fully alive to the fact that the reputation of the University and its power to attract students from the outside depends entirely on the research work and they would be anxious as far as lies in their power and their means allow to assist the Professor in every way they can.

I send you some annotated pages from our prospectus from which you will see the kind of assistance you will have, and the number of classes required. I have always taken Physics II which is a large class and meets twice a week. Physics III is also rapidly increasing owing to the fact that Physics is beginning to be taught properly at school, and our better men are now able to attend Physics III in their first year. Of the second year honours course I have latterly only taken one of the subjects extending over one term at most but several of the assistants are quite capable of taking it. Mr. Petavel's connection with the laboratory is temporary only as we had to make some hurried arrangement to fill Dr. Simpson's place who is going to India. He is taking the Mechanics Classes and looks after the Kite flying. I have a man (Rimmer) training now as a meteorologist (including atmospheric electricity etc.) who has been through our honours courses and is quite good. If he takes Petavel's place next year you would have four assistants (Makower, Stansfield, Russ & Rimmer) each of whom is quite capable to take any lectures. But they are busy of course with laboratory teaching and I like to give them time for research. In consequence I should not give them more than three hours per week lecturing and if possible not throughout the session. Altogether it comes to this that latterly I have given in the first term 2 hours Physics II—sometimes a short course of 8 or 9 lectures on a special subject such as Spectroscopy.—In the second term 5 hours, i.e. Physics II and IV and in this term which is short generally in addition to Physics II one of the third year's honours courses. Otherwise I often replaced the lectures of the third year's honours by private advice in the reading of standard works. It is most important that the third year's honours man should stand on his own feet and not depend on lectures and by present regulations he need not attend any lectures. Often of course it is quite pleasant to give them a short course of lectures especially if they are mathematically inclined.

The division of lectures between himself and the assistant is left to the discretion of the Professor (subject to the theoretical control of the Senate which is never exercised) but of course the Department will not work unless the Professor takes his fair share of the teaching.

There is a sort of complication arising from the fact that Electrochemistry and Electrotechnics are joined to this department of Physics for historical and practical reasons.

Ultimately no doubt the Electrotechnical Department will separate off. Dr. Beattie is now a practically independent lecturer but there is a certain convenience and advantage to have the Professor of Physics to decide when a student knows enough Physics to be drafted off into his Dynamo House. Also the Professor of Physics keeps the control of the heavy current machinery which may be very useful to him. Dr. Hutton has independent charge of Electrochemistry but here also in order to avoid any clashing of demands whether a particular dynamo is to be used in his Department at a particular time or required for physical purposes or by the electrical engineers the Professor of Physics who is the Director of the whole block of buildings has the ultimate control.

In practice no difficulty has ever arisen. A separation of the Departments would involve great expenditures in the duplication of machinery. Separation no doubt will ultimately come but our present system has worked quite well so far.

As regards the money questions our procedure is this:
This time of year the Head of the Department sends in a budget of how much money he will require for new apparatus etc. If his demands are the same as the year before or slightly in excess his budget will be passed as a matter of routine. If he increases his demands he may be called upon to justify the increase before a committee. Once the money is granted the Professor has complete control. He orders the apparatus and when the bills come in he signs them and sends them to the office where they will be paid as a matter of course. Even if he spends more money than he has been granted the money is paid and he will probably hear nothing about it until his next budget is sent in. If the excess is a matter of £20 or £30 nothing is said. If he should spend £100 more than he asked for, he

will probably be told that he ought to estimate more accurately or curtail his expenditure. Much of course depends whether the University happens to be in a flourishing financial condition or not. At present we are fairly well off but the time has been when we were all asked to keep our expenditures as low as possible. Last year I spent about £440 (estimate £420; expenditure £449. 15. od) on apparatus, current expenditure, repairs, fittings etc. But this does not really give you much idea because in the first instance the expenditure on electrotechnics and electrochemistry is included and secondly I am still drawing in addition to the above on a fund collected when the laboratory was built so that the total expenditure was about £100 more. The expenditure on electrotechnics is spasmodic. Several years pass when very little is spent and then some big sum wants paying. It will be better to separate in future the money question of these two Departments (Electrochemistry and Electrotechnology). I have already seen the Vice-Chancellor about it, who agrees—in fact was the first to suggest it. The above does not include the heating, cleaning, gas, water or electricity. (Last year we paid the Corporation £140 for electric light and £80 was spent on cleaning.)

I think however I may sum up by saying that the Council will do what is in their power to keep up the place in as good a position as regards appliances as possible and they are always ready to consider special applications for money if special circumstances arise.

Bad times may of course come financially when one may not always hope to get everything one wants. It is natural of course that owing to my long connection with the place I was placed in a somewhat exceptional position but as long as they feel certain that you will only ask for what is really necessary you will always be able to get it somehow or other. I have never separated the money required for research from that used in ordinary instruction. It might be done, but it is difficult.

I hope I have not given you too rosy a view of our financial condition. Of course we always want more and often I could not get some elaborate piece of apparatus because the money was not there, but then I also often found out a year or two afterwards that I could do quite well without.

A great acquisition has been the establishment last year of a first class instrument maker within 150 yards of the laboratory. He works by agreement on cheap terms for us and is an excellent man. He was assistant at the Royal Institution and constructed a good deal of Dewar's high pressure apparatus. We also have a tinsmith next door and a very excellent glass blower within easy reach. Our own workshop appliance is small.

My formal resignation will go to the Council this week but it will be a few weeks before further steps will be taken.

You would in all probability be communicated with officially and I should like to see some definite arrangement arrived at towards Christmas or the beginning of the New Year. The new Professor would not be required before October next and I should be prepared to carry on the greater part of the work I am doing till Christmas, i.e. if the new Professor wishes to work himself into the laboratory first, he would probably be able to be free entirely of lectures till Christmas but something depends on the state of one's health. I am afraid I have been writing you a very long and disjointed letter. I can only conclude that your answer has considerably relieved my mind. I am so strongly attached to the place that I could not bear to leave my position except to someone who will keep up its reputation and increase it. There is no-one to whom I would leave it with greater freedom from anxiety than yourself. I hope to find a seat on the Council here and you may be sure that I shall always stand up for the interests of the Physical Department.

Yours very sincerely,

ARTHUR SCHUSTER

Rutherford Memorial Lectures

RUTHERFORD: LIFE AND WORK TO THE YEAR 1919, WITH PERSONAL REMINISCENCES OF THE MANCHESTER PERIOD

By H. R. ROBINSON
Queen Mary College, University of London

The first Rutherford Memorial Lecture of the Physical Society; delivered 6 *November* 1942

IN March 1942 the Council of the Physical Society decided that the first two Rutherford Memorial Lectures should be 'reminiscent and personal'. The decision accords with a general precept stated by Rutherford himself in a letter* to Rayleigh in 1936: 'I am sure that we all ought to . . . give some of our recollections of those past and gone before they are lost for good.' In writing this he had in mind a younger generation that shocked him by appearing to 'have the impression that Science only started in their time', and his argument loses nothing of its force from the fact that a veneration for the great figures of the present and the immediate past was not always a conspicuous feature of his private conversation.

Even in a country which is shamefully neglectful of the history of science, and in a world where one country has for years striven mainly to distort it, Rutherford will not easily be forgotten; he has made too deep and wide a mark for that, and there is too much of his work in both the foundations and the superstructure of modern physics. From this point of view, Rutherford stands less than most men in need of any formal memorial, but a Memorial Lecture can still serve a very good purpose by helping to give, especially for the rising generations

* Quoted in Feather, *Lord Rutherford*, page 57.

of physicists, a picture of the man and of the way in which his work was done. I say deliberately, the way in which the work was done, rather than the work itself; for the latter stands, where everyone may see it, in the literature of physics.

The only discernible slackening in the progress of Rutherford's scientific work, from young manhood to the end of his life, was that imposed by the war of 1914–19; at the end of this period he moved from Manchester to Cambridge. It is therefore by an entirely natural—indeed, loosely speaking, by the only possible—dichotomy that the period allotted to this lecture is that which ends with Rutherford's departure from Manchester.

It is obviously impossible, either in the space of an hour's lecture or in the somewhat larger compass allowed to the lecture in its published form, to do justice to Rutherford's life and contributions to science during this period. Any attempt to do this would inevitably lead to the compilation of a mere catalogue of names and facts. Furthermore, even if it were possible, the existing biographies* and obituary notices make it unnecessary. I shall mention, therefore, only such few salient points as are needed to give an outline to the picture; my main aim will be to give some impression of Rutherford in Manchester and of the atmosphere of endeavour and achievement which he maintained in his laboratory. In this way I may be able to add something new to the much that has already been published. Even if some of these additions are trivial—too trivial, perhaps, to find a place in a serious biography—I hope that they may help towards the construction of a faithful picture of Rutherford in his early prime.

I do not think that I underestimate the difficulty of getting an accurate picture. We have, it is true, a very valuable source of information in Rutherford's own correspondence, a great part of which has, through Lady Rutherford's care and foresight, been preserved and filed. This gives us, expressed in

* A. S. Eve's *Rutherford*, the official biography, gives the life and work, with copious extracts from the correspondence. N. Feather's *Lord Rutherford*, a shorter work, gives a sketch of the life, with an excellent connected and critical summary of the work and a few brief extracts from the correspondence.

his own vigorous English, much first-hand information about him that would otherwise have been lost. The facts remain, however, that Rutherford's genius was of a most uncommon kind, which will not, I think, ever be completely analysed, and that his outlook was less simple than many people believed it to be.

My own picture of him, which I have to try to convey in this lecture, is bound to take some of its colour from the circumstances in which I first knew him. When I first met him, he was at the height of his powers and I was a raw student, fresh from school and barely half his age; I began to work with him (naturally in a not very complicated research) two years later. I have stated these facts, much as a junior student might enter in his laboratory note-book, at the beginning of an experiment, the room temperature and barometric pressure, and with the same lack of certainty about their relevance to what follows. It is probable that if I had been at a less impressionable age when I first met him, or more nearly his equal in age or attainments, I should have arrived at my picture of him by a different process, but I do not think it would in the end have been a very different picture. He would possibly have had a very different picture of me, but that at least is quite irrelevant to the present occasion.

New Zealand, 1871–95

Rutherford's paternal grandfather, George Rutherford, a wheelwright, left Scotland in 1842 to settle, with his family, in New Zealand. His son James, born in 1839, married in 1866 Martha Thompson, who had come to New Zealand at the age of twelve, and who for a short time before her marriage worked as a school teacher. Ernest Rutherford, born on 30 August 1871, was the fourth of the twelve children of this marriage. He was born at Brightwater (Spring Grove), not far from Nelson; four years later the family moved to Foxhill, and in 1882 to Havelock, both in the neighbourhood of Nelson. Ernest attended the State primary schools at Foxhill and Havelock, and apparently was very well taught at both schools. In 1886 he won a scholarship which took him to Nelson

College, and at about the same time his family moved to Pungarehu, in North Island—not very far away—where his father, who had previously worked as a wheelwright, farmer, timber contractor and engineer, now concentrated on large-scale flax production.

Nelson College was evidently a good and progressive school, with an excellent headmaster in W. J. Ford and a fine mathematical master in Dr W. S. Littlejohn, who gave Rutherford a sound start in mathematics and physics. Rutherford had a very successful three years in Nelson, winning awards not only in his best subject, mathematics, but also in Latin, French, English literature, history, physics, and chemistry. It is on record that in June 1888 he was top of the Sixth Form in *all* subjects. In the case of French, which he also later took as a degree subject, I feel sure that his success could only have been due to sheer competence and a powerful determination to succeed; although all his physical writings were crystalline in their clarity, I do not think that he had any real affection for the study of languages. Certainly, when Jean Perrin visited Manchester about 1912 or 1913, Rutherford adopted standard British practice in communicating with him—that is, he spoke in English, rather faster and even rather louder than when addressing a compatriot, with no more concession than an occasional *voici* or *voilà*, *oui* or *non*, to Perrin's almost complete incomprehension of rapid colloquial English.

In 1890 a Junior University Scholarship took Rutherford to Canterbury College, Christchurch, where again he established a record of unbroken academic success. It was here, too, that he met, and formed a deep attachment for, Mary Newton, who became his wife in 1900.

In seniority, Canterbury College was the second institution of university rank to be established in New Zealand. Otago University was founded in 1869, Canterbury College in 1873, and the Colleges at Auckland and Wellington in 1882 and 1897; the University of New Zealand was constituted in 1870. At the time of Rutherford's entry Canterbury College was still small; it had about 150 regular students—Rutherford's name is No. 338 in the college register of students—and 7 professors.

Mathematics was taught by Professor C. H. H. Cook, physics and chemistry by Professor A. W. Bickerton, and it is difficult to imagine a more strongly contrasted pair of teachers. Cook was evidently a sound mathematician and an excellent teacher along orthodox lines, with no marked tendency to stray from those lines. On the other hand, Bickerton's outstanding characteristic was a lively and unbounded enthusiasm for experimental science in all its manifestations. Feather* illustrates his widely ranging interest by quoting two of the seven papers down in his name at an annual meeting of the New Zealand Institute (November 1894); they were: 'On molecular attraction' and 'On chlorine as a cure for consumption'. He was most in his element in speculations on such topics as the rejuvenescence of the cosmos; cosmology was in fact his hobby if that is not too light a term. There is a very revealing passage, relating to the beginnings of his cosmological researches, in his book, *The Birth of Worlds and Systems*, published in 1911.† It runs: ' ... although I held South Kensington teaching certificates in thirteen branches of science, I knew but little of Astronomy, so I had to study the subject'. In all his work he was uninhibited by any lack, conscious or unconscious, of essential preliminary technical knowledge, and to the end of his very long life he remained eager to learn and to advance the cause of science. It is doubtful whether Rutherford's scientific curiosity ever needed sharpening from without, but it is certain that if he had needed a stimulus he would have found it in Bickerton's laboratory.

Bickerton was a remarkable man, and, I think, by all but the harshest academic standards, a great man. Rutherford used to speak of him with affection, and in an obituary notice after his death in 1929 he paid tribute to the part he had played, by his enthusiasm and his encouragement of original investigations, 'of whatever kind', in promoting science in New Zealand.

It was in Bickerton's laboratory, under the most primitive—not to say sordid—conditions, that Rutherford did his first

* *Lord Rutherford*, p. 24.

† Rutherford wrote a short preface to this book.

research work. This was on the magnetization of iron in rapidly alternating fields, and it was followed by the invention of an ingenious and highly sensitive magnetic detector of Hertzian waves. These contributions, which would have been remarkable enough as the first performance of a young researcher under any conditions, must be classed very highly indeed in the light of what we know of the facilities and assistance available to Rutherford at the time.

It should be remembered that New Zealand was then a very young country. It had attracted a very fine type of settler, and it is to the everlasting credit of the early settlers that they did so much to develop a sound educational system, in the face of financial shortage and the difficulty of serving a widely scattered population. When George Rutherford entered New Zealand, the number of white settlers was no more than about 2000; there was no rapid increase either in the numbers or the prosperity of the community, and the first two University Colleges were in fact founded when the total white population was a bare quarter of a million, and predominantly agricultural. It so happened that the year in which Rutherford was born coincided with the beginning of a seven-year period of great prosperity throughout the country, and by the end of the period State schools had, by the Education Act of 1877, been made free, secular and compulsory. It is clear from Rutherford's family history that his parents would in any circumstances have been prepared to make all sacrifices that were possible and necessary to secure the best available education for their children; nevertheless, it is an arresting thought that if Rutherford had chanced to be born a very few years earlier, it is highly improbable that he could have got the early training necessary to direct him into physics. No one who knew him can doubt that, whatever his early training had been, he would have become a great man—but he would have been a different kind of great man, and in all probability the whole face of modern physics would be very different from what it is now.

Cambridge, 1895–98

There was, too, an element of chance in the award of the 1851

Exhibition Science Scholarship which enabled him to come to England in 1895. The examiners' first choice was a chemist, J. S. Maclaurin of Auckland, who was a year senior to Rutherford. Maclaurin, for family reasons, did not take up the award, and the scholarship passed to Rutherford. It was, of course, no chance that took him to Cambridge, and to J. J. Thomson at the Cavendish Laboratory. He arrived there just before the beginning of the Michaelmas Term, beating J. S. Townsend by a short head for the distinction of being the first 'advanced student' to enrol under Thomson for the degree of B.A. by research, which was just being instituted in Cambridge for workers from other universities. This passage, from a letter* written to Mary Newton on 3 October 1895, is well worth quoting: 'I am very glad I came to Cambridge. I admire Thomson quite as much as I thought I would, which is saying a good deal.'

Here he continued to work on Hertzian waves with his magnetic detector, and he had notable success in detecting waves at—for the time—very great distances from their source. He soon, however (Easter 1896), dropped this to work with Thomson on the new subject of ions in gases, building up in a remarkably short time a very complete theory of gaseous conduction and determining experimentally many of the characteristic properties of the ions. It is interesting to note that Rutherford's entry into his life's work was determined by two events, both of which were entirely unpredictable at the time of his arrival in Cambridge—namely, the discovery of X-rays by Röntgen in November 1895 and of radioactivity by Becquerel in February 1896. Both these discoveries were largely accidental, and the second of them was made during the following of a false trail from the first—though there was, of course, nothing that can be described as even remotely accidental in either Röntgen's or Becquerel's approach to, or subsequent development of, his discovery.

It is obvious that Thomson and Rutherford's pioneer work on gaseous ionization depended entirely on this timely discovery of suitable ionizing agents. Thomson's earlier work had

* Eve, *Rutherford*, p. 17.

indeed prepared some of the way, but further advance had to await the discovery of a relatively powerful, convenient, and steady means of ionizing gases at ordinary pressures. The Röntgen tube was the first of all such devices—though it is hardly likely that the adjectives 'convenient', 'powerful', and 'steady' would be among the first to occur to a modern radiologist who was asked to work with a tube of the kind available in 1896, fed by an induction coil.

It was almost inevitable that after working on the ions produced by X-rays, Rutherford should go on to examine those produced by the Becquerel rays, and the passage thence to the study of the radiations themselves was almost equally natural. There was, therefore, once again an element of chance—an accident of time and place—in Rutherford's entry into the field of radioactivity. But for this he might well have continued to give his attention to electromagnetic waves, and it is quite likely that he would have risen to fame mainly as a pioneer of wireless communication. From 1898 onwards, however, there was never any element of chance in his choice of research; he made and pursued his own line as few other men have done, and it would scarcely be an exaggeration to say that his subsequent achievement would have been little less imposing or significant if, in the whole period under review, he had been completely oblivious to everything that went on outside his own mind and his own laboratory.

We may with advantage pause here to recall the state of atomic physics at the time of Rutherford's first Cambridge period. It was a time of almost unparalleled activity. Within a very few weeks of the two discoveries already named, there was a remarkable development in electrical theory. Lorentz, the greatest of the pioneers of modern electron theory, quantitatively explained the newly discovered Zeeman splitting of spectral lines in magnetic fields as a consequence of radiation by charged particles. In particular, he showed that the specific charge of the particles had to be assumed to be about one thousand times that of the hydrogen ion in electrolysis. Negative electrons, possessing this property, were isolated for the first time by J. J. Thomson in 1897, and evidence was rapidly accumulated in support of the view that they were constituents of all ordinary matter. This may well be taken as the starting-point of modern electrical and atomic theory.

Soon afterwards, Townsend, Thomson and others measured the electronic charge, *e*, and Townsend's brilliant work on the diffusion of gaseous ions established its identity with the charge carried by a monovalent electrolytic ion. At the same time C. T. R. Wilson was engaged on his investigations of cloudy condensation of gaseous ions, which played an important part in the early determinations of *e*, and which led some years later to the invention of possibly the most searching tool ever put into the hands of atomic physicists. Thus the stage was well set for the part which Rutherford was destined to play upon it.

In the summer of 1898 he left Cambridge to take the Macdonald Research Professorship of Physics at McGill University, Montreal. The decision to leave Cambridge could not have been an easy one to make, for his work was progressing rapidly, and its success had been recognized in 1897 by the award of the valuable Coutts Trotter Studentship of Trinity College. It seems certain that he was influenced by his desire for a position sufficiently assured to justify an early marriage, and the conviction that, as an 'advanced student', he would be prevented by local prejudice from getting such a position in the Cambridge of 1898. It is equally certain that this belief was due to no act of Thomson's, for J.J. had always championed the cause of the research men from other universities, had always treated Rutherford with great personal kindness, and had given him every encouragement in his work. Rutherford, moreover, must have known that of the first three great holders of the Cavendish Chair only one (Rayleigh) had escaped the contamination of undergraduate life at another institution, for Maxwell had studied at Edinburgh University and Thomson at the Owens College, Manchester. However, it is not likely that he was altogether wrong in thinking that lesser men than Thomson had resented the influx of 'advanced students', and it is, moreover, clear that at this stage he had not yet realized that he was himself of the stuff of which

Cavendish Professors are made. Thomson clearly had a very high opinion of him, but Rutherford's excessively modest view of his own powers is clearly enough expressed in a letter* written to Mary Newton (August 1898) on the Montreal appointment. 'It sounds rather comic to myself', he said, 'to have to supervise the research of other men, but I hope I will get along all right.' Anyone with the least knowledge of what he did in McGill will find it much more than 'rather comic' that he should have harboured such doubts; but, in fact, this diffidence was far less uncharacteristic of Rutherford than many people imagine. Years afterwards, when he had made the Macdonald Laboratory world-famous, he showed himself surprised and almost inordinately gratified that foreigners like Hahn and Godleswki should think it worth while to go there to work with him.

There is no doubt that Rutherford could, if he had so chosen, have obtained a more lucrative post than the Macdonald Professorship. He was never much interested in money, and the excellence of the research equipment at McGill was evidently in his eyes a sufficient compensation for the smallness of the salary offered (£500). As he said himself in a letter† to his mother: 'The salaries are small compared with the endowment of the laboratories and the enormous money spent on them, but that is chiefly due to the fact that the money has been advanced by Macdonald, a millionaire, who made his money in tobacco, and he lives on £250, so he reckons a professor should live on £500. However, £500 is not so bad, and as the physical laboratory is the best of its kind in the world, I cannot complain.'

Montreal, 1898–1907

He arrived in Montreal in September 1898, and was soon hard at work. As a newcomer, and as a very young professor with practically no teaching experience, he might have had many difficulties to surmount, but these were largely swept out of

* Eve, *Rutherford*, p. 55.

† Eve, *Rutherford*, p. 57; Feather, *Lord Rutherford*, pp. 61, 62.

his way by his senior colleague in the physics department, Professor John Cox. Cox is perhaps best known in England (though less well known than he ought to be) by his delightful book on *Mechanics*,* an elementary work in which the subject is treated historically. He was not a great research physicist, but he was a scholar and a perfect colleague. He helped Rutherford's research work by shielding him as far as possible from administrative and elementary teaching duties, and he gave him valuable, timely, and reasoned support when some of his colleagues, unable to appreciate the new advances, were inclined to regard them as unsound, gravely revolutionary, and a menace to the reputation of the University. Cox's understanding and wholehearted support must have been worth a great deal to Rutherford in those early days.

The outstanding advance associated with the McGill period was the development in 1902–3 of the transformation or disintegration theory of radioactivity, published as a result of the joint work of Rutherford and Soddy. The disintegration theory was a staggeringly bold hypothesis to come from two comparatively young workers, one in his first independent command, the other barely past the threshold of his scientific career. It must be difficult, if not impossible, for the young physicist or chemist of the present day to realize how extremely bold it was, and how unacceptable to the atomists of the time; it triumphed because, and only because, no other theory was capable of explaining the then known facts of radioactivity.

Among the facts for which an explanation had to be found were: the evolution by radioactive bodies of large amounts of energy, often with no measurable diminution, over long periods of time, in the amount of active matter; the production and gradual disappearance of the emanations; and the complicated behaviour of the active deposits—originally regarded for a time as evidence of an excited or induced radioactivity. Here, in particular, was a mass of experimental data which might well have seemed incomprehensible; the activity of the deposits varied in a most complicated way with the time, its course

* Cambridge University Press, 1904—now out of print.

depending not only on the length of the preliminary exposure to the emanation but also on the type of electroscope used for the measurement—α-, β-, or γ-ray. In some cases an α-ray electroscope would show a rapid initial fall in the activity of the deposit, while a γ-ray electroscope would show a less rapid initial *rise*, the curves having only one thing in common, namely, that all could be represented by the sum of a number of terms, in which each term varied exponentially with the time. The clue was found in the particularly simple rise and decay curves obtained after suitable chemical separations of members of the uranium and thorium series. Starting from this, Rutherford and Soddy developed the theory of successive transformations, which explained all the known facts and, what is even more important, proved an infallible and indispensable guide for further advances. Even if the theory had ultimately proved to be untenable, its formulation and application would rank as major intellectual achievements in the history of physics. This is a point which needs to be stressed, for the younger generation is more likely to be familiar with the ordered simplicity of the radioactive series, as we now know them, than with the chaotic state which preceded the transformation theory, and may therefore underestimate both the magnitude and the difficulty of the advance which was made.

By the time Rutherford left Montreal for Manchester, in 1907, the theory had been established beyond all reasonable doubt, and many of the details of the sequences of transformations had been elucidated. Rutherford had, moreover, established, in his own mind at least, the nature of the alpha-particles and had made rough measurements of their velocities and specific charge. He had also measured, with Barnes, a number of heating effects. He had received many academic honours, his fame was securely established, and he had made of his laboratory what its founder had always hoped it would become, a permanent centre of research in Montreal. Higher education in Canada owes much to Rutherford—and this indebtedness had been generously and repeatedly acknowledged. On the other side of the balance sheet, McGill gave to Rutherford the material needs for an immensely fruitful nine years' work, and he was always ready to point out that the benefits of his association with Canada had been by no means one-sided.

MANCHESTER, 1907–19

Rutherford's election to the Manchester professorship was largely due to the foresight and initiative of Arthur Schuster, who had marked him down some time before as the successor he would wish to see in the Langworthy chair of physics. Schuster was, for a physicist, a wealthy man; moreover, like so many of his race, he knew not only how to be generous, but also to be so with rare discrimination. This he showed when, on retiring at a relatively early age to make way for Rutherford, he enormously increased the strength and improved the balance of the physics department by persuading the University Council to institute a readership in mathematical physics, and by paying the reader's stipend out of his own pocket for some years. Schuster was a fine physicist, with unusually wide interests, and he had built a laboratory that was, for its time, very well designed and equipped, and that could produce adequate supplies of liquid air. It was, naturally, less well equipped than McGill for work in radioactivity, but Rutherford was never a stickler for luxury in apparatus—in fact, if he had a fault as an experimenter, it was that he was too modest in his demands for material equipment—and he was to be found setting up an emanation electroscope in his new laboratory on 6 June 1907, less than three weeks after he had left Montreal.*

Rutherford evidently liked Manchester from the first, and it is a great tribute to his personality that Manchester took to him so warmly—for he was always very plain-spoken, and Lancashire men, almost as markedly as their Yorkshire neighbours, combine a great pride in their own plain-speaking with an even greater intolerance of plain-speaking in others. Nevertheless, Rutherford soon became, and always remained, one of the most popular figures in the University. He had, it is true, as a newcomer is apt to have, a few clashes with vested interests, but as he got much the better of these clashes he bore

* Feather, *Lord Rutherford*, p. 115.

no malice afterwards—or, more accurately, no more malice than sufficed to provide occasional mild amusement to his friends.

His chief handicap in the first weeks was a shortage of radioactive material, which threatened seriously to curtail his opportunities for work. The Vienna Academy arranged almost at once to lend radium for the joint use of Rutherford and of Sir William Ramsay, but it soon became clear that a sharing arrangement between two strong individualists, each of them fully convinced that the interests of science could be best served by his own virtual monopolization of the active material, was unworkable. Rutherford might doubtless have found the arrangement just tolerable if he himself had been given charge of the radium, but he could not easily resign himself to the existing position, which was that Ramsay had possession of the whole supply in his own laboratory at University College, London. Fortunately, the Vienna Academy made another generous loan of 450 mgm. of radium bromide direct to Rutherford for his own use, and this supply, sometimes by diplomacy, sometimes by swift evasive action, and finally by purchase, he was able to keep in his laboratories to the end of his days.

The Vienna radium was received in January 1908. It was put into solution, and simple but extremely efficient arrangements were made for drawing off and purifying the emanation. After this, although at times there was fierce competition in the laboratory for active sources, there was no really chronic shortage of material. Rutherford was exceptionally fortunate in having in the laboratory at this time one of the most distinguished of the pioneer radio-chemists, his old friend, Professor B. B. Boltwood, of Yale, whom he persuaded to come to Manchester for the session of 1907–8, and who shared with him the responsibility of handling the radium.

Rutherford was fortunate also in the men he found in the Manchester laboratory, most of whom gave up the work they were doing and turned to radioactivity.* He was perhaps most

* Spectroscopic research was, however, always kept alive in the laboratory—one result of this being that after the publication of Bohr's theory of spectra, E. J. Evans was able to obtain spectroscopic confirmation of Bohr's attribution of the Pickering and Fowler lines to helium.

fortunate in finding Hans Geiger, a young graduate of Erlangen, who had already done research under Schuster, and William Kay, a young mechanic who soon afterwards became head steward of the laboratories. Kay, besides being a first-rate mechanic, always appeared to have an instinctive knowledge of the anatomy and pathology of any piece of apparatus, however complicated and unfamiliar it might be. In his younger days he was a fine athlete, well known on the amateur running track, but in a very few years the laboratory appeared to become his sole hobby; he used to put in very long hours there, working a week that would have quite rightly been condemned by any trade union. Every physicist knows the importance of the part played by the technical staff of a laboratory (see, for example, Sir J. J. Thomson's *Recollections and Reflections*, page 115); Kay must be ranked high amongst the world's greatest laboratory stewards and lecture assistants, and no account of Rutherford's Manchester period can be complete without some reference to him. Much of the credit for the smooth running of the laboratory is due to his efficiency, and to his evenness of temper, which survived even the assaults of successive generations of heterogeneous and polyglot groups of research workers.

Geiger was a well-trained and capable all-round physicist, with a considerable command of experimental technique and an almost gluttonous appetite for work. His work with Rutherford on the electrical counting of alpha-particles—an amazing technical feat in those days—was completed within a few months, and the resulting paper, together with that on the total charge carried by the particles, was read to the Royal Society in June 1908. Geiger was later appointed Research Assistant and made responsible for training research students in experimental radioactivity. The training course was substantially that described in Makower and Geiger's *Practical Measurements in Radioactivity*, published in 1912.

Rutherford was now attracting experienced workers to Manchester from many other universities, and he had even learnt to accept this as normal. He was so full of ideas for work that he needed every man he could get, and he trained as many as possible of his own honours students for research. It was customary for such students to take a short course of measurements under Geiger as part of their second-year laboratory work, and to begin practically full-time research on a selected problem in their third year at the University. The main degree examination in physics took place at the end of the second year, and a year later there was a paper on modern physics, and more especially radioactivity, for which students were expected to prepare mainly by the reading of current periodical literature. This scheme of undergraduate training, as I experienced it, had the grave disadvantage of leaving wide gaps in our knowledge of some important sections of classical physics—and this is putting it euphemistically, for the word gap normally connotes at least something more or less solid in which a gap can exist.* On the other hand, under Rutherford the scheme did give to all students the chance of seeing physics as a living and growing science; the best students did, as they always will, get hold of their physics somehow, and the system produced a steady stream of men who could, under Rutherford's and Geiger's supervision, play useful parts in radioactive investigations.

Rutherford's most fruitful contribution to general atomic physics arose directly out of the results of an experimental problem which had been given to Ernest Marsden, one of the first of the Manchester trainees. This was the work on the large-angle scattering of alpha-particles, carried out mainly by Geiger and Marsden in collaboration. Approximately in Rutherford's words,† spoken long afterwards, 'I agreed with Geiger that young Marsden, whom he had been training in radioactive methods, ought to begin a research. Why not let him see if any α-particles can be scattered through a large angle? I did not believe that they would be. . . . It was quite the most incredible event that has ever happened to me in my life. It was almost as incredible as if you had fired a 15-inch shell at a piece of tissue-paper and it came back and hit you.'

* In later years, Rutherford considerably stiffened the lecture courses, and himself took a greater part in them.

† Abridged from a report by Mr J. A. Ratcliffe of Rutherford's last public lecture, in *Background to Modern Science*, p. 68 (1938).

Thus originated Rutherford's nuclear theory of the atom, which he worked out in all essential details in 1911, and which changed the whole face of modern physics. Bohr's application of quantum principles to the motions of the electrons of the nuclear atom followed in 1913, when Bohr was back in Denmark after spending some months in Rutherford's laboratory. In the same year Moseley's beautiful work on X-ray spectra still further clarified the picture by establishing the precise significance of the concept of *atomic number*. Rutherford's first public announcement of the nuclear theory had been made in March 1911, and the detailed theory appeared in the *Philosophical Magazine* in June. Bohr's three papers on 'The constitution of atoms and molecules' and Moseley's first paper on 'The high-frequency spectra of the elements', all communicated by Rutherford, appeared in the same journal between July and December 1913. In the meantime, full confirmation of the nuclear model had been obtained by Geiger and Marsden in a very complete investigation of α-particle scattering.

The years 1911–13 may be regarded as marking the end of the first great phase of radioactive investigation, for the outstanding problem of that period was completely solved by Moseley's identification of the atomic number of an element with the number of natural units of positive charge in its nucleus. The radioactive displacement law, which had been built up on purely chemical evidence by Soddy, Fajans, Fleck, Russell and others, could thenceforward be seen as a necessary consequence of nuclear theory. From this time onwards, interest centred on nuclear physics rather than on classical radioactivity, as it might now be termed.

Rutherford's next attack was upon the problems arising out of the collisions of alpha-particles with light nuclei—the earlier work having dealt with collisions with nuclei heavy enough to be sensibly motionless throughout a collision. On the theoretical side the problem was attacked by C. G. Darwin, who was Schuster Reader at the time; the first experiments were made by Rutherford and J. M. Nuttall and by Marsden, who had become Research Assistant in 1912, on Geiger's departure to Charlottenburg. Rutherford was also turning his attention to

Theory of structure of atom

Suppose atom consists of + charge ne at centre + − charge as electrons distributed throughout sphere of radius b.

Force at P on electron $= Ne^2\left\{\frac{1}{r^2} - \frac{r^3}{b^3}\cdot\frac{1}{r^2}\right\}$

$= Ne^2\left\{\frac{1}{r^2} - \frac{r}{b^3}\right\} = X$

Suppose charged particle e mass m moves through atom so that deflection is small but ⊥ distance from centre $= a$

Deflecting force ⊥ direction of motion at P

$= Ne^2\left\{\frac{1}{r^2} - \frac{r}{b^3}\right\}\cos\theta$

Accel ⊥ direction of motion $= dd = \frac{Ne^2}{m}\left\{\frac{1}{r^2} - \frac{r}{b^3}\right\}\frac{a}{r}$

Velocity u acquired in passing through atom ⊥ direction

$u = \int dd \cdot dt = \int da \cdot \frac{ds}{V}$

$= \frac{Ne^2}{mV}\int\left(\frac{1}{r^2} - \frac{r}{b^3}\right)\frac{a}{r}\cdot\frac{r\,dr}{\sqrt{r^2-a^2}}$

$= \frac{2Ne^2}{mV}\int_0 \ldots\, a\left\{\frac{1}{r^3} - \frac{1}{b^3}\right\}\frac{dr}{\sqrt{r^2-a^2}}$

$= \frac{2Ne^2}{mV}\int \ldots$

MS. page of Rutherford's rough notes: early steps in the theory of the nuclear atom problems of β- and γ-ray emission, and with E. N. da C. Andrade, who succeeded Moseley as John Harling Fellow in 1913, he made the first determination of γ-ray wave-lengths by an ingenious modification of the Bragg method of reflection from crystals.

Research on nuclear physics in Manchester was, however, slowed down by the opening of the first phase of the world war. Rutherford's research school was almost completely dispersed, and most of its younger members were soon afterwards engaged, on one side or the other, in the European conflict. Fortunately for the routine work of the department, Rutherford was able to retain Evans, and Bohr came as Schuster Reader in place of Darwin, who was in France. For the next four years much of Rutherford's time was taken up by work for the Government; it is characteristic of him that he contrived in this period to carry through successfully yet another epoch-making research. In experiments which he began in 1917 and ended early in 1919, generally with Kay alone to help in setting up apparatus and counting scintillations, he succeeded in showing that the nitrogen nucleus could be disrupted by the impact of a swift α-particle, with emission of a hydrogen nucleus. This, the first detected example of 'artificial transmutation', was the last work he published from Manchester; its further development belongs to the second Cambridge period.

* * * * *

When I, as a young student, first met Rutherford, in October 1908, he was at the height of his powers—as he had indeed been for many years, and as he remained to the end of his life. Of my predecessors whom he had met a year earlier, at the beginning of his first session in Manchester, he wrote to Boltwood*: 'I find the students here regard a full professor as little short of Lord God Almighty. It is quite refreshing after the critical attitude of Canadian students. It is always a good thing to feel you are appreciated.' I can testify that the same reverence was felt for Rutherford by my generation and by

* 20 October, 1907. Eve, *Rutherford*, p. 167.

succeeding generations of Manchester students—though he was quite wrong in believing, if he really did believe, that all full professors were similarly honoured.

Officially, students specializing in physics had no lectures from the professor in the first year, but in practice we used to attend his elementary lectures as regularly as we could, partly because they were really illuminating, whatever their topic, and partly for the beautiful, and often sensational experiments which Kay prepared for them. It almost seemed at times that the course of the lectures was determined, not by any preconceived plan of Rutherford's, but by Kay's taste in lecture demonstrations; sometimes—not often—in the course of a lecture Rutherford would lower his huge voice to a huge and perfectly audible whisper, and appeal to Kay for information about the experiment he was demonstrating. This in no way detracted from Rutherford's command of his class; Manchester students at that time were far from docile, but he never had trouble, even with the largest classes, largely because of his knack of getting and keeping their interest in what he had to say.

We saw him at his best and most inspiring at the physics colloquium, which met on Friday afternoons. The meetings, at which we were joined by large numbers of chemists and mathematicians who came over to hear Rutherford, were preceded by an enormous tea-party, generally presided over by Lady Rutherford. Rutherford always addressed the first meeting of the session, giving with obvious enjoyment a summary of the main researches carried out in the laboratory during the preceding year. I am fairly certain that this inaugural address was always called 'The progress of physics, 1907–1908', or whatever the session might be, and that the choice of topics was always made in the same way—or, as we should have said a little later, by the same selection principle. I am quite certain that in the atmosphere of sustained and justifiable enthusiasm which Rutherford created at those meetings, no young Manchester student could fail to feel that he was a member of a highly privileged community. I think we all felt that we were living very near the centre of the scientific universe, and maturer consideration has only strengthened my conviction that we were right. The sense of privilege naturally grew stronger in those who went on to do research, even in those of us who were doing relatively humble tasks, and not, like Moseley, things that were going to matter fundamentally in science for years to come.

At this stage it is platitudinous to say that Rutherford was a born researcher, or that he enjoyed, in all senses of the term, an even less common gift for leadership and companionship in research. His gifts are easier to recognize than to analyse, but obviously some analysis is called for in a memorial lecture. I think it wiser not to attempt anything so presumptuous as a formal analysis, but to give a simple and straightforward account of how Rutherford worked, and kept others at work, in Manchester during the years that I knew him.

In the middle years he generally had in the laboratory between fifteen and twenty men engaged in full-time work in radioactivity, and it must be remembered that as a rule a large proportion of these consisted of young workers for whom he had to provide fairly constant supervision as well as the original idea and scheme of attack. The supervision he provided in full measure, in his daily rounds of the laboratory, and he was brimful of ideas—in fact, there was never a time when he had not more problems ready for attack than men available to attack them. He excelled in devising direct and simple methods of attack that could be carried through with a minimum of elaborate or costly apparatus, and at this stage in the history of radioactivity there were many urgent problems requiring only moderately accurate measurements for their solution. His young assistants could therefore have the unusual satisfaction of doing productive work during their apprenticeship, and—a point of some practical importance—Rutherford had the best of reasons for not worrying about the possibility of half-trained men doing irreparable damage to valuable instruments.

Shortage of apparatus for advanced work, especially where high vacua were needed, was undoubtedly a difficulty at times, and I have never been able fully to understand how even

Rutherford managed to keep everyone going. No doubt he was able to tap a number of external sources for special apparatus for his major researches, but much of the work of the laboratory must have been financed out of ordinary income. Dr Norman Smith, a senior member of the Chemistry staff in Manchester in Rutherford's time, and now Registrar of the University, had been kind enough to get for me the details of the annual grants made for apparatus and equipment to the Physics Department during these years. The accounts are slightly complicated by the fact that until 1912 when it became a separate department under the direction of Professor Robert Beattie, Electrotechnics was administered as a sub-department of Physics. Excluding amounts earmarked for electrotechnics, and two special Government grants of £100 each, the average for 1908–14 was under £420 a year, and for 1915–19 under £100 a year. With these grants Rutherford worked wonders, and there can be few instances in the history of science of comparably rich yields from such modest investments.

Earlier vacuum work in the laboratory was done mainly by preliminary exhaustion with a simple Toepler pump, completed when necessary by charcoal in liquid air. Later, a few Gaede rotary mercury pumps were imported, but even those of us who were lucky enough to get one of these could count only on the very intermittent use of an oil pump for the necessary fore-vacuum; we had to put the largest bottle we could get into the pumping train, in order to reduce to a minimum the number of times we had occasion to 'borrow' the Fleuss pump. The general shortage of apparatus obviously called for a good deal of give and take on the part of everyone in the laboratory; on the whole, this did not cause serious trouble, though a few people are still remembered by their greater readiness to take than to give, rather than by the work that they did.

For some years Geiger acted as a watch-dog over the research apparatus, and although he was a jealous guardian his popularity and prestige were high enough to enable him to do this without much friction. Some things he particularly hated to see leaving his charge, and after an interval of thirty years I can still remember his sorrow on handing over to me a battery of small accumulators that I needed for the electrostatic deflection of alpha-particles. This was a battery of 2400 volts, made up of sixty banks each of twenty lead accumulators of a well-known test-tube type. The test-tubes were very fragile, and the whole design of the battery highly vulnerable. Before handing it over, Geiger delivered a little homily: I was never to touch the battery connections while I was standing on the concrete floor; I must always keep a dry wooden board to stand on while making adjustments, and I must always hold one hand firmly behind my back while touching any part of the battery, so that there could be no risk of a circuit being completed through my body. Before I had any chance of expressing surprise at, or gratitude for, his solicitude, he went on, with obviously complete solemnity and singleness of mind: 'You see, if you get a bad shock you may kick out before you realize what you are doing, and the Prof. would not like it if some of the cells got broken.' Geiger, by the way, nearly always referred to Rutherford as 'the Prof', while most other people spoke of him as 'Papa'—the pronunciation and accenting depending upon whether the speaker was or was not an habitué of the local music-halls. Possibly Geiger thought this appellation disrespectful—if he did, he was wrong.

I have already mentioned Rutherford's daily rounds of his research workers; in these he collected information of any new results, performed prodigies of rapid mental arithmetic in interpreting them, made his suggestions for improvements in apparatus or methods of observation, and discussed difficulties that had arisen. Here, going as he was in quick succession from one problem to another, his apparently intuitive grasp of essentials was remarkable to see. It is true, of course, that most of the problems had originated with him; he had a favourite axiom that 'No man should ever have more than one problem given to him'—meaning that after working on one problem a man should know for himself what to do next—but he was far from consistent in honouring this precept. He much too often had another problem waiting for the man before the first was nearly finished. The daily visits to the research men derived much of their stimulating effect from Rutherford's own passionate interest in the course of the work and his obvious impatience to know the result of each experiment; even the laziest worker was bound to be infected with something of his interest and enthusiasm, or at worst to be imbued with a healthy desire to avert his active disapproval. Rutherford himself was human enough to take pleasure in the idea that one of his functions was to 'ginger people up', as he usually put it, and he did not altogether dislike the feeling that he was pushing along a part of his team, as well as leading the rest.

I am sure that the laboratory tea-table, situated in the radioactivity training laboratory, was far from being the least important bench in the laboratory. Rutherford provided tea and biscuits every day, and nearly always attended himself, sitting at the table, with the rest of us perched on stools and the neighbouring benches. It was a period of relaxation and general gossip, but the meeting often resolved itself into an informal colloquium, with Rutherford taking rather more than a chairman's part. It was here, too, and in the frequent hospitality enjoyed by the research men in his own house, that Rutherford's essential friendliness was most apparent. He had in a very high degree that friendly and companionable spirit which is a notable characteristic of people who have spent much of their lives either in New Zealand or Canada. This undoubtedly had its effect in keeping the laboratory working as a more than commonly united family. Rutherford had, moreover, what is not typical either of England or of any Dominion, a curious insensitivity to differences of academic or social standing, within fairly wide limits, and it probably was very good for the morale of a young research student to see himself treated with as much—or as little—respect as an emeritus professor.

Perhaps the greatest single factor in Rutherford's success as a leader was his own obvious and enormous delight in experimentation. In the days of which I am speaking he always seemed to be at his happiest when he was in the laboratory and working with his own hands or designing his own apparatus.

I remember once wasting with him the whole of a fine Saturday afternoon in an obviously rather hopeless effort to purify, with a few dregs of liquid air, a very dirty little sample of radon with which we had hoped to work. The attempt ended with a momentary and quite uncharacteristic lapse on Rutherford's part, which resulted in the admission to the sample of a much larger volume of air than we had previously succeeded in extracting—a slip which brought out the very characteristic remark, 'Well, it's a good job *I* did that, and not you.' I am afraid I felt that the afternoon might have been better spent, but Rutherford's final comment, as he sucked contentedly at his pipe while we cleared up the mess, was: 'Robinson, you know, I *am* sorry for the poor fellows that haven't got labs. to work in!'

This is, perhaps, in one respect a misleading example of Rutherford's delight in experimental work; I have not wished to suggest that his pleasure would have survived a sequence of wasted afternoons or that he could have found permanent satisfaction, as Henry Cavendish did, in working in isolation and with no thought of publication. In fact, he was far from indifferent to questions of priority in discovery—he liked 'to get there first' and to waste as little time as possible in doing it. I never felt more certain of having pleased him than on the one occasion on which I was lucky enough to get some results far more quickly than he had expected. He happened to say one evening, just before he went home to dinner, that he thought it ought to be possible to get evidence of definite groups of secondary β-rays from lead or other heavy elements, and that we must try it some time with the magnetic spectrograph. As the apparatus we had used for the primary β-rays was only partially dismantled, and as there chanced to be a suitable radon source which I could 'borrow' for the night, I made a trial run, and was amazed to find that I could get a measurable photograph with an unexpectedly short exposure. As a result, by the time Rutherford returned, about nine o'clock next morning, I was able to show him four or five magnetic spectra obtained with different fields and different thicknesses of lead. I still remember vividly the impatience with which I awaited his arrival, and ever since that time I have been quite certain that I understand exactly the feelings of a fox-terrier as, after killing a rat, he brings it into the house and lays it on the drawing-room carpet as an offering to his domestic gods.

This story is not so pointless as it may sound; what I want to stress is that, over and above the usual incentives to research, Rutherford's co-workers in Manchester had an unusually powerful stimulus in their leader's enthusiasm and never-failing keenness, and the desire to please him was a far from negligible factor in the output of the laboratory. It lost nothing of its potency from the fact that Rutherford pleased was a vastly more comfortable figure to have in the laboratory than Rutherford displeased; his pleasure and displeasure were obvious enough to the least experienced and the most obtuse. Newcomers soon learnt that the sight of Rutherford singing lustily 'Onward, Christian soldiers' (recognizable chiefly by the words) as he walked round the corridors was an indication that all was going well. I was interested to learn, many years later, that this apparently quite unconscious habit dated at least from the McGill period.* I do not know if this is true of his other habit of intoning a melancholy dirge (never completely identified, for obvious reasons) when work was not going well, or when he had found someone maltreating a treasured piece of apparatus.

It is perhaps unnecessary to add that Rutherford's attitude to the non-radioactive work in progress in the laboratory was relatively detached, spectroscopic investigations, for instance, being regarded with benevolent, rather than passionate, interest. It is easy for anyone who knew the laboratory to realize how it came about that when Andrade arrived he was at once set to work on a γ-ray problem, though previously he had been working on single metal crystals and on ionization in flames. Similarly, although Darwin came as a mathematician without having suffered the tedious preliminary training which is usually imposed on young physicists, it surprised no one very much to see him in the laboratory in shirt

* A. Norman Shaw, *Proc. Phys. Soc.* **50**, 452 (1938).

sleeves, at work on the experimental investigation of a branching radioactive series.

I remarked not long ago that Rutherford was far from indifferent to questions of priority in discovery—he liked to be recognizably first on a new trail. This tendency had probably been accentuated in Canada when, at a time of rapid advance, his distance from Europe caused delays in publication. 'I have to keep going, as there are always people on my track', he wrote to his mother from Montreal in January 1902.* As this is a manifestation of a trait which is liable to be reprehended by critics who are more coldly academic in outlook, or less energetic in exploration, than Rutherford was (and it is not difficult to be either) it would be unfair to let my remark stand without amplification. It was not, I think, true that Rutherford was inordinately anxious for recognition, but rather that his attitude was exceptionally frank; it should be remembered, too, that he was uncommonly generous in assigning credit to others and in the matter of joint authorship. He had always done a large share of the work in any paper which bore his name as part author, and there were many papers to which he had contributed the original idea and much help, but which did not bear his name.

I can think of nothing more that I can usefully add to this account of Rutherford as leader of his Manchester research school. The period is fittingly summed up in Rutherford's own words, in a letter written to Geiger many years later †: 'They were happy days in Manchester and we wrought better than we knew.'

* * * * *

In the nature of things, there can obviously be no young physicist who knew Rutherford as long ago as the Manchester period, and there must be many of the rising generation who have never seen him at any time; it is therefore fitting, if not imperative, that this lecture should contain some attempt at a personal account of the man, as distinct from the physicist, as

* Eve, *Rutherford*, p. 80.

† Ibid., p. 358 (2 September 1932).

he was in middle life. To deal first with externals, he was a powerful and impressive figure. He stood very little, if anything, under six feet high, and his large frame, if never overloaded with fat, was in middle age what is tactfully described as well-covered. It has frequently been said that he had the appearance of a typical farmer; I think it would be more accurate to say that he looked like a town-dweller's somewhat idealized conception of a typical prosperous and good-tempered farmer. He certainly had, in spite of the long hours he spent in the laboratory and his study, the fresh skin and clear eye usually associated with an outdoor life. Captain Oswald Birley's portrait, executed for the Royal Society, has admirably captured the essential Rutherford of a later period; although it was painted in 1932, it is also very recognizably the Rutherford of 1919. A good impression of Rutherford in the early Manchester days may be obtained from a well-known photograph which shows him with Geiger in the laboratory. This photograph and the Birley portrait are reproduced in our *Proceedings* for 1938.* The photograph, naturally, shows the face in repose, and though it is technically good, it fails to give the impression of great power that one always received on meeting Rutherford in the flesh.

It is with considerable diffidence that I approach the task of describing Rutherford's personality. It is never easy to be objective about the recently dead, and Rutherford was so full of vitality to the last that it is difficult even now to realize that it is over five years since he died. My task is simple in one respect only, namely, that I know nothing about him that there is any need to suppress or whitewash. If there is ever a revival of the unpleasant practice of making literary capital by caricaturing the less agreeable foibles of the truly great, none of its practitioners will be able to make anything of Rutherford, for he had none of the meaner faults.

I do not suggest that he was a copy-book hero, for this he was not, and I cannot think off-hand of any description (except perhaps that of 'intellectual') that would have offended him

* *Proc. Phys. Soc.* **50**, facing pp. 455 and 466 (1938); also reproduced in the present book facing p. 6 and Frontispiece

more deeply. On the whole, he suffered fools far less gladly than is enjoined upon us, but if the folly remained outside certain fairly well-defined limits, Rutherford was as likely as the next man to treat the fool tolerantly, or even kindly. He found it difficult to tolerate pomposity or pretentiousness—or, more accurately, he did not try very hard to tolerate them—and he was very impatient of anyone who discoursed at greater length than he liked—when, for instance, he wanted to take the floor himself, or to go away and do something else. On such occasions he could be, and frequently was, quite ruthless, though after he had thoroughly trounced the offender (and, to do him justice, on occasion when the offender had surprised him by coming back with a well-placed retort) his temper was generally soon restored.

Crimes against apparatus he kept in a special category; for such crimes he had little forgiveness and an uncomfortably long memory. In this respect he was uncommonly like Uncle Pentstemon, who at Mr Polly's wedding, it may be remembered, could see in the bride's elder sister only the young fiend who, many years before, had mucked up his mushroom bed with her clumsy great feet. Similarly, although Rutherford was at any rate after the first few seconds, eminently reasonable about any accident that could fairly be ascribed to ill-luck, his view of a co-worker was apt to be coloured for many years by recollections of a bad case of carelessness.

I have already mentioned his outstanding friendliness, which was a very real characteristic, with no trace of self-consciousness or seeking after popularity, and no taint of the cultivated toothy smile which sometimes simulates friendship; in fact his oldest friend, if he arrived inopportunely, was more likely to be received with a grunt than a smile. Few men can have made more friends, or lost fewer, than he did, and it was delightful to see his pleasure in the company of old friends like Elliot Smith or Boltwood. He liked rejoicing with his friends, and was quick in sympathy with their major misfortunes, though at times he might hugely enjoy the contemplation of their minor mishaps. Like most men who keep their hair, but are not perfectly confident that they will always do so, he took a keen and not quite seemly interest in the signs of approaching baldness in his contemporaries and his juniors, but in most other respects he gave the lie to La Rochefoucauld's best-known maxim.

His mood in the laboratory was generally one of good humour, and frequently boisterous good humour, but he suffered from occasional moods of deep depression, which sometimes lasted for two or three days. As Bohr* put it, when speaking after a public dinner at which Rutherford was the guest of honour: 'To the pupils in his laboratory it is often as if the sun suddenly began to shine when he arrives in the morning; but sometimes it is as if the sky was darkened by a thundercloud'. On bad days he was apt to be unreasonable, and one avoided contact with him as far as possible, but he generally cheered up by tea-time, or earlier if he could be made to laugh, even against himself. I once failed to notice that he was in a bad mood, and I unwisely asked him to authorize the payment of a few shillings for new spring balances for the sonometers in the elementary laboratory. So badly had the time been chosen that this precipitated a tempest, and 'Why must you always have money? Why can't you learn to improvise? Why don't you hang beakers on the ends of the wires and load them by pouring in water?' I must have been in an unusually obstinate mood myself, for I ventured to ask him to calculate the size of a beaker large enough to hold 25 pounds of water, and to guess its probable cost and almost certain fate. This did the trick; in a few seconds he laughed, and soon afterwards he was carolling 'Onward, Christian soldiers' as he went on his round. As a matter of fact, his rare bouts of ill-humour did practically nothing to dispel the cheerful atmosphere which his normal good fellowship created and maintained in the laboratory, and his grumblings were usually so utterly unreasonable that it was difficult for anyone to take them very seriously, or to give them any personal application. When they were not unreasonable, they were made directly to the man concerned, they were usually salutary, they were not unnecessarily repeated, and I do not think they were often

* Eve, *Rutherford*, p. 363.

resented for long. Rutherford was a fairly hard taskmaster, but he spared himself no more than he spared others, and his laboratory housed a very happy family, with remarkably few subterranean rumblings against its head.

The only persistent rumbling had its origin in causes common to most universities of that time, and not peculiar to Rutherford's department. Manchester University was a very good university (and still is; I used the past tense only because I was speaking of a period in the past), but it was expanding rapidly, and it had little money to spare for salaries. Junior staff salaries in science were commonly £125–£150, and the term *junior* in this connection was used very elastically. Some men who had tastes they could not gratify on less than £3 a week, or who wished to marry, undoubtedly found Rutherford's attitude unsympathetic, and his views on the advantages of plain living and high thinking somewhat exaggerated. It is probable that his attitude was largely defensive, and that he was, in fact, putting the best face he could on his own lack of power to move against the general policy of the University, but I think it is true that he did show some lack of imagination in this respect. It should be added that his own personal tastes were extraordinarily simple, and that throughout his life he was almost fantastically indifferent to motives of personal gain. Money meant little to him, and he was perhaps always surprised to find that other people had uses for it. His own instincts were generous and hospitable; he could be generous even with his time, which he valued more than money, and he was surprisingly tolerant of the well-intentioned cranks who pester eminent scientists and of foolish amateurs who wanted to borrow radium, of which they did not appreciate the value, to exhibit at popular lectures. 'Seal up some emanation residues in a glass tube with some dirt and a little zinc sulphide, and send it to them', he would say. 'It will look like a million pounds worth of radium, and nobody will know the difference.'

I have already mentioned the excessive humility of Rutherford's estimate of himself at the time of his Montreal appointment. This was naturally soon modified by the brilliant success of his work, and there is an unmistakable and very human note of triumph in the Preface to the second edition of his *Radioactivity* (1905), where he 'apologizes' for bringing out what was 'almost a new work' of 580 pages barely fifteen months after the issue of a first edition in 399 pages; he refrained from pointing out how much of the new material was directly due to his own activity. Before he left Montreal, he was indisputably supreme in his own subject; no imaginable share of humility could have prevented him from realizing this, and only an entirely misplaced modesty could have led him to deny it. He took the eminently sensible course of thoroughly and openly enjoying the fame he had earned and the occasions of its public recognition, and he liked to see his friends sharing his enjoyment. He was, however, innately and fundamentally much more modest about his achievements than was always apparent to the casual observer, and he made no pretence of special knowledge outside his own subject. I have a pleasant recollection of him, seated in a class that contained many of his own students, industriously taking notes of a course of lectures on the theory of probability given by Professor Horace Lamb, and if Lamb had given us exercises to work out, I should not have been surprised to see Rutherford handing in his exercises with the rest. He had these other signs of essential modesty: he would not only defer to the opinions of authorities in other subjects, but he would also listen with every appearance of respectful attention to quite junior workers in his own subject, and even to people who were merely plausible humbugs; it is not suggested that he always allowed such people to influence his judgement.

* * * * *

I fully realize that the account I have given may be indicted on the ground that it has dealt mainly with the more superficial aspects of Rutherford's work and personality. This choice of treatment has been made quite deliberately. There were, of course, depths and subtleties in Rutherford's mind that are far from apparent in the simplicity and directness of his final approach to and attack upon a physical problem. It is more true of Rutherford than of most men that we cannot

'parcel out
His intellect by geometric rules,
Split like a province into round and square',

and I know that not only more, but vastly more, subtlety than I can command would still be inadequate for even a rough analysis of his genius.

The simplicity of his experimental methods was easy enough to observe. It was neatly summed up by Moseley in a few half-serious words at the end of a discussion on methods he and I were going to use for measuring ionization currents. We decided to use Townsend's induction balance, with which the electrometer deflection is nullified by regulation of a potentiometer circuit attached to a condenser. 'But,' said Moseley, 'Rutherford will think it very effeminate of us to use a null method when we might measure the deflection instead.' Similarly in his appearance and his life outside his work there were many things to suggest the same kind of deceptive simplicity—such as his large build, suggestive rather of latent than active power, his faintly bucolic appearance, his almost schoolboyish sense of fun, and even, in those days, his habitual pipe-smoking. He was a heavy smoker, and it was noticeable that, like many men who work constantly at high pressure, he burnt a great deal more tobacco than he smoked. He was also an inveterate borrower of matches (a venial sin in days when safeties could be purchased almost anywhere at a penny a dozen boxes), and his habit of pocketing the borrowed box was, so far as I can remember, his sole concession to the popular legend of professorial absent-mindedness.

He had read widely and well; just how widely was difficult to know, for he never had the habit of dragging in literary allusions by the coat-tails—they emerged only by chance, and at rare intervals. It was, however, a safe guess that when he turned to fiction for relaxation it would most probably, though not certainly, be to a simple narrative and not to an elaborately psychological novel, and that he would revel in a book like *David Harum*. That he had a subtle and penetrating mind, working at times by ways that were quite inscrutable, was obvious to all who worked with him; its quality should be obvious to all who read his work. That he had a simpler side, which he liked to keep in the foreground, and which enabled him to enjoy simple things, was his and his friends' good fortune.

This lecture began with a quotation from Rutherford. It may fittingly end with a quotation from another great physicist, von Helmholtz, taken from an address* given almost exactly sixty years before the date of Rutherford's death. I am sure it will strike the same chord in any of Rutherford's men that it struck in me when I first read it over thirty years ago. Von Helmholtz was speaking of his own great teacher, Johannes Müller, and after stressing the importance to the student of 'daily mental intercourse with teachers from whom he learns something of the workings of the thoughts of independent minds', he went on to say: 'Anyone who has once come in contact with one or more men of the first rank must have had his whole mental measuring-rod altered for the rest of his life.'

Acknowledgements

I have pleasure in thanking Dr Norman Smith, Registrar of the Victoria University of Manchester, for compiling and sending to me lists of the workers in the Manchester laboratories, with the relevant dates, and the details of the grants made to the Physics Department for apparatus during Rutherford's tenure of the Langworthy Professorship. Also Dr Norman Feather, for suggesting a slide of a portion of Rutherford's rough preliminary draft of the theory of the nuclear atom, for the loan of a suitable page of the manuscript and for authorizing its reproduction here. References to Eve's *Rutherford* and Feather's *Lord Rutherford* have, wherever possible, been indicated in the text.

* Von Helmholtz, 'On Academic Freedom in German Universities', October 1877.

LORD RUTHERFORD: MANCHESTER, 1907–19: A PARTIAL PORTRAIT

By A. S. RUSSELL

Christ Church, Oxford

Lecture delivered 8 *December* 1950

A MEMORIAL lecture must necessarily be in part biographical, and biography, we are told, cannot avoid incursion into autobiography. You will forgive me, therefore, I am sure, if I speak of myself this afternoon as well as of my subject. I am not a physicist—not even a nuclear physicist—but an inorganic chemist, a former pupil and admirer of Lord Rutherford. I think I am the only one since their Montreal days who has worked with both Rutherford and Soddy, so, whatever else I am ignorant of, at least I should be acquainted with the great disintegration theory of radioactivity which these young men sprung on the learned, timid, rather unbelieving, and, as yet, unquantized, world of physics in 1902 and 1903. I don't intend, however, to take you today quite so far back into ancient history as that. I shall begin in 1907 and stop in 1919. That embraces the great middle period of Rutherford's life of discovery that followed the twelve years spent at Cambridge and Montreal, and preceded the eighteen years of his return to Cambridge till his death in 1937. The Manchester period, like the others, was a great period, perhaps the greatest, and it was almost certainly the happiest period of a particularly happy life.

Ernest Rutherford, his New Zealander wife, Mary Newton, and their six-year-old and only child, Eileen, settled in Manchester in a medium-sized, well-planned, admirably warmed house in Withington, on the main road to the South from the University. It was in this house that Professor and Mrs

Rutherford were hospitable hosts in a hospitable University. Supper in the white-painted dining room on Saturdays and Sundays preceded pow-wows till all hours in the study on the first floor; tea on Sundays in the drawing room often followed a spin on the Cheshire roads in the motor. Manchester in 1907 was the Manchester of the *Guardian* and the Hallé Concerts and of Miss Horniman's Repertory Company, where, among the younger members of the company, were Lewis Casson, not then knighted, and Sybil Thorndike, not yet 'Damed'; the Manchester of cotton, liberalism, Free Trade, and the Manchester school; the home of the Hopkinsons, Ramsbothams, Cleggs, and Marsdens as well as the scarcely less Lancastrian Behrens and Schusters, Simons and Zimmerns. At the University Tout and Tait were great names in history, Alexander in philosophy, Schuster in physics, Elliot Smith in anatomy, and Perkin in chemistry. (It is interesting to note that in Perkin's laboratory in 1907 there was a young graduate destined, like Rutherford, to win the 1851 Exhibition scholarship, to become a professor overseas before obtaining a chair at one of the older Universities in England, to gain the Nobel Prize for Chemistry and the Copley Medal, and to become the President of the Royal Society—Sir Robert Robinson.) In that safe and easy world before the *débâcle* of 1914 prices were low. They had to be, for Universities and students were on the whole poor. A research student could then 'manage' at a University like Manchester on a bare hundred pounds a year. Stipends, except to those with very special qualifications, were, by today's standards, fantastic. Rutherford himself had £1,600 a year—a very high salary for those distant days. His regular staff in the department of physics, consisting of nine graduates, also had £1,600 a year—but divided between them—four at the bottom of the list having but £125 a year. You will be glad to know that all of these have had rises since, in more senses than one. One of the nine still remains on the Manchester Physics staff, one would have obtained the Nobel Prize for physics had he not been killed in the 1914–1919 war—H. G. J. Moseley—two became heads of Cambridge colleges and the remaining five professors.

Rutherford impressed me—an impressionable Scot from Glasgow—from the first even more by his kindness and generous outlook on life than by his undoubted great ability in physics. He was a man who never did dirty tricks. It was delightful to be in the daily company of one who could overlook trifles and not harp on real or imaginary grievances or failures. He had been brought up in New Zealand as a presbyterian and, although in his Manchester period he was no churchgoer, he had preserved in the serious part of his life the great puritan qualities. When relaxed or off duty he had, as you all know, a wonderful manner, the manner of one who always seemed to be in tearing spirits. His talk abounded in banter and slang, in wisecrack and epigram, in burlesque and misquotation. Strangers, not knowing the serious man he was, and meeting him away from worry and responsibility, might also gasp at his exuberance, and, certainly, if they were unaware of his other side, they would gain a wrong impression of the man. His loud laugh, his assertive, even boastful, manner at times, and the loud voice, were only parts of him. He had, as I have said, the best of the puritan qualities of heart: a clear, honest, simple integrity, steady composure in the face of difficulties, gentleness on occasion, intelligence, a slow and cautious way of reaching conclusions of importance, a habit of understatement, kindness of heart, decency, and profound and loyal affection for home, parents, and pupils. This was undoubtedly the side of himself he showed to Nature when he was brooding over her secrets or describing what he had done in the scientific journals. He kept his mind instinctively on what was good and positive in the investigations he was making, and, no doubt, he was the better able to do this because he could let off steam, as it were, in moments when no critical person was present. He has been well described as a tribal leader by one of his biographers. That is very true. He could be aggressive, even hard, when his work, or that of his pupils, was being stymied, as he thought, by incompetence. But he was fundamentally fair and fundamentally humble. He hated pretentiousness with the derision of a Mark Twain. 'The vanity of the man was just terrible', he would say, 'I couldn't hear what the man was saying for looking at it'. Or, again, of some nincompoop in high position (such were usually referred to as 'johnnies'): 'That man is like the Euclidean point: he has position without magnitude.' He seemed to have the personal qualities, as well as the gifts in science, to enable a large band of devoted research workers continuously to adhere to him. And, despite this, in the Manchester days, he was no despot, not even a benevolent despot, as he has been described. He showed little envy or jealousy of the position or the work of others. When he got angry with anyone it was because they were interfering, not with his personal success, but merely with the good prospects of the cause. He was by no means unconscious of his greatness, but he had none of the common self-applause that exaggerates what is ordinary into something supreme, and sets down what is in fact good fortune to his own foresight and penetration. Rutherford had supremely foresight and penetration in addition to good fortune. He *was* fortunate, to be sure. He was fortunate in getting the 1851 Exhibition scholarship from New Zealand precisely at the time that X-rays were being discovered and in having J. J. Thomson at Cambridge as his mentor. It was fortunate, too, that radioactivity was such a simple subject. How admirable that it was atomic and not molecular, that the spontaneity of the disintegration was unaffected by any chemical or physical condition, that disintegration, wherever it occurred, followed one law only, that never more than one particle at a time was ejected by the disintegrating atom, and that altogether there were two kinds of particles only! He was fortunate always in his co-workers (and never more so, may I say, than when he was the Cavendish professor at Cambridge). But the basis of good fortune for him was not luck or chance. It resided, no doubt, in the times and the places where he was; but it derived supremely from the character and personality of the man himself and his intellectual gifts.

What were those gifts? His greatest gift was surely his insight into scientific problems. He always saw further ahead in his work in physics than any of his contemporaries and saw more deeply. He saw what was important and what trivial in ideas and results, so that neither time nor pains were lost in following roads that led nowhere. He had been brought up in the physical world of continuity, of induction, of waves, and of the mathematical theories then dominant. He had almost to make a clean break with this environment, almost to invent discontinuity, to imagine paradoxically that by a proper study of the smallest thing in nature, the atom, the main secrets of the physical universe would ultimately be disclosed. And in the study of the atom we now see how wise he was to concentrate on the α-particle and to regard as secondary the β-particle and the γ-wave.

His other great gift was to design experiments that asked of Nature the most pertinent questions and then to brood for long over the answers. In this respect he was of the great company of Newton and Faraday. They knew what to ask and how to pay attention not so much to what Nature was saying as to what Nature was whispering. In this Rutherford was an artist. All his experiments had style. Let me illustrate: One of the early experiments he did at Manchester was with Royds on the identification of the α-particle with the atom of helium. He had known for years that the α-particle was likely to be the helium atom, but he had to make assurance doubly sure. A glass tube blown so thin that it allowed the α-particle easily to penetrate its walls was shown to be gas-tight. Filled with radon it was surrounded by a second glass tube highly evacuated. In this tube it was simple to show that helium accumulated with the passage of time as it got filled by the particles entering it. Then, in 1908, how beautiful, as well as how accurate, was Rutherford's determination of Avogadro's number! He counted accurately the number of α-particles emitted in a given time by a known mass of radium and determined also the value of the charges the particles were carrying. From these data he obtained a value of Avogadro's number which was 40 per cent different from the best of earlier determinations but which is still within 3 per cent of the best determinations of today. Or again, think of the simplicity of the device developed by Geiger and himself to register a single α-particle. A wire charged almost to breaking potential and connected to an electrometer was inserted in a tube into which a very small stream of α-particles was allowed to enter. As one particle entered, its feeble ionization increased greatly by the ionization from collision, sufficed to cause a discharge easily registered by an electrometer. Or think of the work on the scattering of α-particles by thin films of metal where the number scattered through a given angle was counted by well-rested eyes in a dark room by the flashes which each one individually gave on a screen of zinc sulphide; or the comparison of two very disparate standards of γ-radiation by putting each in turn on an optical bench at such distances from a measuring instrument that a constant result was recorded, and then invoking the inverse square law for the calculation. On a backward view one saw the beauty of the method of investigation as well as the ease with which the truth was arrived at. The minimum of fuss went with the minimum chance of error. With one movement from afar Rutherford, so to speak, threaded the needle first time.

Rutherford's Manchester work has often been described and will be merely summarized now. It comprised a wide study of α-particles till about 1911, then an investigation of the scattering of α-particles by metallic screens which led to the enunciation of the great nuclear theory of the atom in 1913, and, thirdly, the work begun in 1913, but much interrupted by the war, which culminated in the successful disintegration of the nucleus of nitrogen in 1917. There was an admirable description of the co-operation between Rutherford and his pupils in Dr Marsden's lecture last year. Rutherford was always the creator of ideas and the main driving force, but while he made the fullest use of their willing help he never 'ran' his pupils or played the dictator, even a benevolent one. It was a reasonably free community. Geiger, Boyle, Boltwood, Bohr, Fajans, Hevesy, Gray, and Andrade were among the more notable arrivals in the laboratory from other Universities. Russ, Makower, Chadwick, Darwin, Marsden, Nuttall, Robinson, and Moseley were among those on the regular staff. Of these, Professor Robinson and Dr Marsden have already given a Rutherford Memorial lecture to you. Sir James Chadwick would have been in my place this afternoon had he not unfortunately become ill, and Sir Charles Darwin, I am glad to see, is with us now.

Moseley from the first was recognized by his colleagues as the most original and gifted on the regular staff after the professor himself. He was a nice man but not 'hail-fellow-well-met'. He was an Etonian not at all amiable to fools and time wasters. He rarely let any loose statement pass in conversation without either a total denial of its validity or a considerable and often pungent modification of the original formulation. He was one of the few who contradicted Rutherford. He worked by choice towards the end of his time mainly through the night, and was one of the hardest workers the laboratory had ever had. Geiger was too much of an Olympian for me to know well. Gentle, without being docile, and aloof, he seemed in laboratory hours to live entirely for the work. He was a beautiful experimenter of the Sir James Dewar type, splendid with his hands. Like many Germans, he loved good music and good dinners. The four young demonstrators who were native to the laboratory, Marsden, Chadwick, Robinson, and Nuttall, had two things in common, devotion to work and a high sense of humour. They were, moreover, quite content with the meagre stipends which the University paid to them. Bohr was one of a small group who advised on mathematical theory as well as carrying out their own research work. His coming to Manchester just at the right time to give Rutherford the maximum help on the mathematical side of the nuclear theory of the atom was indeed providential. Bohr came to England from Denmark in 1912 to work at Cambridge, and at Cambridge he might have stayed out his time had he felt he fitted in there. A chance visit to Rutherford weakened his original intention. He felt instinctively he could fit in better with him than at Cambridge. When Bohr dallied with the idea of coming to Manchester Rutherford persuaded him not to alter his original plan too precipitately. 'Stay in Cambridge as long as you can', said Rutherford in effect. 'It's a good place and there's plenty going forward there. You'll like it the better the longer you are there. And, in any case, Manchester is always here. It won't run away.' Almost the next thing we heard, however, was that Dr and Mrs Bohr had settled in Manchester, and the rest of the story: how Bohr co-operated on the nuclear theory of the atom and rescued the Periodic Classification of the elements from the curves and spirals and whatnots in which it had got unfortunately embedded, is it not one of the best known pieces of history in science?

Here I may interpose a few stories, characteristic rather than funny, to illustrate the man. Rutherford loved chaffing his younger research workers on occasion at tea-time in his laboratory. As I was the only Scot amongst them I came in for a good deal of chaff on the real or supposed foibles of Scotsmen. He thought them an over-scholarshipped and over-praised lot. 'You young fellows come down here from across the border with such testimonials written by your Scots professors that, why man alive!, if Faraday or Clerk Maxwell were competing against you they wouldn't even get on to the short list.' One day he told us he had picked up a delightful phrase from one of the novels of H. G. Wells: 'a fellow of the Royal Society in the sight of God', and thereafter, on occasion, the young Scotsman of science was not only, on paper, miles better than Maxwell and Faraday, 'but already at twenty-four a fellow of the Royal Society in the sight of God'. I once saw Rutherford genuinely surprised. We had been out on a laboratory visit to a works where one of the products was a plated glass teapot. (These were quite popular at one time.) The inner piece of glass held the warm tea, the outer faced the world. Between was deposited some white metal which shone brightly. It was as though a glass mirror had been fashioned into a teapot. To make polite conversation Rutherford asked the man showing him the teapot what metal was used for the plating. He was quite staggered when the man replied 'Platinum'. Platinum in those days was very rare and never spoken lightly of. Moreover, it happened that just at that time Rutherford had shown that what afterwards was called the nucleus of platinum had a charge of about one hundred positive units. Rutherford was consequently emotionally interested in platinum, and so expressed his incredulity about the answer given in a loud and sustained 'Wh-a-a-at?' He wasn't going to be fobbed off with sales talk or have his leg even lightly pulled. 'Platinum?' repeated Rutherford, 'Platinum? Platinum?' 'Yes', quietly answered the man, almost apologizing for the word. 'This isn't a case of "only the best being good enough" for these teapots. It's a case of the most expensive being the cheapest', and he started talking of thinness of films and coverage power and details of that sort. 'But do you really mean platinum?', asked Rutherford again, giving the man one more chance to withdraw. 'Oh, yes', said the man, quite cheerfully. 'It's platinum all right', and then to bring it right down to the level of the Nobel Prizeman in Chemistry, he added: 'One of the osmium, iridium family of metals' and then, turning to me to clinch the matter, he said, 'atomic weight 195·2.' The moment he said that, I knew, somehow, that it was platinum. Platinum, in fact, it really was. Rutherford, genuinely surprised but not yet defeated, then retaliated by asking how much was the cost of plating a single teapot. All he evidently wanted to know was whether it was five shillings, one shilling or what. It was clear from the way the question was received by the man that we were in for a long *viva.* 'Grade A or grade B?' he asked. Rutherford, at a venture, murmured rather boredly 'B'. 'Grade A is better', he was encouraged to believe. 'All right then', roared Rutherford, 'grade A'. 'We don't actually quote for single teapots', resumed the conscientious man. 'I'll quote you the fiftieth of the cost of fifty'. 'All right', shouted Rutherford, whose patience had almost given out. 'Wholesale or retail?', continued the exasperating man, and there would have been a scene had not the answer to Rutherford's 'wholesale' put everyone in high good humour. For the answer that came at long last, given calmly and weightedly, as though empires depended upon it, was, believe it or not, twopence three-farthings! I can still hear Rutherford's long and loud laugh as he heard the unexpected news, and for some time afterwards he had a new story to work off on his friends.

May I give one more story, not funny, not even very complimentary to Rutherford himself, but characteristic of his boisterous manner to strangers, the antithesis, as I have said, of his working and brooding manner? One day at a formal luncheon a bishop started to tell me a story of how he had met my professor at an earlier meal. Knowing that Rutherford was a New Zealander, he had asked him how many people there were in the South Island. He had been quite genuinely surprised to learn in answer that it was only about 250,000. He had imagined till then that the population was of the order of three or four millions. To indicate his surprise, and to get confirmation of the smallness of his figure, he compared it to Rutherford with the population of an English town 'As I spoke to him of this', continued the bishop to me, 'I saw your professor's face flush. You could almost see the blood flowing up the neck and flooding the face . . . '. Just at that interesting point the chairman at the luncheon proposed the health of the King. We rose, and I never heard the end of the story—at least from the bishop. A few days later, however, as I arrived a little late for the laboratory tea, I came in at the professor's words: ' . . . bishop in gaiters. It was perfectly ludicrous. He thought there ought to be about four millions there. "Quarter of a million?", he said to me incredulously. "Do you mean to say there are only 250,000 there? Only about the population of Stoke-on-Trent?".' It was then that I realized why Rutherford had got excited in the bishop's story. The idea of comparing his lovely South Island with some place in England like Stoke-on-Trent! So I waited for the conclusion of the bishop's story. And it came 'So I said to him', continued Rutherford, and then he paused and looked kindly at us all. 'I hope there are none of you here from Stoke-on-Trent. So I said to him: "Maybe the population is only about that of Stoke-on-Trent. But let me tell you, sir, that every single man in the South Island of New Zealand could eat up the whole population of Stoke-on-Trent, every day, before breakfast, and still be hungry".'

Rutherford loved pungent phrases and liked to use them in talk. He did not pretend to originate them. He was content to pass them on. I have mentioned already the wheeze about the Euclidean point and Wells's gibe about the young F.R.S. in the sight of God. Phrases like 'a mere flea in the ocean', 'trembling like an aspic', 'keeping your nose to the gridiron', 'Athens the crater of civilization' were constantly interlarded into conversation, and he could use them with great effect whenever he wanted to. (These are not actually his. I have borrowed them to illustrate.)

I now raise the question with you: Why were the inorganic chemists so slow in the years immediately preceding 1914 in arriving at the conceptions of isotopes and atomic number? When we realize the importance of these conceptions in the nuclear physics of today, as well as in inorganic chemistry, we cannot but criticize the casual manner in which the earlier chemists eventually arrived at them. Crookes was the first to put forward the idea that developed later into that of isotopes. In 1886 he formulated his suggestion of meta-elements. He imagined that an element such as iodine might have atomic masses other than that of 127. The most prevalent mass in Nature would be 127. There would be an appreciable concentration, however, of masses of, say, 126 and 128, smaller concentrations of masses of 125 and 129, and so on. These deviations from 127 would not suffice to make an appreciable difference in the ordinary chemical reactions of the different masses. They would reveal themselves, however, in certain physical properties such as spectra. Thus the different iodine atoms would be 'non-separable' chemically (to use the phrase of 1910), but with regard to the seven series of bands in the absorption spectrum of iodine Crookes imagined that 'some of these molecules may emit some of the series, others others, and in the jumble of all these molecules, to which the name "iodine vapour" is given, the whole seven series are contributors'. That certainly was an idea, an idea well worthy of a great chemist. Crookes, indeed, was a kind of Rutherford of chemistry but a solitary worker, entirely without the 'tribal leadership' qualities.

The curtain descended on this novel theory for twenty years. It rose again in 1906. In that year Otto Hahn discovered a new product, radio-thorium, in the thorium disintegration series, and later found that although it differed from thorium by 4 in atomic mass it could not be separated from it by any chemical reaction to which it had been put. In 1907 McCoy and Ross confirmed this 'non-separability', as it began to be called. In 1908 Boltwood found that uranium differed from every other known radio-element in expelling on disintegration not one, but two α-particles. It was concluded, in consequence, that ordinary uranium consisted of two uraniums, each expelling a single α-particle on disintegration, although it was not then known by how much the two differed in atomic mass. In 1909 Strömholm and Svedberg found that radium, thorium X and actinium X were non-separable, and in the next year Soddy, and independently Marckwald, found that mesothorium 1 and radium were also non-separable, a result, it appeared, that Hahn had himself known for some years. The work of Keetman in 1909, however, turned out to be of most consequence. In finding that ionium and thorium, which were known to differ in atomic mass by 2, were non-separable he had gone 'all out' to effect a chemical separation. The other workers had contented themselves with showing that their non-separable pairs of radio-elements were extremely similar. Keetman tried every chemical and physical device that was available before he had to confess himself defeated. Moreover, in all the other cases the concentration of one of the non-separable radio-elements was known from its half-value period to be below what is called 'weighable amount'. In Keetman's preparation, on the other hand, ionium was present to the extent of about 1 per cent. The excuse that non-separability was due simply to adsorption of a vanishingly small concentration of a radio product on a compound similar to but not necessarily identical with it could no longer be urged. Keetman made it quite clear that non-separability was not just an extreme case of 'difficulty of separation', but something probably fundamental. This was confirmed by Rossi and myself in Rutherford's laboratory. We were given a preparation of thorium that contained at least 2 per cent of ionium, if the half-value of ionium then accepted (and since confirmed) were not many times smaller than was thought. We took the opposite view to that of Crookes. He had imagined that chemical non-separability would be revealed by differences in spectra. We imagined that there would be no difference whatever in the arc spectra of ionium and thorium. Rossi, who was an experienced spectroscopist, was unable to find the slightest difference between the arc spectrum of pure thorium and the mixed spectra of thorium and ionium in conditions when the presence of one-quarter of 1 per cent of impurity would have been easily detected.

With the fact of non-separability, with about forty radio-elements somehow to be 'explained' or fitted into the Periodic Table, and, as we now know, only ten places above the position of lead available, it must strike you as odd that the chemist hesitated for so long to distribute the radio-elements in the available places of the Table. That would have given us at once the idea of isotopes. It would have given us also the displacement laws, and from the displacement laws it would have been seen that the number of positive charges carried by an atom was more important than its mere atomic mass. Note that it would not have given us the absolute values of the atomic numbers of thorium and uranium; that had to wait for the work of Moseley and of Bohr, but it would have given us the atomic numbers of all the radio-elements relative to that of one of them arbitrarily chosen—and this as early as 1911, a year before Rutherford and his co-workers were evolving the idea of atomic numbers from their experiments on the scattering of α-particles by elements like gold and platinum, and two years before Moseley's classical work on the X-ray spectra of the elements. In defence of his apparent lack of insight, or even courage, the chemist could have advanced two points. He could argue that it is unwise to erect into a principle the mere fact that some analytical chemists had failed to effect certain separations. Inability to do something that seemingly ought to be done is surely better met with 'the more fool, you' retort than with the acceptance of a new principle. He could argue also that in 1911 you could not, in fact, 'trust' the Periodic Classification. As a classification it was obviously not periodic. The rare-earth elements demonstrably did not fit in. There were difficulties over the atomic weights of argon and potassium and other pairs of adjacent elements and, worst of all, there was no criterion for limiting the numbers of elements that might be heavier than lead or lighter than hydrogen.

The real difficulty with the inorganic chemist in that period, however, was not that Mendeléef's periodic classification in its development had never kept pace with discovery (so that it always appeared to critical minds more a help to the student or a mnemonic for the memorizer than a true principle in embryo), but that the climate of opinion in inorganic chemistry then was adverse to any kind of speculation or even theorizing. Chemistry, we were always being told, was an experimental science. No good ever came from pontificating on the ways of Nature from the comfort of an armchair. The laboratory bench, not the sofa, we were sarcastically told, was where the truth would be found. And so no inorganic chemist of eminence, not Ramsay, Crookes, Mme. Curie, Soddy, Hahn, Marckwald, or Welsbach, took the final and decisive step in 1911. In the previous year Soddy in comparing a radio-element with its parent expelling an α-particle fastened on the idea of valency. Uranium in expelling an α-particle dropped its valency from 6 to 4; thorium in doing the same dropped its valency from 4 to 2; radium in producing radon dropped its valency from 2 to 0. Valency was the property insisted on. Position, now so simple and obvious an idea, was not then thought of.

I end by speaking very briefly of a point, raised by any consideration of the Life of Lord Rutherford, which has not been much discussed by those who have preceded me in addressing you. The point is the paramount importance of the great man in science. I believe from the bottom of my heart two things in this connection. One is that we cannot afford in science not to know anything that possibly can be discovered. Knowledge has no doubt a bad side, but its credit is enormously greater than its debit in a decent world; life on the whole is enriched by it. The other is that in the pursuit of knowledge we cannot afford to do without the great man. Rutherford often said in his modest way that men of science are not dependent on the ideas of a single man, but on the combined wisdom of thousands of men, all thinking of the same problem, and each doing his part in adding to the great structure of knowledge going up. In some sciences, and in the practical applications of scientific knowledge, the statement is probably truer than most of us realize. But is it altogether true of a fundamental science like physics? Surely it is nearer the mark to say that the more fundamental the science the greater is the need of the big advances which only great men can make. At the least they save us years of waiting while the team of talented workers, however well organized, make their belated discovery. And there are cases, I assert, where if the great man does not do his work the darkness remains permanently unpierced. Where should we be today in physics if Rutherford had not lived among us and given generously of his great endowment? By probing the atom to its very depth he not only revealed great truth and great beauty; he showed us by example what one man can do when he makes the most of his great gifts. His life in Meredith's phrase, may have been 'a little holding', but it was 'lent to do a mighty work'. That such as he have lived among us must raise our hopes of man's worth and dignity in these dark days.

MEMORIES OF RUTHERFORD

By P. M. S. BLACKETT

Physics Department, Imperial College, London

Lecture delivered 26 *November* 1954

ANYONE like myself who had the good luck to come under the direct influence of Rutherford is apt, when faced with some tricky problem in the tactics or strategy of scientific research, to ask himself 'what would Rutherford have done?'. I want today to talk about some of the ways in which I think the study of Rutherford's remarkable career of scientific research and discovery can help us in our present-day problems. Of course, this looking for advice to the actions of the great men of the past has also its dangers, since circumstances change and so it is necessary to change the tactics and strategy of research accordingly. Moreover, one should learn from Rutherford's few mistakes as well as from his many successes.

My own personal contact with Lord Rutherford started in 1921 when I graduated in Physics at the Cavendish Laboratory, Cambridge. Rutherford started me on my first research, gave me my problem and encouraged and inspired me in subsequent years. Until 1933, with short intervals abroad, I worked first as research student and later as a member of his teaching staff. I was indeed lucky to be a member of the Cavendish Laboratory during these exciting and unrivalled years. Not only were many important discoveries made, particularly in the wonder-years 1932–3, but also the period showed a transition from the simple apparatus of Rutherford's earlier epoch to the great machines which are now dominating so large a part of the subject of nuclear structure which he largely himself created.

There are four main points of Rutherford's forty-two years

of scientific achievement. The first was during the Montreal period from 1898 to 1907. It will be remembered that in 1896 Becquerel discovered radioactivity and soon afterwards Marie and Pierre Curie isolated first polonium and then radium. Rutherford started energetically to examine this new phenomenon and within a few years of experimentation and deduction evolved with Soddy the transmutation theory of radioactivity. Radioactive atoms were shown to be unstable and to change spontaneously into atoms of different nature with precisely defined mean lives and with the emission of characteristic radiations. It is most interesting to recall that the isolation of the first material showing the characteristic exponential decay with time was made by investigations of what appeared at first sight to be an irritating inability to get consistent measurement of the radioactivity of thorium. Rutherford and his colleagues soon found that the measured intensity of ionization of a thorium source depended upon whether the door of the laboratory was open or shut! Air draughts were soon shown to be the responsible agents and it became clear that a radioactive gas, emitted from the thorium, was being blown about the room, and so affected the electroscope capriciously. Rutherford immediately investigated the properties of this gas. He passed it at slow speed down a tube and showed that its activity decayed to half strength every so many centimetres down the tube. From the known velocity of the gas, it was deduced that the activity of the radioactive gas decreased to half its strength every minute whatever its original strength. Thus was the first case of exponential radioactive decay discovered. May every young scientist remember this story and not fail to keep his eyes open for the possibility that an irritating failure of his apparatus to give consistent results may once or twice in a lifetime conceal an important discovery.

The second peak of Rutherford's career belongs to the early period at Manchester from 1907 to 1914, where he quickly collected round him a brilliant band of young colleagues—Geiger, Marsden, Nuttall, Moseley, Chadwick, Robinson, Andrade, Darwin, Bohr. The unexpected experimental discovery that α-particles are sometimes scattered through large angles led Rutherford to the nuclear theory of the atom in which it is supposed that all the positive charge in an atom is concentrated on a massive nucleus, ten thousand times smaller than an atom as a whole. Rutherford characteristically said he was as surprised to find that α-particles were deflected through more than 90° by a thin gold foil as if he had seen a 15-inch naval projectile deflected through more than 90° by a piece of paper. This remark and innumerable other examples show that Rutherford possessed an extremely concrete and vivid pictorial and mechanical imagination. He visualized α-particles and atoms as material objects interacting like the rigid bodies of elementary dynamical textbooks. Rutherford saw that one could only get forces large enough to deflect an α-particle through a large angle if the positive electric charge in the atom was concentrated in a very small space. In this way he was led to the very simple and very beautiful theory of the scattering of α-particles by the nucleus which laid the foundations of, or rather at once established, the nuclear theory of the atom. This was probably the greatest of all Rutherford's great discoveries. Soon after it was made, Niels Bohr welded Rutherford's nuclear atom with Planck's quantum theory of radiation into the beautiful Bohr model of the electronic structure of the atom.

The third peak of Rutherford's personal achievement was the demonstration toward the end of the Manchester period that certain light atomic nuclei could be disrupted by the impact of energetic α-particles from radioactive substances. In 1919 on a laboratory bench in a lower room of the present Physics building of Manchester University, Rutherford with his gifted assistant Kay, using an apparatus of great simplicity, showed that α-particles from radium C could disrupt a nitrogen nucleus and eject fast hydrogen nuclei. Thus was born the vast modern subject of nuclear physics, which now gives such fertile research problems to so many of the world's physicists and, incidentally, such headaches to so many of the world's statesmen.

Progress in the first decade of Rutherford's professorship at Cambridge from 1919 to his death in 1937 was rather slower, as the limitations of then existing technical methods of detecting atomic particles became apparent. However, steady progress was made on many important lines. Rutherford and Chadwick made further studies of the disintegration of light elements and of the anomalous scattering of α-particles, and Ellis made important researches on the spectra of β-rays. In 1921 Rutherford had set me the problem of attempting to use C. T. R. Wilson's beautiful cloud chamber method to photograph the disintegration of nitrogen nuclei, which he had observed by means of scintillations. This meant making an automatic cloud chamber which would take a very large number of photographs. After three years' preliminary work mainly concerned with the development of an automatic cloud chamber, I succeeded in 1924 in taking within a few months some 25 thousand photographs showing the tracks of 400 thousand α-particles, and amongst these tracks discovered six which clearly represented the process of atomic disintegration discovered previously by Rutherford. The novel result deduced from these photographs was that the α-particle was itself captured by the nitrogen nucleus with the ejection of a hydrogen atom, so producing a new and then unknown isotope of oxygen, ^{17}O.

The fourth peak of Rutherford's great achievement was the middle period in the Cavendish, particularly the years 1932 to 1933. These two years saw the discovery of the neutron by Chadwick and the disintegration of the nucleus by Cockcroft and Walton using artificially accelerated particles. Though inspired by Rutherford's foresight and encouragement, these discoveries were less his personal work and more the work of his colleagues. The engineering scale of such experiments as Cockcroft's and Walton's was beyond the scope of the individual physicist. Cockcroft was, of course, an electrical engineer turned physicist. Cockcroft's and Walton's work, together with that of Lawrence at Berkeley, inaugurated the Machine Age of nuclear physics, of which the present high points are the Cosmotron at Brookhaven and the Bevatron at Berkeley. On the other hand, Chadwick's discovery of the neutron was truly in the Rutherford tradition and needed little apparatus but much inspiration and physical intuition. Chadwick's paper announcing the discovery describes simple well-designed experiments and is a model of clear physical thinking.

Exciting discoveries were also made in these years in other laboratories. In 1932 Carl Anderson in California discovered the positron among the cosmic rays. This was confirmed by the discovery of cosmic-ray showers of positive and negative electrons by Occhialini and myself early in 1933 using our new counter-controlled cloud chamber method. In 1934 Irene Curie and Frederick Joliot discovered radioactivity induced by impact of α-particles on elements and Fermi discovered similar radioactivity induced by the impact of neutrons. The years 1932 to 1934 surely cannot be equalled in the history of science in this stream of first-class discoveries. Rutherford died shortly before the quite unexpected discovery of fission of uranium by Hahn in 1938, which in a sense was the last of the great discoveries of nuclear physics proper, as distinct from the physics of the elementary particles. Thus Rutherford did not live to see the culmination of the subject that was so much his own; nor consequently did it fall to him to compete with the military and political problems to which Hahn's discovery gave rise.

Looking back over this wonderful list of important discoveries, one cannot but feel surprised that some of them were not made many years previously. This is particularly true of the discovery of the positron and of induced radioactivity. Throughout the nineteen-twenties several workers in different laboratories were measuring the β-ray spectra from radioactive sources emitting strong γ-rays and surrounded by lead or platinum foils. Now it is known today that, in addition to the negative electrons emitted by the metal due to the incident γ-rays, positive electrons are also emitted amounting to a few per hundred. Thus there must have been enormous numbers of positrons available for discovery in many of the β-ray spectrometers then in use. If someone had reversed the magnetic field and made a long exposure, he would have undoubtedly discovered the positrons any time up to a decade before the actual discovery by Anderson.

Then again, the discovery of induced radioactivity was really a rather simple matter—when one knew how to do it. It was only necessary to let a strong source of α-particles bombard a light element such as boron and to examine its radioactivity to find that new unstable elements, in the case of boron a new form of nitrogen, were created. These new elements produce positrons in their spontaneous decay into another element. Cockcroft has suggested that this discovery was not made in the Cavendish Laboratory because they did not then use Geiger counters. Rutherford himself had tended to concentrate his attention on α-particles and protons rather than on β-particles. However, many of his younger colleagues were studying β-activity and still failed to discover induced radioactivity. When one looks back on the history of the subject and notes that Rutherford himself was the first user of counting techniques of α-particles and when one considers the great number of radioactive experiments of all kinds that were done under Rutherford's direction and, moreover, that some of his students were set deliberately to look for induced radioactivity, one is more and more astonished that it was only in 1934 that the discovery was made, and then not in the Cavendish. Research workers today can learn from these two cases not to assume that all the obvious experiments have been done or that their predecessors have not missed some exciting phenomena.

Looking at his scientific career as a whole we see that Rutherford's output of important scientific discovery began in 1895 when he first went to Cambridge and only ended 42 years later with his death in 1937. Only Newton and Faraday can be at all compared with him in the magnitude and duration of their output. Rutherford possessed great physical energy and power of work and concentration—without these even his experimental genius could not have borne such fruit. He had a great belief in his own powers and was not particularly modest about them—in conversation. As was once said of someone else, he had not very much to be modest about. But in print he was most modest. It is amusing in retrospect to note that his paper in 1919 in which he described the disintegration of nitrogen nuclei, and so opened the way to the detailed study of nuclear structure, was entitled 'Collision of α-particles with light atoms. Part 4: An anomalous effect in nitrogen'*.

Rutherford's single-minded and passionate interest in the nucleus led him sometimes to decry the importance and interest of other branches of physics and still more so of other sciences. Though this depreciation was more jocular than serious, his prestige was such that even a joke from Rutherford's mouth was apt to become a dogma in lesser men's minds. No very young physicist could be totally unaffected by his famous crack: 'All science is either physics or stamp collecting', or by the often implied assumption that it only needed some further progress in physics to allow us to deduce from first and physical principles the facts and laws of the lesser sciences like chemistry. Rutherford undoubtedly should have been sympathetic to Compte's hierarchy of sciences with physics placed right at the top, and with each science deducible in principle from the next one higher up the list. However, whatever 'philosophic truth' this scheme may have, the limitations of calculation, even with the electronic machines of the future, will still leave the different sciences largely autonomous in their own fields.

I remember as a young research worker gradually realizing on the one hand the severe limitations of deductive physics as set by the limitations of calculation, and on the other the vast experimental and intellectual achievements of other sciences—for instance, organic chemistry.

In 1924 I spent a year at Göttingen working under James Franck, then in the full flow of experimental discovery and occupied with laying the experimental foundation of the quantum theory of the excitation of spectra, and of the physics of stationary states. I remember how very grudging was Rutherford's permission for me to leave the Cavendish for a year (my first sin) and to study the outside of the atom rather than the nucleus (my second sin).

Rutherford was, of course, right in believing that nuclear

* Reprinted on p. 308

physics was one of the greatest, if not the greatest single branch of physics: he did not, I think, realize as clearly as he might have done (in spite of his friendship with and great admiration for Niels Bohr) that it was just from the study of the electronic structure of atoms that the new laws of quantum and wave theory were emerging, which were essential tools for the understanding of the nucleus. The explanation of Rutherford's twenty-year-old phenomenological theory of radioactive decay arose when Gamow and Gurney independently applied to the nucleus the new wave-mechanical concepts derived from the study of the outside of atoms and their interaction with radiation.

We can see now how it was that the direct study of the nucleus itself, because of its innate complexity and of the experimental difficulties, was not able then to lead, and could hardly even now itself have led, to the necessary revolution in methods of physical thought. These had to come from the simpler and experimentally more accessible electronic structures of atoms.

Let us turn again for a moment to the technical methods by which Rutherford achieved his astonishing output of important discoveries. Great emphasis has often and rightly been laid on the simplicity of his apparatus and their perfect fitness for the matter in hand. In this respect, as in many others, Rutherford and Faraday were alike. Faraday can have used very few pieces of apparatus which he did not construct himself and none that he could not have constructed. This was also true of a large part of Rutherford's personal work, certainly of the work in Montreal and that in Manchester. But by the nineteen-twenties things were beginning to alter. Apparatus had got more complicated and research teams had grown bigger. Thus the personal part that Rutherford himself played in the work diminished, as was inevitable, if only because of the increased calls on his time for all kinds of outside activities. Rutherford was lucky in that as well as being an experimental genius he succeeded in finding a field which was so new and full of exciting possibilities and new results that only simple apparatus was required. He certainly showed genius in designing simple apparatus exactly and perfectly arranged for the purpose. However, when young, he had perhaps a slightly undue contempt for those physicists who were more interested in instrument design than in finding new facts. In a well-known passage he writes of a colleague in 1899, 'As a matter of fact, I don't quite class myself in the same order as Callendar who was more of an engineering type than a physicist and who took more pride in making a piece of apparatus than in discovering a scientific truth—but this is between ourselves'. And even in the Cavendish period when apparatus was inevitably getting more complicated, Rutherford could be disconcertingly unappreciative of experimental and constructional difficulties. I can confirm from personal experience what others have said, that Rutherford took only a minimal interest in one's work during these years of laborious constructional work: indeed, he was often so impatient for results that the young research student had often to exert some will-power to resist being unduly hurried. His own main personal results had been achieved with apparatus of exquisite simplicity—a simplicity arising both from his genius and from the nature of his chosen work—and he was slow to admit that these days were over for the time being, and complexity of apparatus was likely to grow and grow.

Once physical results arose from a student's experiment, then Rutherford became the stimulating and genial visitor to one's room. Rutherford's main rôle in these later Cavendish days (when, of course, he was already a man of affairs with many calls on his time) was to give the new student a fertile problem, leave him to it for a year or two, ignore all the years of travail, but welcome the eventual results with enthusiasm. It is surprising how well the method worked.

Rutherford once said he had never given a student a dud problem! Napoleon is reported to have once said, 'There are no bad soldiers, only bad generals'. Rutherford might have adapted this remark to some of his colleagues (and I think he certainly would have, if he had thought of it, for he had a sharp tongue particularly in the dark room while counting scintillations), 'There are no bad research students, only bad professors'.

It is hardly necessary to point the contrast between these early days and the present time with its huge nuclear accelerating machines costing millions of pounds and requiring teams of engineering physicists working for years on their design and construction. Not only, however, are the machines expensive and big but the actual experiments carried out with them are often of extreme complexity demanding very elaborate electronic equipment which is far beyond the range of a single research worker. Thus modern research work tends more and more to be inevitably organized in teams of young men, in which the engineer, the electronic expert and the physicist (both experimental and theoretical) all play their part. But still we can learn much from Rutherford's attitude and always remember that complication is not an end in itself but a means to an end. Often a little more thought and care, perhaps a little more genius, can simplify an apparatus, although, however, not perhaps to the level of Rutherford's classic apparatus.

Rutherford would have greatly appreciated a story which was current at the end of the second world war. In some Defence laboratory where some complicated instrument for sighting a gun was being designed, which comprised many ingenious electronic and mechanical devices, a young research worker went up one morning very excited to his superior, and said, 'Sir, I have made a discovery. If you take a rod and rest its centre on a solid support, then if you press one end down, the other end goes up. This will save six valves'.

Much has been written of Rutherford's astonishing flair not only for the design of experiments but for interpreting them in what turned out to be the correct manner. He seemed to have a nose for the right answer. Among the mental ingredients were not only a very clear-cut method of picturing the happenings of atomic particles, but also a great knowledge of the order of magnitude of physical quantities. He was extremely good at mental arithmetic and always knew how big any quantities were almost by instinct. But in general he did not like abstract theoretical physics. There is a well-known story dating back to 1910 when Willy Wien was explaining to Rutherford that Newton was wrong in the matter of relative velocity, which was 'not the vector sum of the two velocities $U + V$, but that the expression according to Einstein must be divided by $1 + UV/c^2$. Wien added, 'But no Anglo-Saxon can understand relativity'. No,' laughed Rutherford, 'they have too much sense.' A year later he wrote as follows: 'I was rather struck in Brussels by the fact that Continental people do not seem to be in the least interested to form a physical idea as a basis of Planck's theory. They are quite content to explain everything on a certain assumption and do not worry their heads about the real cause of a thing. I must, I think, say that the English point of view is much more physical and much to be preferred.' Later developments of the quantum theory and wave mechanics were somewhat outside Rutherford's sphere except in so far as they suggested new experiments. However, he was extremely quick to see the real point of some of the new theories. In 1913 he wrote to Bohr, 'Your ideas as to the mode of origin of spectra in hydrogen are very ingenious and seem to work out very well; but the mixture of Planck's ideas and the old mechanics make it very difficult to form a physical idea of what is the basis of it all. There appeared to me one grave difficulty in your hypothesis, which I have no doubt that you fully realize, namely, how does an electron decide what frequency it is going to vibrate at when it passes from one stationary state to the other? It seems to me that you have to assume that the electron knows beforehand where it is going to stop'. Here Rutherford, of course, put his finger right on one of the most important points of the new quantum theory. Much later in the Cambridge time he jokingly referred to theorists. 'They play games with their symbols, but we in the Cavendish turn out the real facts of Nature'.

It has often been remarked that Rutherford used very little mathematics but when he did want mathematics he used it to great effect. The exponential theory of radioactive decay and growth worked out in the earlier period was very elegant and not nearly so obvious as it seems today. Of course, his greatest achievement in the use of mathematics was the application of the Newtonian laws of hyperbolic orbital motion to the scattering of α-particles.

Quite in keeping with his very factual mind and his flair for finding the simple and direct way of attacking a problem was a certain impatience with over-subtle analysis of results, and particularly in the over-emphasis on the theory of errors. A story is told, but with what authority I do not know, that once a research student brought Rutherford some results and started an elaborate discussion of their probable significance in the light of error theory. Rutherford became more and more impatient and finally burst out with, 'Do forget about the theory of errors and go back to your laboratory and do the experiment again'. Whether apocryphal or not, this story does usefully warn one against concentrating too much on the statistical analysis of random errors and too little on the possible presence of consistent errors: experience constantly shows the latter to be often much larger than expected.

I think it is fair to say that Rutherford deliberately sought fields of research in which little mathematical reasoning was needed for their interpretation; and, of course, he was brilliantly successful in finding such fields. And in spite of the huge development of theoretical physics in recent decades there are still such fields of research. It is quite clear that much of the stream of discovery in physics since his death has been largely uninfluenced by abstract theoretical considerations. Rutherford would have been in his element with the new unstable elementary particles.

REMINISCENCES OF THE FOUNDER OF NUCLEAR SCIENCE AND OF SOME DEVELOPMENTS BASED ON HIS WORK*

By NIELS BOHR

IT has been a pleasure for me to accept the invitation from the Physical Society to contribute to the series of Rutherford Memorial Lectures in which, through the years, several of Rutherford's closest collaborators have commented on his fundamental scientific achievements and communicated reminiscences about his great human personality. As one who in early youth had the good fortune to join the group of physicists working under Rutherford's inspiration, and owes so much to his warm friendship through the many succeeding years, I welcome the task of recalling some of my most treasured remembrances. Since it is impossible, of course, in a single lecture to attempt a survey of the immense and many-sided life-work of Ernest Rutherford and its far-reaching consequences, I shall confine myself to periods of which I have personal recollections and to developments I have followed at close hand.

I

The first time I had the great experience of seeing, and listening to Rutherford was in the autumn of 1911 when, after my university studies in Copenhagen, I was working in Cambridge with J. J. Thomson, and Rutherford came down from Manchester to speak at the annual Cavendish Dinner. Although I did not on this occasion come into personal contact with

* The present text is an elaborated version, completed in 1961, of the lecture delivered without a prepared manuscript at a meeting of The Physical Society of London at the Imperial College of Science and Technology on 28 November 1958.

Rutherford I received a deep impression of the charm and power of his personality by which he had been able to achieve almost the incredible wherever he worked. The dinner took place in a most humorous atmosphere and gave the opportunity for several of Rutherford's colleagues to recall some of the many anecdotes which already then were attached to his name. Among various illustrations of how intensely he was absorbed in his researches, a laboratory assistant in the Cavendish was reported to have noted that of all the eager young physicists who through the years had worked in the famous laboratory, Rutherford was the one who could swear at his apparatus most forcefully.

From Rutherford's own address I especially remember the warmth with which he greeted the latest success of his old friend C. T. R. Wilson who by the ingenious cloud chamber method had just then obtained the first photographs of tracks of α-rays exhibiting clear cases of sharp bends in their usual remarkably straight path. Of course, Rutherford was thoroughly acquainted with the phenomenon which only a few months before had led him to his epoch-making discovery of the atomic nucleus; but that such details of the life history of α-rays could now be witnessed directly by our eyes, he admitted to be a surprise, causing him extreme pleasure. In this connection, Rutherford spoke most admiringly of the persistence with which Wilson already during their comradeship in the Cavendish had pursued his researches on cloud formation with ever more refined apparatus. As Wilson later told me, his interest in these beautiful phenomena had been awakened when as a youth he was watching the appearance and disappearance of fogs as air currents ascended the Scottish mountain ridges and again descended in the valleys.

A few weeks after the Cavendish Dinner I went up to Manchester to visit one of my recently deceased father's colleagues who was also a close friend of Rutherford. There I again had the opportunity to see Rutherford who in the meantime had attended the inaugural meeting of the Solvay Council in Brussels where he had met Planck and Einstein for the first time. During the conversation, in which Rutherford spoke with characteristic enthusiasm about the many new prospects in physical science, he kindly assented to my wish to join the group working in his laboratory when in the early spring of 1912 I should have finished my studies in Cambridge where I had been deeply interested in J. J. Thomson's original ideas on the electronic constitution of atoms.

In those days many young physicists from various countries had gathered around Rutherford, attracted by his genius as a physicist and by his unique gifts as a leader of scientific co-operation. Although Rutherford was always intensely occupied with the progress of his own work, he had the patience to listen to every young man, when he felt he had any idea, however modest, on his mind. At the same time, with his whole independent attitude, he had only little respect for authority and could not stand what he called 'pompous talk'. On such occasions he could even sometimes speak in a boyish way about venerable colleagues, but he never permitted himself to enter into personal controversies, and he used to say: 'There is only one person who can take away one's good name, and that is oneself!'

Naturally, to trace in every direction the consequences of the discovery of the atomic nucleus was the centre of interest of the whole Manchester group. In the first weeks of my stay in the laboratory I followed on Rutherford's advice an introductory course on the experimental methods of radioactive research which under the experienced instruction of Geiger, Makower, and Marsden was arranged for the benefit of students and new visitors. However, I rapidly became absorbed in the general theoretical implications of the new atomic model and especially in the possibility it offered of a sharp distinction as regards the physical and chemical properties of matter, between those directly originating in the atomic nucleus itself and those primarily depending on the distribution of the electrons bound to it at distances very large compared with nuclear dimensions.

While the explanation of the radioactive disintegrations had to be sought in the intrinsic constitution of the nucleus, it was evident that the ordinary physical and chemical characteristics of the elements manifested properties of the surrounding electron system. It was even clear that owing to the large mass of the nucleus and its small extension compared with that of the whole atom, the constitution of the electron system would depend almost exclusively on the total electric charge of the nucleus. Such considerations at once suggested the prospect of basing the account of the physical and chemical properties of every element on a single integer, now generally known as the atomic number, expressing the nuclear charge as a multiple of the elementary unit of electricity.

In the development of such views, I was encouraged not least by discussions with George Hevesy who distinguished himself among the Manchester group by his uncommonly broad chemical knowledge. In particular, as early as 1911, he had conceived the ingenious tracer method which has since become so powerful a tool in chemical and biological research. As Hevesy has himself humorously described, he was led to this method by the negative results of elaborate work undertaken as a response to a challenge by Rutherford, who had told him that 'if he was worth his salt' he ought to be helpful by separating the valuable radium D from the large amount of lead chloride, extracted from pitchblende and presented to Rutherford by the Austrian government.

My views took more definite shape in conversations with Hevesy about the wonderful adventure of those Montreal and Manchester years, in which Rutherford and his collaborators, after the discoveries of Becquerel and Madame Curie, had built up the science of radioactivity by progressively disentangling the succession and interconnections of radioactive disintegrations. Thus, when I learned that the number of stable and decaying elements already identified exceeded the available places in the famous table of Mendeleev, it struck me that such chemically inseparable substances, to the existence of which Soddy had early called attention and which later by him were termed 'isotopes', possessed the same nuclear charge and differed only in the mass and intrinsic structure of the nucleus. The immediate conclusion was that by radioactive decay the element, quite independently of any change in its atomic weight, would shift its place in the periodic table by two steps down or one step up, corresponding to the decrease or increase in the nuclear charge accompanying the emission of α- or β-rays, respectively.

When I turned to Rutherford to learn his reaction to such ideas, he expressed, as always, alert interest in any promising simplicity but warned with characteristic caution against overstressing the bearing of the atomic model and extrapolating from comparatively meagre experimental evidence. Still such views, probably originating from many sides, were at that time livelily discussed within the Manchester group and evidence in their support was rapidly forthcoming, especially through chemical investigations by Hevesy as well as by Russell.

In particular, a strong support for the idea of the atomic number as determining the general physical properties of the elements was obtained from spectroscopic investigations by Russell and Rossi of mixtures of ionium and thorium which pointed to the identity of the optical spectra of these two substances in spite of their different radioactive properties and atomic weights. On the basis of an analysis of the whole evidence then available the general relationship between the specified radioactive processes and the resulting change of the atomic number of the element was indicated by Russell in a lecture to the Chemical Society in the late autumn of 1912.

In this connection it is interesting that when after further research, especially by Fleck, the radioactive displacement law in its complete form was enunciated a few months later by Soddy working in Glasgow, as well as by Fajans in Karlsruhe, these authors did not recognize its close relation to the fundamental features of Rutherford's atomic model, and Fajans even regarded the change in chemical properties evidently connected with the electron constitution of the atoms as a strong argument against a model according to which the α- as well as the β-rays had their origin in the nucleus. About the same time, the idea of the atomic number was independently introduced by van den Broek in Amsterdam, but in his classification of the elements a different nuclear charge was still ascribed to every stable or radioactive substance.

Staff and Research Students of Manchester University Physics Department, 1913

T. S. Taylor A. S. Russell

H. Richardson J. M. Nuttall B. Williams W. Kzy

A. B. Wood E. Green R. H. Wilson S. Oba E. Marsden H. Gerrard J. Chadwick F. W. Whaley H. G. J. Moseley

H. Robinson D. C. H. Florance Miss M. White J. N. Pring Prof. E. Rutherford W. Makower E. J. Evans C. G. Darwin

So far, the primary object of the discussions within the Manchester group was the immediate consequences of the discovery of the atomic nucleus. The general programme of interpreting the accumulated experience about the ordinary physical and chemical properties of matter on the basis of the Rutherford model of the atom presented, however, more intricate problems which were to be clarified gradually in the succeeding years. Thus in 1912, there could only be question of a preliminary orientation as to the general features of the situation.

From the outset it was evident that, on the basis of the Rutherford model, the typical stability of atomic systems could by no means be reconciled with classical principles of mechanics and electrodynamics. Indeed, on Newtonian mechanics, no system of point charges admits of a stable static equilibrium, and any motion of the electrons around the nucleus would according to Maxwell's electrodynamics give rise to a dissipation of energy through radiation accompanied by a steady contraction of the system, resulting in the close combination of the nucleus and the electrons within a region of extension far smaller than atomic dimensions.

Still, this situation was not too surprising, since an essential limitation of classical physical theories had already been revealed by Planck's discovery in 1900 of the universal quantum of action which, especially in the hands of Einstein, had found such promising application in the account of specific heats and photo-chemical reactions. Quite independent of the new experimental evidence as regards the structure of the atom, there was therefore a widespread expectation that quantum concepts might have a decisive bearing on the whole problem of the atomic constitution of matter.

Thus, as I later learned, A. Haas had in 1910 attempted, on the basis of Thomson's atomic model, to fix dimensions and periods of electronic motions by means of Planck's relation between the energy and the frequency of a harmonic oscillator. Further, J. Nicholson had in 1912 made use of quantized angular momenta in his search for the origin of certain lines in the spectra of stellar nebulae and the solar corona. Above all, however, it deserves mention that, following early ideas of

Nernst about quantized rotations of molecules, N. Bjerrum already in 1912 predicted the band structure of infra-red absorption lines in diatomic gases and thereby made a first step towards the detailed analysis of molecular spectra eventually achieved on the basis of the subsequent interpretation, by quantum theory, of the general spectral combination law.

Early in my stay in Manchester in the spring of 1912 I became convinced that the electronic constitution of the Rutherford atom was governed throughout by the quantum of action. A support for this view was found not only in the fact that Planck's relation appeared approximately applicable to the more loosely bound electrons involved in the chemical and optical properties of the elements, but especially in the tracing of similar relationships as regards the most firmly bound electrons in the atom revealed by the characteristic penetrating radiation discovered by Barkla. Thus, measurements of the energy necessary to produce the Barkla radiation by electron bombardment of various elements, performed by Whiddington at the time when I was staying in Cambridge, exhibited simple regularities of the kind to be expected from an estimate of the firmest binding energy of an electron rotating in a Planck orbit round a nucleus with a charge given by the atomic number. From Lawrence Bragg's recently published Rutherford Lecture I have been very interested to learn that William Bragg, then in Leeds, in his first investigation of X-ray spectra, based on Laue's discovery in 1912, was fully aware of the bearing of Whiddington's results on the connection between the Barkla radiation and the ordering of the elements in Mendeleev's table, a problem which through Moseley's work in Manchester soon was to receive such complete elucidation.

During the last month of my stay in Manchester I was mainly occupied with a theoretical investigation of the stopping power of matter for α- and β-rays. This problem, which originally was discussed by J. J. Thomson from the point of view of his own atomic model, had just been re-examined by Darwin on the basis of the Rutherford model. In connection with the considerations mentioned above regarding the frequencies involved in the electron binding in the atom, it occurred to me that the transfer of energy from the particles to the electrons could be simply treated in analogy to the dispersion and absorption of radiation. In this way, it proved possible to interpret the results of the stopping power measurements as additional support for ascribing to hydrogen and helium the atomic numbers 1 and 2 in conformity with general chemical evidence, and in particular with Rutherford and Royds' demonstration of the formation of helium gas by the collection of α-particles escaping from thin-walled emanation tubes. Also for the more complex case of heavier substances, approximate agreement was ascertained with the expected atomic numbers and the estimated values for the binding energies of the electrons, but the theoretical methods were much too primitive to yield more accurate results. As is well known, an appropriate treatment of the problem by modern methods of quantum mechanics was first achieved in 1930 by H. Bethe.

Although Rutherford just at that time was concentrating on the preparation of his great book *Radioactive Substances and Their Radiations*, he nevertheless followed my work with a constant interest which gave me the opportunity to learn about the care which he always took in the publications of his pupils. After my return to Denmark I was married in mid-summer 1912, and on our wedding trip in August to England and Scotland, my wife and I passed through Manchester to visit Rutherford and deliver the completed manuscript of my paper on the stopping problems. Both Rutherford and his wife received us with a cordiality which laid the foundation of the intimate friendship that through the many years connected the families.

II

After settling down in Copenhagen I remained in close contact with Rutherford, to whom I regularly reported about the development of the work on general atomic problems which I had started in Manchester. Common to Rutherford's answers, which were always very encouraging, was the spontaneity and joy with which he told about the work in his laboratory. It was indeed the beginning of a long correspondence, which lasted over twenty-five years and which revives, every time I look into it, my memories of Rutherford's enthusiasm for the progress in the field he had opened up, and the warm interest he took in the endeavours of everyone trying to contribute to it.

My letters to Rutherford in the autumn of 1912 concerned the continued endeavours to trace the role of the quantum of action for the electronic constitution of the Rutherford atom including problems of molecular bindings and radiative and magnetic effects. Still the stability question presented in all such considerations intricate difficulties stimulating the search for a firmer hold. However, after various attempts to apply quantum ideas in a more consistent manner it struck me in the early spring of 1913 that a clue to the problem of atomic stability directly applicable to the Rutherford atom was offered by the remarkably simple laws governing the optical spectra of the elements.

On the basis of the extremely accurate measurements of the wavelengths of spectral lines by Rowland and others, and after contributions by Balmer and by Schuster, Rutherford's predecessor in the Manchester chair, the general spectral laws were most ingeniously clarified by Rydberg. The principal result of the thorough analysis of the conspicuous series in the line spectra and their mutual relationship was the recognition that the frequency ν of every line in the spectrum of a given element could be represented with unparalleled accuracy as $\nu = T' - T''$, where T' and T'' are two among a multitude of spectral terms T characteristic of the element.

This fundamental combination law obviously defied ordinary mechanical interpretation and it is interesting to recall how in this connection Lord Rayleigh had pertinently stressed that any general relationship between the frequencies of the normal modes of vibration of a mechanical model would be quadratic and not linear in these frequencies. For the Rutherford atom we should not even expect a line spectrum since, according to ordinary electrodynamics, the frequencies of radiation accompanying the electronic motion would change continuously with the energy emitted. It was therefore natural to attempt to base the explanation of spectra directly on the combination law.

In fact, accepting Einstein's idea of light quanta or photons with energy $h\nu$, where h is Planck's constant, one was led to assume that any emission or absorption of radiation by the atom is an individual process accompanied by an energy transfer $h(T' - T'')$, and to interpret hT as the binding energy of the electrons in some stable, or so-called stationary, state of the atom. In particular, this assumption offered an immediate explanation of the apparently capricious appearance of emission and absorption lines in series spectra. Thus, in emission processes we witness the transition of the atom from a higher to a lower energy level, whereas in the absorption processes we have in general to do with a transfer of the atom from the ground state, with the lowest energy, to one of its excited states.

In the simplest case of the hydrogen spectrum, the terms are with great accuracy given by $T_n = R/n^2$, where n is an integer and R the Rydberg constant. Thus, the interpretation indicated led to a sequence of decreasing values for the binding energy of the electron in the hydrogen atom, pointing to a steplike process by which the electron, originally at a large distance from the nucleus, passes by radiative transitions to stationary states of firmer and firmer binding, characterized by lower and lower n-values, until the ground state, specified by $n = 1$, is reached. Moreover, a comparison of the binding energy in this state with that of an electron moving in a Keplerian orbit round the nucleus yielded orbital dimensions of the same order as the atomic sizes derived from the properties of gases.

On the basis of the Rutherford atomic model, this view also immediately suggested an explanation of the appearance of the Rydberg constant in the more complex spectra of other elements. Thus it was concluded that we were here faced with transition processes involving excited states of the atom, in which one of the electrons had been brought outside the region occupied by the other electrons bound to the nucleus, and therefore exposed to a field of force resembling that surrounding a unit charge.

The tracing of a closer relation between the Rutherford atomic model and the spectral evidence obviously presented intricate problems. On the one hand, the very definition of the charge and mass of the electron and the nucleus rested entirely on an analysis of physical phenomena in terms of the principles of classical mechanics and electromagnetism. On the other hand, the so-called quantum postulate, stating that any change of the intrinsic energy of the atom consists in a complete transition between two stationary states, excluded the possibility of accounting on classical principles for the radiative processes or any other reaction involving the stability of the atom.

As we know today the solution of such problems demanded the development of a mathematical formalism, the proper interpretation of which implied a radical revision of the foundation for the unambiguous use of elementary physical concepts and the recognition of complementary relationships between phenomena observed under different experimental conditions. Still at that time some progress could be made by utilizing classical physical pictures for the classification of stationary states based on Planck's original assumptions on the energy states of a harmonic oscillator. In particular, a starting point was offered by the closer comparison between an oscillator of given frequency and the Keplerian motion of an electron around a nucleus, with a frequency of revolution depending on the binding energy.

In fact, just as in the case of a harmonic oscillator, a simple calculation showed that for each of the stationary states of the hydrogen atom the action integrated over an orbital period of the electron could be identified with nh, a condition which in the case of circular orbits is equivalent to a quantization of the angular momentum in units $h/2\pi$. Such identification involved a fixation of the Rydberg constant, in terms of the charge e and mass m of the electron and Planck's constant, according to the formula

$$R = \frac{2\pi^2 me^4}{h^3}$$

which was found to agree with the empirical value within the accuracy of the available measurements of e, m, and h.

Although this agreement offered an indication of the scope for the use of mechanical models in picturing stationary states, of course the difficulties involved in any combination of quantum ideas and the principles of ordinary mechanics remained. It was therefore most reassuring to find that the whole approach to the spectral problems fulfilled the obvious demand of embracing the classical physical description in the limit where the action involved is sufficiently large to permit the neglect of the individual quantum. Such considerations presented indeed the first indication of the so-called correspondence principle expressing the aim of representing the essentially statistical account of quantum physics as a rational generalization of the classical physical description.

Thus, in ordinary electrodynamics the composition of the radiation emitted from an electron system should be determined by the frequencies and amplitudes of the harmonic oscillations into which the motion of the system can be resolved. Of course no such simple relation holds between the Keplerian motion of an electron around a heavy nucleus and the radiation emitted by transitions between the stationary states of the system. However, in the limiting case of transitions between states for which the values of the quantum number n are large compared with their difference it could be shown that the frequencies of the components of the radiation, appearing as the result of the random individual transition processes, coincide asymptotically with those of the harmonic components of the electron motion. Moreover, the fact that in a Keplerian orbit, in contrast to a simple harmonic oscillation, there appears not only the frequency of revolution but also higher harmonics, offered the possibility of tracing a classical analogy as regards the unrestricted combination of the terms in the hydrogen spectrum.

Still, the unambiguous demonstration of the relation between the Rutherford atomic model and the spectral evidence was for a time hindered by a peculiar circumstance. Already twenty years before, Pickering had observed in the spectra of distant stars a series of lines with wavelengths exhibiting a close numerical relationship with the ordinary hydrogen spectrum. These lines were therefore generally ascribed to hydrogen and were even thought by Rydberg to remove the apparent contrast between the simplicity of the hydrogen spectrum and the complexity of the spectra of other elements, including those of the alkalis, whose structure comes nearest the hydrogen spectrum This view was also upheld by the eminent spectroscopist A. Fowler who just at that time, in laboratory experiments with discharges through a mixture of hydrogen and helium gas, had observed the Pickering lines and new related spectral series.

However, the Pickering and Fowler lines could not be included in the Rydberg formula for the hydrogen spectrum, unless the number n in the expression for the spectral terms were allowed to take half integrals as well as integral values; but this assumption would evidently destroy the asymptotic approach to the classical relationship between energy and spectral frequencies. On the other hand, such correspondence would hold for the spectrum of a system consisting of an electron bound to a nucleus of charge Ze, whose stationary states are determined by the same value nh of the action integral. Indeed, the spectral terms for such a system would be given by Z^2R/n^2, which for $Z = 2$ yields the same result as the introduction of half-integral values of n in the Rydberg formula. Thus, it was natural to ascribe the Pickering and Fowler lines to helium ionized by the high thermal agitation in the stars and in the strong discharges used by Fowler. Indeed, if this conclusion were confirmed, a first step would have been made towards the establishment of quantitative relationships between the properties of different elements on the basis of the Rutherford model.

III

When in March 1913 I wrote to Rutherford, enclosing a draft of my first paper on the quantum theory of atomic constitution, I stressed the importance of settling the question of the origin of the Pickering lines and took the opportunity of asking whether experiments to that purpose could be performed in his laboratory, where from Schuster's days appropriate spectroscopic apparatus were available. I received a prompt answer, so characteristic of Rutherford's acute scientific judgement and helpful human attitude, that I shall quote it in full:

'March 20 1913.

'Dear Dr. Bohr.

I have received your paper safely and read it with great interest, but I want to look over it again carefully when I have more leisure. Your ideas as to the mode of origin of spectrum and hydrogen are very ingenious and seem to work out well; but the mixture of Planck's ideas with the old mechanics make it very difficult to form a physical idea of what is the basis of it. There appears to me one grave difficulty in your hypothesis, which I have no doubt you fully realise, namely, how does an electron decide what frequency it is going to vibrate at when it passes from one stationary state to the other? It seems to me that you would have to assume that the electron knows beforehand where it is going to stop.

There is one criticism of minor character which I would make in the arrangement of the paper. I think in your endeavour to be clear you have a tendency to make your papers much too long, and a tendency to repeat your statements in different parts of the paper. I think that your paper really ought to be cut down, and I think this could be done without sacrificing anything to clearness. I do not know if you appreciate the fact that long papers have a way of frightening readers, who feel that they have not time to dip into them.

I will go over your paper very carefully and let you know what I think about the details. I shall be quite pleased to send it to the Phil. Mag. but I would be happier if its volume could be cut down to a fair amount. In any case I will make any corrections in English that are necessary.

I shall be very pleased to see your later papers, but please take to heart my advice, and try to make them as brief as possible consistent with clearness. I am glad to hear that you are coming over to England later and we shall be very glad to see you when you come to Manchester.

By the way, I was much interested in your speculations in regard to Fowler's spectrum. I mentioned the matter to

Evans here, who told me that he was much interested in it, and I think it quite possible that he may try some experiments on the matter when he comes back next term. General work goes well, but I am held up momentarily by finding that the mass of the α-particle comes out rather bigger than it ought to be. If correct it is such an important conclusion that I cannot publish it until I am certain of my accuracy at every point. The experiments take a good deal of time and have to be done with great accuracy.

Yours very sincerely,
E. Rutherford.

P.S. I suppose you have no objection to my using my judgement to cut out any matter I may consider unnecessary in your paper? Please reply.'

Rutherford's first remark was certainly very pertinent, touching on a point which was to become a central issue in the subsequent prolonged discussions. My own views at that time, as expressed in a lecture at a meeting of the Danish Physical Society in October 1913, were that just the radical departure from the accustomed demands on physical explanation involved in the quantum postulate should of itself leave sufficient scope for the possibility of achieving in due course the incorporation of the new assumptions in a logically consistent scheme. In connection with Rutherford's remark, it is of special interest to recall that Einstein, in his famous paper of 1917 on the derivation of Planck's formula for temperature radiation took the same starting point as regards the origin of spectra, and pointed to the analogy between the statistical laws governing the occurrence of spontaneous radiation processes and the fundamental law of radioactive decay, formulated by Rutherford and Soddy already in 1903. Indeed, this law, which allowed them at one stroke to disentangle the multifarious phenomena of natural radioactivity then known, also proved the clue to the understanding of the later observed peculiar branching in spontaneous decay processes.

The second point raised with such emphasis in Rutherford's letter brought me into a quite embarrassing situation. In fact, a few days before receiving his answer I had sent Rutherford a considerably extended version of the earlier manuscript; the additions especially concerning the relation between emission and absorption spectra and the asymptotic correspondence with the classical physical theories. I therefore felt the only way to straighten matters was to go at once to Manchester and talk it all over with Rutherford himself. Although Rutherford was as busy as ever, he showed an almost angelic patience with me, and after discussions through several long evenings during which he declared he had never thought I should prove so obstinate, he consented to leave all the old and new points in the final paper. Surely both style and language were essentially improved by Rutherford's help and advice, and I have often had occasion to think how right he was in objecting to the rather complicated presentation and especially to the many repetitions caused by reference to previous literature. This Rutherford Memorial Lecture has therefore offered a welcome opportunity to give a more concise account of the actual development of the arguments in those years.

During the following months, the discussion about the origin of the spectral lines ascribed to helium ions took a dramatic turn. In the first place, Evans was able to produce the Fowler lines in discharges through helium of extreme purity, not showing any trace of the ordinary hydrogen lines. Still, Fowler was not yet convinced and stressed the spurious manner in which spectra may appear in gas mixtures. Above all he noted that his accurate measurements of the wavelengths of the Pickering lines did not exactly coincide with those calculated from my formula with $Z = 2$. An answer to the last point was, however, easily found, since it was evident that the mass m in the expression for the Rydberg constant had to be taken not as the mass of a free electron but as the so-called reduced mass $mM(m + M)^{-1}$, where M is the mass of the nucleus. Indeed taking this correction into account, the predicted relationship between the spectra of hydrogen and ionized helium was in complete agreement with all the measurements. This result was at once welcomed by Fowler who took the opportunity of pointing out that also in the spectra of other elements series were observed in which the ordinary Rydberg constant had to be multiplied by a number close to four. Such series spectra, which are generally referred to as spark spectra, could now be recognized as originating from excited ions in contrast to the so-called arc spectra due to excited neutral atoms.

Continued spectroscopical investigations were in the following years to reveal many spectra of atoms, from which not only one but even several electrons were removed. In particular, the well-known investigations of Bowen led to the recognition that the origin of the nebular spectra discussed by Nicholson had to be sought, not in new hypothetical elements, but in atoms of oxygen and nitrogen in a highly ionized state. Eventually the prospect arose of arriving, by analysis of the processes by which the electrons one by one are bound to the nucleus, at a survey of the binding of every electron in the ground state of the Rutherford atom. In 1913, of course, the experimental evidence was still far too scarce, and the theoretical methods for classification of stationary states were not yet sufficiently developed to cope with so ambitious a task.

IV

In the meantime, the work on the electronic constitution of the atom gradually proceeded, and soon again I permitted myself to ask Rutherford for help and advice. Thus, in June 1913 I went to Manchester with a second paper which, besides a continued discussion of the radioactive displacement law and the origin of the Barkla radiation, dealt with the ground state of atoms containing several electrons. As regards this problem, I tried tentatively to arrange the electron orbits in closed rings resembling the shell structure originally introduced by J. J. Thomson in his early attempt to account by his atomic model for the periodicity features in Mendeleev's table of the elements.

In Rutherford's laboratory, I met on that occasion Hevesy and Paneth, who told me of the success of the first systematic investigations by the tracer method of the solubility of lead sulphide and chromate, which at the beginning of that year they had carried out together in Vienna. In every way, these repeated visits to Manchester were a great stimulation and gave me the welcome opportunity to keep abreast of the work in the laboratory. At that time, assisted by Robinson, Rutherford was busily engaged in the analysis of β-ray emission and, in co-operation with Andrade, studied γ-ray spectra. Moreover, Darwin and Moseley were then intensely occupied with refined theoretical and experimental investigations on the diffraction of X-rays in crystals.

A special opportunity to see Rutherford again soon arose in connection with the meeting of the British Association for the Advancement of Science in Birmingham in September 1913. At the meeting, attended by Madame Curie, there was in particular a general discussion about the problem of radiation with the participation of such authorities as Rayleigh, Larmor, and Lorentz, and especially Jeans who gave an introductory survey of the application of quantum theory to the problem of atomic constitution. His lucid exposition was, in fact, the first public expression of serious interest in considerations which outside the Manchester group were generally received with much scepticism. An incident which amused Rutherford and us all was the remark of Lord Rayleigh in response to a solemn request by Sir Joseph Larmor to express his opinion on the latest developments. The prompt reply from the great veteran, who in earlier years had contributed so decisively to the elucidation of radiation problems, was: 'In my young days I took many views very strongly and among them that a man who has passed his sixtieth year ought not to express himself about modern ideas. Although I must confess that today I do not take this view quite so strongly, I keep it strongly enough not to take part in this discussion!'

On my visit to Manchester in June I had discussed with Darwin and Moseley the question of the proper sequence for the arrangement of the elements according to their atomic number, and learned then for the first time about Moseley's plans to settle this problem by systematic measurements of the high-frequency spectra of the elements by the Laue-Bragg method. With Moseley's extraordinary energy and gifts of purposeful experimentation his work developed astonishingly quickly, and already in November 1913 I received a most interesting letter from him with an account of his important results and with some questions regarding their interpretation on the lines which had proved applicable to the optical spectra.

In modern history of physics and chemistry few events have from the outset attracted such general interest as Moseley's discovery of the simple laws allowing an unambiguous assignment of the atomic number to any element from its high-frequency spectrum. Not only was the decisive support of the Rutherford atomic model immediately recognized, but also the intuition which had led Mendeleev at certain places in his table to depart from the sequence of increasing atomic weights was strikingly brought out. In particular, it was evident that Moseley's laws offered an unerring guide in the search for as yet undiscovered elements fitting into vacant places in the series of atomic numbers.

Also as regards the problem of the configuration of the electrons in the atom, Moseley's work was to initiate important progress. Certainly, the predominance, in the innermost part of the atom, of the attraction exerted by the nucleus on the individual electrons over their mutual repulsion afforded the basis for an understanding of the striking similarity between Moseley's spectra and those to be expected for a system consisting of a single electron bound to the bare nucleus. The closer comparison, however, brought new information pertaining to the shell structure of the electronic constitution of the atoms.

An important contribution to this problem was soon after given by Kossel, who, as the origin of the K, L and M types of Barkla radiation, pointed to the removal of an electron from one of the sequence of rings or shells surrounding the nucleus. In particular he ascribed the K_α and K_β components of Moseley's spectra to individual transition processes by which the electron lacking in the K shell is replaced by one of the electrons in the L and M shells, respectively. Proceeding in this way, Kossel was able to trace further relationships between Moseley's measurements of the spectral frequencies which permitted him to represent the whole high-frequency spectrum of an element as a combination scheme in which the product of any of the terms and Planck's constant was to be identified with the energy required to remove an electron from a shell in the atom to a distance from the nucleus beyond all the shells.

In addition, Kossel's views offered an explanation of the fact that the absorption of penetrating radiation of increasing wavelength practically begins with an absorption edge representing the complete removal in one step of an electron of the respective shell. The absence of intermediate excited states was assumed to be due to the full occupation of all shells in the ground state of the atom. As is well known, this view eventually found its final expression through Pauli's formulation in 1924 of the general exclusion principle for electron binding states, inspired by Stoner's derivation of finer details of the shell structure of the Rutherford atom from an analysis of the regularities of the optical spectra.

V

In the autumn of 1913 another stir among physicists was created by Stark's discovery of the surprisingly large effect of electric fields on the structure of the lines in the hydrogen spectrum. With his vigilant attention to all progress in physical science, Rutherford, when he had received Stark's paper from the Prussian Academy, at once wrote to me: 'I think it is rather up to you at the present time to write something on the Zeeman and electric effects, if it is possible to reconcile them with your theory.' Responding to Rutherford's challenge, I tried to look into the matter, and it was soon clear to me that in the effects of electric and magnetic fields we had to do with two very different problems.

The essence of Lorentz's and Larmor's interpretations of Zeeman's famous discovery in 1896 was that it pointed directly to electron motions as the origin of line spectra in a way largely independent of special assumptions about the binding mechanism of the electrons in the atom. Even if the origin of the spectra is assigned to individual transitions between stationary states, the correspondence principle thus led one, in view of Larmor's general theorem, to expect a normal Zeeman effect for all spectral lines emitted by electrons bound in a field of central symmetry, as in the Rutherford atom. Rather did the appearance of so-called anomalous Zeeman effects present new puzzles which could only be overcome more than ten years later when the complex structure of the lines in series spectra was traced to an intrinsic electron spin. A most interesting historical account of this development, to which important contributions were given from various sides, can be found in the well-known volume recently published in memory of Pauli.

In the case of an electric field, however, no effect proportional to its intensity was to be expected for the radiation emitted by a harmonic oscillator, and Stark's discovery therefore definitely excluded the conventional idea of elastic vibrations of electrons as the origin of line spectra. Still, for a Keplerian motion of the electron around the nucleus even a comparatively weak external electric field will through secular perturbations produce considerable changes in the shape and orientation of the orbit. By the study of particular cases in which the orbit remains purely periodic in the external field it was possible, by arguments of the same type as those applied to the stationary states of the undisturbed hydrogen atom, to deduce the order of magnitude of the Stark effect and especially to explain its rapid rise from line to line within the hydrogen spectral series. Yet these considerations clearly showed that for an explanation of the finer details of the phenomenon, the methods for a classification of stationary states of atomic systems were not sufficiently developed.

In just this respect a great advance was achieved in the following years by the introduction of quantum numbers specifying components of angular momenta and other action integrals. Such methods were first suggested by W. Wilson in 1915 who applied them to electron orbits in the hydrogen atom. However, owing to the circumstance that on Newtonian mechanics every orbit in this case is simply periodic with a frequency of revolution depending only on the total energy of the system, no physical effects were disclosed. Still, the velocity dependence on the electron mass, predicted by the new mechanics of Einstein, removes the degeneracy of the motion and introduces a second period in its harmonic components through a continual slow progression of the aphelion of the Keplerian orbit. In fact, as was shown in Sommerfeld's famous paper of 1916, the separate quantization of the angular momentum and of the action in the radial motion permitted a detailed interpretation of the observed fine structure of the lines in the spectra of the hydrogen atom and helium ion.

Moreover, the effect of magnetic and electric fields on the hydrogen spectrum was treated by Sommerfeld and Epstein who by a masterly application of the methods for quantization of multi-periodic systems were able, in complete accordance with observations, to derive the spectral terms by the combination of which the resolution of the hydrogen lines appears. The compatibility of such methods with the principle of adiabatic invariance of stationary states, which Ehrenfest had formulated in 1914 in order to meet thermodynamical requirements, was secured by the circumstance that the action integrals to which the quantum numbers refer according to classical mechanics are not modified by a variation of the external field slow compared with the characteristic periods of the system.

Further evidence of the fruitfulness of the approach was derived from the application of the correspondence principle to the radiation emitted by multiperiodic systems, permitting qualitative conclusions regarding the relative probabilities for the different transition processes. These considerations were not least confirmed by Kramers's explanation of the apparently capricious variations in the intensities of the Stark effect components of the hydrogen lines. It was even found possible to account by the correspondence argument for the absence of certain types of transitions in other atoms, beyond those which, as pointed out by Rubinowicz, could be excluded by the conservation laws for energy and angular momentum applied to the reaction between the atom and the radiation.

With the help of the rapidly increasing experimental evidence about the structure of complicated optical spectra, as well as the methodical search for finer regularities in the high-frequency spectra by Siegbahn and his collaborators, the classification of the binding states in atoms containing several electrons continually advanced. In particular, the study of the way in which the ground states of the atoms could be built up by the successive bindings of the electrons to the nucleus led to a gradual elucidation of the shell structure of the electronic configuration in the atom. Thus, although such essential elements of the explanation as the electron spin were still unknown, it became in fact possible within about ten years of Rutherford's discovery of the atomic nucleus to achieve a summary interpretation of many of the most striking periodicity features of Mendeleev's table.

The whole approach, however, was still of largely semi-empirical character, and it was soon to become clear that for an exhaustive account of the physical and chemical properties of the elements, a radically new departure from classical mechanics was needed in order to incorporate the quantum postulate in a logically consistent scheme. To this well-known development we shall have occasion to return, but I shall first proceed with the account of my reminiscences of Rutherford.

VI

The outbreak of the first world war brought about an almost complete dissolution of the Manchester group, but I was lucky to remain in close contact with Rutherford who in the spring of 1914 had invited me to succeed Darwin in the Schuster Readership of Mathematical Physics. On our arrival in Manchester in early autumn, after a stormy voyage round Scotland, my wife and I were most kindly received by the few of our old friends who remained in the laboratory after the departure of colleagues from abroad and the participation in military duties by most of the British. Rutherford and his wife were at that time still in America on their way back from a visit to their relatives in New Zealand, and it goes without saying that their safe return to Manchester some weeks later was greeted by all of us with great relief and joy.

Rutherford was himself soon drawn into military projects, especially concerning the development of methods of sound tracing of submarines, and teaching the students was almost entirely left to Evans, Makower and me. Still, Rutherford found time to continue his own pioneer work, which already before the end of the war was to give such great results, and showed the same warm interest as ever in the endeavours of his collaborators. As regards the problem of atomic constitution, a new impulse was given by the publication in 1914 of the famous experiments by Franck and Hertz on the excitation of atoms by electron impact.

On the one hand these experiments, carried out with mercury vapour, gave most conspicuous evidence of the stepwise energy transfer in atomic processes; on the other hand the value of the ionization energy of mercury atoms apparently indicated by the experiments was less than half of that to be expected from the interpretation of the mercury spectrum. One was therefore led to suspect that the ionization observed was not directly related to the electronic collisions but was due to an accompanying photo-effect on the electrodes, produced by the radiation emitted by the mercury atoms on their return from the first excited state to the ground state. Encouraged by Rutherford, Makower and I planned experiments to investigate this point, and an intricate quartz apparatus with various electrodes and grids was constructed with the help of the competent German glass-blower in the laboratory who in the earlier days had made the fine α-ray tubes for Rutherford's investigations on the formation of helium.

With his liberal human attitude Rutherford had tried to obtain permission for the glass-blower to continue his work in England in the war time, but the man's temper, not uncommon for artisans in his field, and releasing itself in violent super-patriotic utterances, eventually led to his internment by the British authorities. Thus when our fine apparatus was ruined by an accident in which its support caught fire, there was no help to reconstruct it, and when also Makower shortly afterwards volunteered for military service, the experiments were given up. I need hardly add that the problem was solved with the expected result quite independently by the brilliant investigations of Davis and Gauthier in New York in 1918, and I have only mentioned our fruitless attempts as an indication of the kind of difficulties with which work in the Manchester laboratory was faced in those days, and which were very similar to those the ladies had to cope with in their households.

Still, Rutherford's never-failing optimism exerted a most encouraging influence on his surroundings and I remember how at the time of a serious set-back in the war Rutherford quoted the old utterance ascribed to Napoleon about the impossibility of fighting the British because they were too stupid to understand when they had lost. To me it was also a most pleasant and enlightening experience to be admitted to the monthly discussions among a group of Rutherford's personal friends including Alexander, the philosopher, the historian Tout, the anthropologist Elliot Smith, and Chaim Weizmann, the chemist who thirty years later was to become the first president of Israel and for whose distinctive personality Rutherford had great esteem.

A terrible shock to us all was the tragic message in 1915 of Moseley's untimely death in the Gallipoli campaign, deplored so deeply by the community of physicists all over the world, and which not least Rutherford, who had endeavoured to get Moseley transferred from the front to less dangerous duties, took much to heart.

In the summer of 1916 my wife and I left Manchester and returned to Denmark where I had been appointed to the newly created professorship of theoretical physics in the University of Copenhagen. Notwithstanding the ever-increasing difficulties of postal communication, a steady correspondence with Rutherford was kept up. From my side, I reported about the progress with the work on a more general representation of the quantum theory of atomic constitution which at that time was further stimulated by the development as regards the classification of stationary states, already referred to. In that connection, Rutherford took an interest in what news I could give from the Continent and in particular of my first personal contact with

Sommerfeld and Ehrenfest. In his own letters, Rutherford also gave a vivid description of how, in spite of the increasing difficulties and the pressure of other obligations, he strove to continue his investigations in various directions. Thus in the autumn of 1916, Rutherford wrote about his intense interest in some surprising results regarding the absorption of hard γ-rays produced by high voltage tubes which had just then become available.

In the next years, Rutherford was more and more occupied with the possibilities of producing nuclear disintegrations by means of fast α-rays and already in a letter on 9 December 1917 he writes: 'I occasionally find an odd half-day to try a few of my own experiments and have got I think results that will ultimately prove of great importance. I wish you were here to talk matters over with. I am detecting and counting the lighter atoms set in motion by α-particles, and the results, I think, throw a good deal of light on the character and distribution of forces near the nucleus. I am also trying to break up the atom by this method. In one case, the results look promising but a great deal of work will be required to make sure. Kay helps me and is now an expert counter.' A year later, 17 November 1918, Rutherford in his characteristic manner announced further progress: 'I wish I had you here to discuss the meaning of some of my results in collision of nuclei. I have got some rather startling results, I think, but it is a heavy and long business getting *certain* proofs of my deductions. Counting weak scintillations is hard on old eyes, but still with the aid of Kay I have got through a good deal of work at odd times in the past four years.'

In Rutherford's famous papers in the *Philosophical Magazine*, 1919, containing the account of his fundamental discovery of controlled nuclear disintegrations, he refers to the visit to Manchester, in November 1918, of his old collaborator Ernest Marsden who at the Armistice had got leave from military service in France. With his great experience of scintillation experiments from the old Manchester days when, in collaboration with Geiger, he performed the experiments which led Rutherford to his discovery of the atomic nucleus, Marsden helped him to clear up some apparent anomalies in the statistical distribution of the high-speed protons released by the bombardment of nitrogen with α-rays. From Manchester, Marsden returned to New Zealand to take up his own university duties, but kept in close contact with Rutherford through the years.

In July 1919, when after the Armistice travelling was again possible, I went to Manchester to see Rutherford, and learned in more detail about his great new discovery of controlled, or so-called artificial, nuclear transmutations, by which he gave birth to what he liked to call 'modern Alchemy', and which in the course of time was to give rise to such tremendous consequences as regards man's mastery of the forces of nature. Rutherford was at that time almost alone in the laboratory and, as told in his letters, the only help in his fundamental researches, apart from Marsden's short visit, was his faithful assistant William Kay, who by his kindness and helpfulness through the years had endeared himself to everyone in the laboratory. During my visit, Rutherford also spoke about the great decision he had had to make in response to the offer of the Cavendish professorship in Cambridge left vacant by the retirement of J. J. Thomson. Certainly, it had not been easy for Rutherford to decide to leave Manchester after the many rich years there, but of course he had to follow the call to succeed the unique series of Cavendish professors.

VII

From the beginning Rutherford gathered around him in the Cavendish laboratory a large and brilliant group of research workers. A most notable figure was Aston who through many years had worked with J. J. Thomson and already during the wartime had started the development of mass spectroscopic methods which was to lead to the demonstration of the existence of isotopes of almost every element. This discovery, which gave such a convincing confirmation of Rutherford's atomic model, was not entirely unexpected. Already in the early Manchester days it was understood that the apparent irregularities in the sequence of the atomic weights of the elements when they were ordered according to their chemical properties suggested that even for the stable elements the nuclear charge could not be expected to have a unique relation to the nuclear mass. In letters to me in January and February 1920, Rutherford expressed his joy in Aston's work, particularly about the chlorine isotopes which so clearly illustrated the statistical character of the deviations of chemical atomic weights from integral values. He also commented humorously on the lively disputes in the Cavendish laboratory about the relative merits of different atomic models to which Aston's discovery gave rise.

It was a great help in the continuation of Rutherford's own pioneering work on the constitution and disintegrations of atomic nuclei as well as in the management of the great laboratory, that from the very beginning he was joined by James Chadwick from the old Manchester group, who returned from a long detention in Germany where at the outbreak of the war he had been working in Berlin with Geiger. Among Rutherford's collaborators in the early Cambridge years were also Blackett and Ellis, both coming from a career in the defence services, Ellis having been initiated to physics by Chadwick during their comradeship under German imprisonment. A further asset to the group at the Cavendish was the arrival, a few years later, of Kapitza, who brought with him ingenious projects, in particular for the production of magnetic fields of hitherto unheard-of intensities. In this work he was from the start assisted by John Cockcroft, who with his singular combination of scientific and technological insight was to become such a prominent collaborator of Rutherford.

At the beginning, Charles Darwin, whose mathematical insight had been so helpful in the Manchester years, shared with Ralph Fowler responsibility for the theoretical part of the activities at the Cavendish. In collaboration, they made at that time important contributions to statistical thermodynamics and its application to astrophysical problems. After Darwin's departure for Edinburgh, the principal theoretical adviser and teacher in Cambridge right up to the second world war was Fowler, who had become Rutherford's son-in-law. Not only did Fowler with enthusiastic vigour participate in the work at the Cavendish, but he also soon found numerous gifted pupils who benefited from his inspiration. Foremost among these were Lennard-Jones and Hartree, who both contributed, each along his own line, to the development of atomic and molecular physics, and especially Dirac, who from his early youth distinguished himself by his unique logical power.

Ever since I left Manchester in 1916, I had of course tried to use the experience gained in Rutherford's laboratory and it is with gratitude that I recall how Rutherford from the very outset most kindly and effectively supported my endeavours in Copenhagen to create an institute to promote intimate collaboration between theoretical and experimental physicists. It was a special encouragement that already in the autumn of 1920, when the Institute building was nearing completion, Rutherford found time to visit us in Copenhagen. As a token of appreciation the University conferred upon him an honorary degree and on that occasion he gave a most stimulating and humorous address which was long remembered by all present.

For the work in the new Institute it was of great benefit that we were joined shortly after the war by my old friend from the Manchester days, George Hevesy, who during the more than twenty years he worked in Copenhagen carried out many of his famous physico-chemical and biological researches, based on the isotopic tracer method. A special event, in which Rutherford took great interest, was the application of Moseley's method by Coster and Hevesy in 1922 to the successful search for the missing element now called hafnium, the properties of which gave strong additional support to the interpretation of the periodic system of the elements. An auspicious start was given to the general experimental work by a visit, at the opening of the laboratory, of James Franck, who during the following months most kindly instructed the Danish collaborators in the refined technique of excitation of atomic spectra by electron bombardment which he had so ingeniously developed together with Gustav Hertz.

The first among the many distinguished theoretical physicists who stayed with us for a longer period was Hans Kramers who as a quite young man came to Copenhagen during the war and proved to be such an invaluable asset to our group during the ten years he worked with us until, in 1926, he left his position as lecturer in the Institute to take over a professorship in Utrecht. Shortly after Kramers's arrival in Copenhagen came two promising young men, Oscar Klein from Sweden and Svein Rosseland from Norway, who already in 1920 made their names known by pointing to the so-called collisions of the second kind, in which atoms are transferred by electron bombardment from a higher to a lower stationary state with gain of velocity for the electron. Indeed, the occurrence of such processes is decisive for ensuring thermal equilibrium in a way analogous to the induced radiative transitions which played an essential rôle in Einstein's derivation of Planck's formula for temperature radiation. The consideration of collisions of the second kind proved particularly important for the elucidation of the radiative properties of stellar atmospheres, to which at that time Saha, working in Cambridge with Fowler, made such fundamental contributions.

The group at the Copenhagen Institute was joined in 1922 by Pauli, and two years later by Heisenberg, both pupils of Sommerfeld, and who, young as they were, had already accomplished most brilliant work. I had made their acquaintance and formed a deep impression of their extraordinary talent in the summer of 1922 during a lecturing visit to Göttingen, which initiated a long and fruitful co-operation between the group working there under the leadership of Born and Franck, and the Copenhagen group. From the early days our close connection with the great centre in Cambridge was maintained especially by longer visits to Copenhagen of Darwin, Dirac, Fowler, Hartree, Mott, and others.

VIII

Those years, when a unique co-operation of a whole generation of theoretical physicists from many countries created step by step a logically consistent generalization of classical mechanics and electromagnetism, have sometimes been described as the 'heroic' era in quantum physics. To everyone following this development, it was an unforgettable experience to witness how, through the combination of different lines of approach and the introduction of appropriate mathematical methods, a new outlook emerged regarding the comprehension of physical experience. Many obstacles had to be overcome before this goal was reached, and time and again decisive progress was achieved by some of the youngest among us.

The common starting point was the recognition that, notwithstanding the great help which the use of mechanical pictures had temporarily offered for the classification of stationary states of atoms in isolation or exposed to constant external forces, it was clear, as already mentioned, that a fundamentally new departure was needed. Not only was the difficulty of picturing the electronic constitution of chemical compounds on the basis of the Rutherford atomic model more and more evident, but insurmountable difficulties also arose in any attempts to account in detail for the complexity of atomic spectra, especially conspicuous in the peculiar duplex character of the arc spectrum of helium.

The first step to a more general formulation of the correspondence principle was offered by the problem of optical dispersion. Indeed, the close relation between the atomic dispersion and the selective absorption of spectral lines so beautifully illustrated by the ingenious experiments of R. W. Wood and P. V. Bevan on the absorption and dispersion in alkali vapours, suggested from the very beginning a correspondence approach. On the basis of Einstein's formulation of the statistical laws for the occurrence of radiation-induced transitions between stationary states of an atomic system, Kramers in 1924 succeeded in establishing a general dispersion formula, involving only the energies of these states and the probabilities of spontaneous transitions between them. This theory, further developed by Kramers and Heisenberg included even new dispersion effects connected with the appearance, under the influence of the radiation, of possibilities for transitions not present in the unperturbed atom, and an analogue to which is the Raman effect in molecular spectra.

Shortly afterwards an advance of fundamental significance was achieved by Heisenberg who in 1925 introduced a most ingenious formalism, in which all use of orbital pictures beyond the general asymptotic correspondence was avoided. In this bold conception, the canonical equations of mechanics are retained in their Hamiltonian form, but the conjugate variables are replaced by operators subject to a non-commutative algorism involving Planck's constant as well as the symbol $\sqrt{-1}$. In fact, by representing the mechanical quantities by hermitian matrices with elements referring to all possible transition processes between stationary states, it proved possible without any arbitrariness to deduce the energies of these states and the probabilities of the associated transition processes. This so-called quantum mechanics, to the elaboration of which Born and Jordan as well as Dirac from the outset made important contributions, opened the way to a consistent statistical treatment of many atomic problems which hitherto were only amenable to a semi-empirical approach.

For the completion of this great task, the emphasis on the formal analogy between mechanics and optics, originally stressed by Hamilton, proved most helpful and instructive. Thus, pointing to the similar rôles played by the quantum numbers in the classification of stationary states by means of mechanical pictures, and by the numbers of nodes in characterizing the possible standing waves in elastic media, L. de Broglie had already in 1924 been led to a comparison between the behaviour of free material particles and the properties of photons. Especially illuminating was his demonstration of the identity of the particle velocity with the group velocity of a wave-packet built up of components with wavelengths confined to a small interval, and each related to a value of the momentum by Einstein's equation between the momentum of a photon and the corresponding wavelength of radiation. As is well known, the pertinence of this comparison soon received a decisive confirmation with the discoveries by Davisson and Germer and by George Thomson of selective scattering of electrons in crystals.

The culminating event of this period was Schrödinger's establishment in 1926 of a more comprehensive wave mechanics in which the stationary states are conceived as proper solutions of a fundamental wave-equation, obtained by regarding the Hamiltonian of a system of electric particles as a differential operator acting upon a function of the co-ordinates which define the configuration of the system. In the case of the hydrogen atom, not only did this method lead to a remarkably simple determination of the energies of the stationary states, but Schrödinger also showed that the superposition of any two proper solutions corresponded to a distribution of electric charge and current in the atom which on classical electrodynamics would give rise to the emission and resonance absorption of a monochromatic radiation of a frequency coinciding with some line of the hydrogen spectrum.

Similarly, Schrödinger was able to explain essential features of the dispersion of radiation by atoms by representing the charge and current distribution of the atom perturbed by the incident radiation as the effect of a superposition of the proper functions defining the manifold of possible stationary states of the unperturbed system. Particularly suggestive was the derivation on such lines of the laws of the Compton effect, which in spite of the striking support it gave to Einstein's original photon idea, at first presented obvious difficulties for a correspondence treatment, attempting to combine conservation of energy and momentum with a division of the process in two separate steps, consisting in an absorption and an emission of radiation resembling radiative transitions between the stationary states of an atomic system.

This recognition of the wide scope of arguments implying the use of a superposition principle similar to that of classical electromagnetic field theory, which was only implicitly contained in the matrix formulation of quantum mechanics, meant a great advance in the treatment of atomic problems. Still, it was from the beginning obvious that wave mechanics did not point to any less radical modification of the classical physical approach than the statistical description envisaged by the correspondence principle. Thus, I remember how, on a visit of Schrödinger to Copenhagen in 1926, when he gave us a most impressive account of his wonderful work, we argued with him that any procedure disregarding the individual character of the quantum processes would never account for Planck's fundamental formula of thermal radiation.

Notwithstanding the remarkable analogy between essential features of atomic processes and classical resonance problems, it must indeed be taken into account that in wave mechanics we are dealing with functions which do not generally take real values, but demand the essential use of the symbol $\sqrt{-1}$ just as the matrices of quantum mechanics. Moreover, when dealing with the constitution of atoms with more than one electron or collisions between atoms and free electric particles, the state functions are not represented in ordinary space but in a configuration space of as many dimensions as there are degrees of freedom in the total system. The essentially statistical character of the physical deductions from wave mechanics was eventually clarified by Born's brilliant treatment of general collision problems.

The equivalence of the physical contents of the two different mathematical formalisms was completely elucidated by the transformation theory formulated independently by Dirac in Copenhagen and Jordan in Göttingen, which introduced in quantum physics possibilities for the change of variables similar to those offered by the symmetrical character of the equations of motion in classical dynamics in the canonical form given by Hamilton. An analogous situation is met with in the formulation of a quantum electrodynamics incorporating the photon concept. This aim was first achieved in Dirac's quantum theory of radiation treating phases and amplitudes of the harmonic components of the fields as non-commuting variables. After further ingenious contributions by Jordan, Klein, and Wigner, this formalism found, as is well known, essential completion in the work of Heisenberg and Pauli.

A special illustration of the power and scope of the mathematical methods of quantum physics is presented by the peculiar quantum statistics pertaining to systems of identical particles where we have to do with a feature as foreign to classical physics as the quantum of action itself. Indeed, any problem which calls for relevant application of Bose-Einstein or

Fermi-Dirac statistics in principle excludes pictorial illustration. In particular, this situation left room for the proper formulation of the Pauli exclusion principle, which not only gave the final elucidation of the periodicity relations in Mendeleev's table, but in the following years proved fertile for the understanding of most of the varied aspects of the atomic constitution of matter.

A fundamental contribution to the clarification of the principles of quantum statistics was afforded by Heisenberg's ingenious explanation in 1926 of the duplicity of the helium spectrum. In fact, as he showed, the set of stationary states of atoms with two electrons consists of two non-combining groups corresponding to symmetric and antisymmetric spatial wave functions, respectively associated with opposite and parallel orientations of the electron spins. Shortly afterwards Heitler and London succeeded on the same lines in explaining the binding mechanism in the hydrogen molecule and thereby opened the way for the understanding of homopolar chemical bonds. Even Rutherford's famous formula for the scattering of charged particles by atomic nuclei had as was shown by Mott, to be essentially modified when applied to collisions between identical particles like protons and hydrogen nuclei or α-rays and helium nuclei. However, in the actual experiments of large-angle scattering of fast α-rays by heavy nuclei, from which Rutherford drew his fundamental conclusions, we are well within the range of validity of classical mechanics.

The increasing use of more and more refined mathematical abstractions to ensure consistency in the account of atomic phenomena found in 1928 a temporary climax in Dirac's relativistic quantum theory of the electron. Thus the concept of electron spin, to the treatment of which Darwin and Pauli had made important contributions, was harmoniously incorporated in Dirac's spinor analysis. Above all, however, in connection with the discovery of the positron by Anderson and Blackett, Dirac's theory prepared the recognition of the existence of antiparticles of equal mass but opposite electric charges and opposite orientations of the magnetic moment relative to the spin axis. As is well known, we have here to do with a development which in a novel manner has restored and enlarged that isotropy in space and reversibility in time which has been one of the basic ideas of the classical physical approach.

The wonderful progress of our knowledge of the atomic constitution of matter and of the methods by which such knowledge can be acquired and interrelated has indeed carried us far beyond the scope of the deterministic pictorial description brought to such perfection by Newton and Maxwell. Following this development at close hand, I have often had occasion to think of the dominating influence of Rutherford's original discovery of the atomic nucleus, which at every stage presented us with so forceful a challenge.

IX

In all the long and rich years during which Rutherford worked with untiring vigour in the Cavendish I often came to Cambridge where on Rutherford's invitation I gave several courses of lectures on theoretical problems including the epistemological implications of the development of quantum theory. On such occasions it was always a great encouragement to feel the open mind and intense interest with which Rutherford followed the progress in the field of research which he had himself so largely initiated and the growth of which should carry us so far beyond the horizon which limited the outlook at the early stages.

Indeed, the extensive use of abstract mathematical methods to cope with the rapidly increasing evidence about atomic phenomena brought the whole observational problem more and more to the foreground. In its roots this problem is as old as physical science itself. Thus the philosophers in ancient Greece, who based the explanation of the specific properties of substances on the limited divisibility of all matter, took it for granted that the coarseness of our sense organs would forever prevent the direct observation of individual atoms. In such respect the situation has been radically changed in our days by the construction of amplification devices like cloud chambers and the counter mechanisms originally developed by Rutherford and Geiger in connection with their measurements of the numbers and charges of α-particles. Still, the exploration of the world of atoms was, as we have seen, to reveal inherent limitations in the mode of description embodied in common language developed for the orientation in our surroundings and the account of events of daily life.

In words conforming with Rutherford's whole attitude, one may say that the aim of experimentation is to put questions to nature, and of course Rutherford owed his success in this task to his intuition in, shaping such questions so as to permit the most useful answers. In order that the inquiry may augment common knowledge it is an obvious demand that the recording of observations as well as the construction and handling of the apparatus, necessary for the definition of the experimental conditions, be described in plain language. In actual physical research this demand is amply satisfied with the specification of the experimental arrangement through the use of bodies like diaphragms and photographic plates, so large and heavy that their manipulation can be accounted for in terms of classical physics, although of course the properties of the materials of which the instruments, as well as our own bodies, are built up depend essentially on the constitution and stability of the component atomic systems defying such account.

The description of ordinary experience presupposes the unrestricted divisibility of the course of the phenomena in space and time and the linking of all steps in an unbroken chain in terms of cause and effect. Ultimately this viewpoint rests on the fineness of our senses which for perception demands an interaction with the objects under investigation so small that in ordinary circumstances it is without appreciable influence on the course of events. In the edifice of classical physics this situation finds its idealized expression in the assumption that the interaction between the object and the tools of observation can be neglected or, at any rate, compensated for.

The element of wholeness, symbolized by the quantum of action and completely foreign to classical physical principles, has, however, the consequence that in the study of quantum processes any experimental inquiry implies an interaction between the atomic object and the measuring tools which, although essential for the characterization of the phenomena, evades a separate account if the experiment is to serve its purpose of yielding unambiguous answers to our questions. It is indeed the recognition of this situation which makes the recourse to a statistical mode of description imperative as regards the expectations of the occurrence of individual quantum effects in one and the same experimental arrangement, and which removes any apparent contradiction between phenomena observed under mutually exclusive experimental conditions. However contrasting such phenomena may at first sight appear, it must be realized that they are complementary in the sense that taken together they exhaust all information about the atomic object which can be expressed in common language without ambiguity.

The notion of complementarity does not imply any renunciation of detailed analysis limiting the scope of our inquiry, but simply stresses the character of objective description, independent of subjective judgment, in any field of experience where unambiguous communication essentially involves regard to the circumstances in which evidence is obtained. In logical respect such a situation is well known from discussions about psychological and social problems where many words have been used in a complementary manner since the very origin of language. Of course we are here often dealing with qualities unsuited to the quantitative analysis characteristic of so-called exact sciences, whose task, according to the programme of Galileo, is to base all description on well-defined measurements.

Notwithstanding the help which mathematics has always offered for such a task it must be realized that the very definition of mathematical symbols and operations rests on simple logical use of common language. Indeed, mathematics is not to be regarded as a special branch of knowledge based on the accumulation of experience, but rather as a refinement of general language, supplementing it with appropriate tools to represent relations for which ordinary verbal communication is imprecise or too cumbersome. Strictly speaking, the mathematical formalism of quantum mechanics and electrodynamics merely offers rules of calculation for the deduction of expectations about observations obtained under well-defined experimental conditions specified by classical physical concepts. The exhaustive character of this description depends not only on the freedom, offered by the formalism, of choosing these conditions in any conceivable manner, but equally on the fact that the very definition of the phenomena under consideration for their completion implies an element of irreversibility in the observational process emphasizing the fundamentally irreversible character of the concept of observation itself.

Of course all contradictions in the complementary account in quantum physics were beforehand excluded by the logical consistency of the mathematical scheme upholding every demand of correspondence. Still, the recognition of the reciprocal latitude for the fixation of any two canonically conjugate variables, expressed in the principle of indeterminacy formulated by Heisenberg in 1927, was a decisive step towards the elucidation of the measuring problem in quantum mechanics. Indeed it became evident that the formal representation of physical quantities by non-commuting operators directly reflects the relationship of mutual exclusion between the operations by which the respective physical quantities are defined and measured.

To gain familiarity with this situation the detailed treatment of a great variety of examples of such arguments was needed. Notwithstanding the generalized significance of the superposition principle in quantum physics an important guide for the closer study of observational problems was repeatedly found in Rayleigh's classic analysis of the inverse relation between the accuracy of image-forming by microscopes and the resolving power of spectroscopic instruments. In this connection not least Darwin's mastery of the methods of mathematical physics often proved helpful.

With all appreciation of Planck's happy choice of words when introducing the concept of a universal 'quantum of action', or the suggestive value of the idea of 'intrinsic spin', it must be realized that such notions merely refer to relationships between well-defined experimental evidence which cannot be comprehended by the classical mode of description. Indeed, the numbers expressing the values of the quantum or spin in ordinary physical units do not concern direct measurements of classically defined actions or angular momenta, but are logically interpretable only by consistent use of the mathematical formalism of quantum theory. In particular, the much-discussed impossibility of measuring the magnetic moment of a free electron by ordinary magnetometers is directly evident from the fact that in Dirac's theory the spin and magnetic moment do not result from any alteration in the basic Hamiltonian equation of motion, but appear as consequences of the peculiar non-commutative character of the operator calculus.

The question of the proper interpretation of the notions of complementarity and indeterminacy was not settled without lively disputes, in particular at the Solvay meetings of 1927 and 1930. On these occasions Einstein challenged us with his subtle criticism which especially gave the inspiration to a closer analysis of the rôle of the instruments in the measuring process. A crucial point, irrevocably excluding the possibility of reverting to causal pictorial description, was the recognition that the scope of unambiguous application of the general conservation laws of momentum and energy is inherently limited by the circumstance that any experimental arrangement, allowing the location of atomic objects in space and time, implies a transfer, uncontrollable in principle, of momentum and energy to the fixed scales and regulated clocks indispensable for the definition of the reference frame. The physical interpretation of the relativistic formulation of quantum theory ultimately rests on the possibility of fulfilling all relativity exigencies in the account of the handling of the macroscopic measuring apparatus.

This circumstance was especially elucidated in the discussion of the measurability of electromagnetic field components raised by Landau and Peierls as a serious argument against the consistency of quantum field theory. Indeed, a detailed investigation in collaboration with Rosenfeld showed that all the predictions of the theory in this respect could be fulfilled when due regard was taken to the mutual exclusiveness of the fixation of the values of electric and magnetic intensities and the specification of the photon composition of the field. An analogous situation is met with in positron theory where any arrangement suited for measurements of the charge distribution in space necessarily implies uncontrollable creation of electron pairs.

The typical quantum features of electromagnetic fields do not depend on scale, since the two fundamental constants—the velocity of light c and the quantum of action h—do not allow of any fixation of quantities of dimensions of a length or time interval. Relativistic electron theory, however, involves the charge e and mass m of the electron, and essential characteristics of the phenomena are limited to spatial extensions of the order h/mc. The fact that this length is still large compared with the 'electron radius' e^2/mc^2, which limits the unambiguous application of the concepts of classical electromagnetic theory, suggests, however, that there is still a wide scope for the validity of quantum electrodynamics, even though many of its consequences cannot be tested by practical experimental arrangements, involving measuring instruments sufficiently large to permit the neglect of the statistical element in their construction and handling. Such difficulties would of course also prevent any direct inquiry into the close interactions of the fundamental constituents of matter, whose number has been so largely increased by recent discoveries, and in the exploration of their relationships we must therefore be prepared for a new approach transcending the scope of present quantum theory.

It need hardly be stressed that such problems do not arise in the account of the ordinary physical and chemical properties of matter, based on the Rutherford atomic model, in the analysis of which use is only made of well-defined characteristics of the constituent particles. Here the complementary description offers indeed the adequate approach to the problem of atomic stability, with which we were faced from the very beginning. Thus, the interpretation of spectral regularities and chemical bonds refers to experimental conditions mutually exclusive of those which permit exact control of the position and displacement of the individual electrons in the atomic systems.

In this connection, it is of decisive importance to realize that the fruitful application of structural formulae in chemistry rests solely on the fact that the atomic nuclei are so much heavier than the electrons that in comparison with molecular dimensions the indeterminacy in the position of the nuclei can be largely neglected. When we look back on the whole development we recognize indeed that the discovery of the concentration of the mass of the atom within a region so small compared with its extension has been the clue to the understanding of an immense field of experience embracing the crystalline structure of solids as well as the complex molecular systems which carry the genetic characters of living organisms.

As is well known, the methods of quantum theory have also proved decisive for the clarification of many problems regarding the constitution and stability of the atomic nuclei themselves. To some early disclosed aspects of such problems I shall have occasion to refer in continuing the account of my reminiscences of Rutherford, but it would be beyond the scope of this Memorial Lecture to attempt a detailed account of the rapidly increasing insight in the intrinsic nuclear constitution, brought about by the work of the present generation of experimental and theoretical physicists. This development reminds indeed the elders among us of the gradual clarification of the electronic constitution of the atom in the first decades after Rutherford's fundamental discovery.

X

Every physicist is of course acquainted with the imposing series of brilliant investigations with which Rutherford to the very end of his life augmented our insight into the properties and constitution of atomic nuclei. I shall therefore here mention only a few of my remembrances from those years when I often had occasion to follow the work in the Cavendish laboratory and learned in talks with Rutherford about the trend of his views and the problems occupying him and his collaborators.

With his penetrating intuition, Rutherford was early aware of the strange and novel problems presented by the existence and stability of composite nuclei. Indeed, already in the Manchester time he had pointed out that any approach to these problems demanded the assumption of forces of short range between the nuclear constituents, of a kind essentially different from the electric forces acting between charged particles. With the intention of throwing more light on the specific nuclear forces, Rutherford and Chadwick, in the first years in Cambridge, performed thorough investigations of anomalous scattering of α-rays in close nuclear collisions.

Although much important new evidence was obtained in these investigations, it was more and more felt that for a broader attack on nuclear problems the natural α-ray sources were not sufficient and that it was desirable to have available intense beams of high energy particles produced by artificial acceleration of ions. In spite of Chadwick's urge to start the construction of an appropriate accelerator, Rutherford was during several years reluctant to embark upon such a great and expensive enterprise in his laboratory. This attitude is quite understandable when one considers the wonderful progress which Rutherford hitherto had achieved with the help of very modest experimental equipment. The task of competing with natural radioactive sources must also have appeared quite formidable at that time. The outlook, however, was changed by the development of quantum theory and its first application to nuclear problems.

Rutherford himself had as early as 1920 in his second Bakerian lecture clearly pointed out the difficulties of interpreting α-ray emission from nuclei on the basis of the simple mechanical ideas which had proved so helpful in explaining the scattering of α-particles by nuclei, since the velocity of the ejected particles was not large enough to allow them by reversal to re-enter the nuclei against the electric repulsion. However, the possibilities of penetration of particles through potential barriers was soon recognized as a consequence of wave mechanics, and in 1928 Gamow, working in Göttingen, as well as Condon and Gurney in Princeton, gave on this basis a general explanation of α-decay and even a detailed account of the relationship between the lifetime of the nucleus and the kinetic energy of the emitted α-particles, in conformity with the empirical regularities found by Geiger and Nuttall in the early Manchester days.

When in the summer of 1928 Gamow joined us in Copenhagen, he was investigating the penetration of charged particles into nuclei by a reverse tunnel effect. He had started this work in Göttingen and discussed it with Houtermans and Atkinson, with the result that the latter were led to suggest that the source of solar energy might be traced to nuclear transmutations induced by impact of protons with the great thermal velocities which according to Eddington's ideas were to be expected in the interior of the sun.

During a brief visit to Cambridge in October 1928, Gamow discussed the experimental prospects arising from his theoretical considerations with Cockcroft, who by more detailed estimates convinced himself of the possibility of obtaining observable effects by bombardment of light nuclei with protons of an energy far smaller than that of α-particles from natural radioactive sources. As the result appeared promising, Rutherford accepted Cockcroft's proposal to build a high-voltage accelerator for such experiments. Work on the construction of the apparatus was started by Cockcroft at the end of 1928 and was continued during the following year with the collaboration of Walton. The first experiments they made with accelerated protons in March 1930, in which they looked for gamma rays emitted as a result of the interaction of the protons with the target nuclei, gave no result. The apparatus then had to be rebuilt owing to a change of laboratory and, as is well known, production of high-speed α-particles by proton impact on lithium nuclei was obtained in March 1932.

These experiments initiated a new stage of most important progress, during which both our knowledge of nuclear reactions and the mastery of accelerator techniques rapidly increased from year to year. Already Cockcroft and Walton's first experiments gave results of great significance in several respects. Not only did they confirm in all details the predictions of quantum theory as regards the dependence of the reaction cross-section on the energy of the protons, but it was also possible to connect the kinetic energy of the emitted α-rays with the masses of the reacting particles which were at that time known with sufficient accuracy thanks to Aston's ingenious development of mass spectroscopy. Indeed, this comparison offered the first experimental test of Einstein's famous relation between energy and mass, to which he had been led many years before by relativity arguments. It need hardly be recalled how fundamental this relation was to prove in the further development of nuclear research.

The story of Chadwick's discovery of the neutron presents similar dramatic features. It is characteristic of the broadness of Rutherford's views that he early anticipated the presence in nuclei of a heavy neutral constituent of a mass closely coinciding with that of the proton. As gradually became clear, this idea would indeed explain Aston's discoveries of isotopes of nearly all elements with atomic masses closely approximated by multiples of the atomic weight of hydrogen. In connection with their studies of many types of α-ray induced nuclear distintegrations Rutherford and Chadwick made an extensive search for evidence concerning the existence of such a particle. However, the problem came to a climax through the observation by Bothe and the Joliot-Curies of a penetrating radiation resulting from the bombardment of beryllium by α-particles. At first this radiation was assumed to be of γ-ray type, but with Chadwick's thorough familiarity with the multifarious aspects of radiative phenomena he clearly perceived that the experimental evidence was not compatible with this view.

Indeed, from a masterly investigation, in which a number of new features of the phenomenon were revealed, Chadwick was able to prove that one was faced with momentum and energy exchanges through a neutral particle, the mass of which he determined as differing from that of the proton by less than one part in a thousand. On account of the ease with which neutrons, compared with charged particles, can pass through matter without transfer of energy to the electrons and penetrate into atomic nuclei, Chadwick's discovery opened great possibilities of producing new types of nuclear transmutations. Some most interesting cases of such new effects were immediately demonstrated in the Cavendish by Feather, who obtained cloud chamber pictures showing nitrogen nuclei disintegrating under α-particle release by neutron bombardment. As is well known, continued studies in many laboratories along such lines were rapidly to increase our knowledge of nuclear constitution and transmutation processes.

In the spring of 1932, at one of our yearly conferences at the Copenhagen Institute, where as always we were happy to see many of our former collaborators, one of the main topics of discussion was of course the implications of the discovery of the neutron, and a special point raised was the apparently strange circumstance that in Dee's beautiful cloud chamber pictures no interaction whatever was observed between the neutrons and the electrons bound in the atoms. In relation to this point, it was argued that owing to the dependence in quantum physics of the scattering cross-section on the reduced mass of the colliding particles, this fact would not be inconsistent even with the assumption of short range interaction between the neutron and an electron of strength similar to that between the neutron and a proton. A few days later, I got a letter from Rutherford touching incidentally on this point, and which I cannot resist quoting in full:

April 21st 1932.

'My dear Bohr,

I was very glad to hear about you all from Fowler when he returned to Cambridge and to know what an excellent meeting of old friends you had. I was interested to hear about your theory of the Neutron. I saw it described very nicely by the scientific correspondent of the Manchester Guardian, Crowther, who is quite intelligent in these matters. I am very pleased to hear that you regard the Neutron with favour. I think the evidence in its support, obtained by Chadwick and others, is now complete in the main essentials. It is still a moot point how much ionization is, or should be, produced to account for the absorption, disregarding the collisions with nuclei.

It never rains but it pours, and I have another interesting development to tell you about of which a short account should appear in Nature next week. You know that we have a High Tension Laboratory where steady D.C. voltages can be readily obtained up to 600,000 volts or more. They have recently been examining the effects of a bombardment of light elements by protons. The protons fall on a surface of the material inclined at 45° to the axis of the tube and the effects produced were observed at the side by the scintillation method, the zinc sulphide screen being covered with sufficient mica to stop the protons. In the case of lithium brilliant scintillations are observed, beginning at about 125,000 volts and mounting up very rapidly with voltage when many hundreds per minute can be obtained with a protonic current of a few milliamperes. The α-particles apparently had a definite range, practically independent of voltage, of 8 cms, in air. The simplest assumption to make is that the lithium 7 captures a proton breaking up with the emission of two ordinary α-particles. On this view the total energy liberated is about 16 million volts and this is of the right order for the changes in mass involved, assuming the Conservation of Energy.

Later special experiments will be made to test the nature of the particles but from the brightness of the scintillations and the trail in a Wilson chamber it seems probable they are α-particles. In experiments in the last few days similar effects have been observed in Boron and Fluorine but the ranges of the particles are smaller although they look like α-particles. It may be Boron, 11, captures a proton and breaks up into three alphas, while fluorine breaks up into oxygen and an alpha. The energy changes are in approximate accord with these conclusions. I am sure you will be much interested in these new results which we hope to extend in the near future.

It is clear that the α-particle, neutron and proton will probably give rise to different types of disintegration and it may be significant that so far results have only been observed in $4n+3$ elements. It looks as if the addition of the 4th proton leads at once to the formation of an α-particle and the consequent disintegration. I suppose, however, the whole question should be regarded as the result of one process rather than of steps.

I am very pleased that the energy and expense in

getting high potentials has been rewarded by definite and interesting results. Actually they ought to have observed the effect a year or so ago but did not try it in the right way. You can easily appreciate that these results may open up a wide line of research in transmutation generally.

We are all very well at home and I start lectures to-morrow. With best wishes to you and Mrs Bohr

Yours ever

Rutherford

Beryllium shows some queer effects—still to be made definite.

I shall possibly refer to these experiments in the Royal Society discussion on nuclei on Thursday April 25.'

Of course, in reading this letter, it must be borne in mind that my previous visits to Cambridge had kept me acquainted with the work in progress in the Cavendish laboratory, so that Rutherford had no need to specify the individual contributions of his collaborators. The letter is indeed a spontaneous expression of his exuberant joy in the great achievements of those years and his eagerness in pursuing their consequences.

* * * * *

XI

As a true pioneer, Rutherford never relied merely on intuition, however far it carried him, but was always on the look-out for new sources of knowledge which could possibly lead to unexpected progress. Thus, also in Cambridge Rutherford and his collaborators continued with great vigour and steadily refined apparatus the investigations of the radioactive processes of α- and β-decay. The important work of Rutherford and Ellis on β-ray spectra revealed the possibility of a clear distinction between intra-nuclear effects and the interaction of the β-particle with the outer electron system and led to the clarification of the mechanism of internal conversion. Moreover, Ellis' demonstration of the continuous spectral distribution of the electrons directly emitted from the nucleus raised a puzzling question about energy conservation, which was eventually answered by Pauli's bold hypothesis of the simultaneous emission of a neutrino, affording the basis for Fermi's ingenious theory of β-decay. By the great improvement of accuracy in measurements of α-ray spectra by Rutherford, Wynn-Williams and others, much new light was thrown on the fine structure of these spectra and their relation to the energy levels of the residual nucleus resulting from the α-decay. A special adventure at an earlier stage was the discovery of the capture of electrons by α-rays which, after the first observation of the phenomenon in 1922 by Henderson, was explored by Rutherford in one of his most masterly researches. As is well known, this work, which brought so much information about the process of electron capture, was to attract new attention a few years after Rutherford's death when, with the discovery of the fission processes of heavy nuclei by neutron impact, the study of the penetration of highly charged nuclear fragments through matter, where electron capture is the dominating feature, came into the foreground.

Great progress both as regards general outlook and experimental technique was initiated in 1933 by the discovery by Frederic Joliot and Irene Curie of so-called artificial β-radioactivity produced by nuclear transmutations initiated by α-ray bombardment. I need hardly here remind how by Enrico Fermi's brilliant systematic investigations of neutron-induced nuclear transmutations, radioactive isotopes of a great number of elements were discovered and much information gained about nuclear processes initiated by capture of slow neutrons. Especially the continued study of such processes revealed most remarkable resonance effects of a sharpness far surpassing that of the peaks in the cross-section of α-ray induced reactions first observed by Pose and to Gurney's explanation of which, on the basis of the potential well model, Gamow at once drew Rutherford's attention.

Already Blackett's observations with his ingenious automatic cloud chamber technique had shown that in the very process investigated in Rutherford's original experiments on artificial nuclear disintegrations, the incident α-particle remained incorporated in the residual nucleus left after proton escape.

It now became clear that all types of nuclear transmutations within a large energy region take place in two well-separated steps. Of these the first is the formation of a relatively long-lived compound nucleus, while the second is the release of its excitation energy as a result of a competition between the various possible modes of disintegration and radiative processes. Such views, in which Rutherford took a vivid interest, were the theme for the last course of lectures which on Rutherford's invitation I gave in 1936 in the Cavendish laboratory.

Less than two years after Rutherford's death in 1937, a new and dramatic development was initiated by the discovery of the fission processes of the heaviest elements by his old friend and collaborator in Montreal, Otto Hahn, working in Berlin with Fritz Strassmann. Immediately after this discovery Lise Meitner and Otto Frisch, then working in Stockholm and Copenhagen, and now both in Cambridge, made an important contribution to the understanding of the phenomenon by pointing out that the critical decrease in stability of nuclei of high charge was a simple consequence of the balancing of cohesive forces between the nuclear constituents and the electrostatic repulsion. A closer investigation of the fission process in collaboration with Wheeler showed that many of its characteristic features could be accounted for in terms of the mechanism of nuclear reactions involving as a first step the formation of a compound nucleus.

In Rutherford's last years he found in Marcus Oliphant a collaborator and friend whose general attitude and working power reminds us so much of his own. At that time new possibilities of research were opened by Urey's discovery of the heavy hydrogen isotope ^{2}H or deuterium, and by the construction of the cyclotron by Lawrence, who in his first investigations on nuclear disintegrations by deuteron beams obtained a number of new striking effects. In the classical experiments of Rutherford and Oliphant, in which by bombardment of separated lithium isotopes with protons and deuterons they were led to the discovery of ^{3}H, or tritium, and ^{3}He, the foundation was indeed created for the vigorous modern attempt to apply thermonuclear reactions to the realization of the full promises of atomic energy sources.

From the very beginning of his radioactive researches Rutherford was acutely aware of the wide perspectives they opened in several directions. In particular, he early took deep interest in the possibility of arriving at an estimate of the age of the earth and of understanding the thermal equilibrium in the crust of our planet. Even if the liberation of nuclear energy for technological purposes was still to come, it must have been a great satisfaction for Rutherford that the explanation of the hitherto completely unknown source of solar energy as a result of the development he had initiated had come within the horizon in his lifetime.

XII

When we look back on Rutherford's life we perceive it, of course, against the unique background of his epoch-making scientific achievements, but our memories will always remain irradiated by the enchantment of his personality. In earlier Memorial Lectures several of Rutherford's closest co-workers have recalled the inspiration which emanated from his vigour and enthusiasm and the charm of his impulsive ways. Indeed, in spite of the large and rapidly expanding scope of Rutherford's scientific and administrative activities the same spirit reigned in the Cavendish as we all had enjoyed so much in the early Manchester days.

A faithful account of Rutherford's eventful life from childhood till his last days has been written by his old friend from the Montreal period, A. S. Eve. Especially the many quotations in Eve's book from Rutherford's astonishingly large correspondence give a vivid impression of his relations with colleagues and pupils all over the world. Eve also does not fail to report some of the humorous stories which constantly grew around Rutherford, and to which I alluded in a speech, reproduced in his book, when Rutherford for the second and last time visited us in Copenhagen in 1932.

Characteristic of Rutherford's whole attitude was the warm interest he took in any one of the many young physicists with whom he came into contact for shorter or longer periods.

Thus I vividly remember the circumstances of my first meeting in Rutherford's office in the Cavendish with the young Robert Oppenheimer, with whom I was later to come into such close friendship. Indeed, before Oppenheimer entered the office Rutherford, with his keen appreciation of talents, had described the rich gifts of the young man which in the course of time were to create for him his eminent position in scientific life in the United States.

As is well known, Oppenheimer, shortly after his visit to Cambridge, during his studies in Göttingen was among the first who called attention to the phenomenon of particle penetration through potential barriers, which should prove basic for the ingenious explanation of α-decay by Gamow and others. After his stay in Copenhagen, Gamow came in 1929 to Cambridge, where his steady contributions to the interpretation of nuclear phenomena were highly appreciated by Rutherford, who also greatly enjoyed the bizarre and subtle humour which Gamow unfolded in daily intercourse and to which he later gave so abundant expression in his well-known popular books.

Of the many young physicists from abroad working in the Cavendish laboratory in those years, one of the most colourful personalities was Kapitza, whose power of imagination and talent as a physical engineer Rutherford greatly admired. The relationship between Rutherford and Kapitza was very characteristic of them both and was, notwithstanding inevitable emotional encounters, marked from first to last by a deep mutual affection. Such sentiments were also behind Rutherford's efforts to support Kapitza's work after his return to Russia in 1934 and were from Kapitza's side most movingly expressed in a letter which I received from him after Rutherford's death.

When in the beginning of the nineteen-thirties as an extension to the Cavendish, the Mond laboratory was created on Rutherford's initiative for the promotion of Kapitza's promising projects, Kapitza wanted in its decoration to give expression for his joy in Rutherford's friendship. Still, the carving of a crocodile on the outer wall caused comments which could only be appeased by reference to special Russian folklore about animal life. Above all, however, the relief of Rutherford, in Eric Gill's artistic interpretation, placed in the entrance hall, deeply shocked many of Rutherford's friends. On a visit to Cambridge I confessed that I could not share this indignation, and this remark was so welcomed that Kapitza and Dirac presented me with a replica of the relief; installed above the fireplace in my office at the Copenhagen Institute, it has since given me daily enjoyment.

When in recognition of his position in science Rutherford was given a British peerage he took a keen interest in his new responsibilities as a member of the House of Lords, but there was certainly no change in the directness and simplicity of his behaviour. Thus I do not remember any more severe utterance of his to me than, when at a Royal Society Club dinner in a conversation with some of his friends I had referred to him in the third person as Lord Rutherford, he furiously turned on me with the words: 'Do you lord me?'

In the nearly twenty years during which Rutherford, right up to his death, worked with undiminished energy in Cambridge, my wife and I kept in close touch with him and his family. Almost every year we were hospitably received in their beautiful home in Newnham Cottage at the backs of the old colleges, with the lovely garden in which Rutherford found relaxation and the upkeep of which gave Mary Rutherford much enjoyable work. I remember many peaceful evening hours in Rutherford's study spent discussing not merely new prospects of physical science but also topics from many other fields of human interest. In such conversation one was never tempted to overrate the interest of one's own contributions since Rutherford after a long day's work was apt to fall asleep as soon as the discourse seemed pointless to him. One then just had to wait until he woke up and resumed the conversation with usual vigour as if nothing had happened.

On Sundays Rutherford regularly played golf in the morning with some close friends and dined in the evening in Trinity College where he met many eminent scholars and enjoyed discussions on the most different subjects. With his insatiable curiosity for all aspects of life, Rutherford had great esteem for his learned colleagues; however, I remember how he once remarked on our way back from Trinity that to his mind so-called humanists went a bit too far when expressing pride in their complete ignorance of what happened in between the pressing of a button at their front door and the sounding of a bell in the kitchen.

Some of Rutherford's utterances have led to the misunderstanding that he did not fully appreciate the value of mathematical formalisms for the progress of physical science. On the contrary, as the whole branch of physics, created so largely by himself, rapidly developed, Rutherford often expressed admiration for the new theoretical methods, and even took interest in questions of the philosophical implications of quantum theory. I remember especially how at my last stay with him a few weeks before his death he was fascinated by the complementary approach to biological and social problems and how eagerly he discussed the possibility of obtaining experimental evidence on the origin of national traditions and prejudices by such unconventional procedures as the interchange of newborn children between nations.

A few weeks later, at the Centenary celebrations for Galvani in Bologna, we learned with sorrow and consternation of Rutherford's death, and I went at once to England to attend his funeral. Having been with them both so shortly before and found Rutherford in full vigour and in the same high spirits as always, it was under tragic circumstances, indeed, that I met Mary Rutherford again. We talked about Ernest's great life in which from their early youth she had been so faithful a companion, and how to me he had almost been as a second father. On one of the following days, Rutherford was buried in Westminster Abbey, close to the sarcophagus of Newton.

The memory which Rutherford has left us remains to everyone who had the good fortune to know and come close to him a rich source of encouragement and fortitude. The generations who in coming years pursue the exploration of the world of atoms will continue to draw inspiration from the work and life of the great pioneer.

Reprints of Original Papers

The Nature of the α Particle from Radioactive Substances. By Professor E. Rutherford, *F.R.S., and* T. Royds, *M.Sc.*, 1851 *Exhibition Science Scholar* *.

The *Philosophical Magazine*, Series VI, **17**, 281–286 (1909)

THE experimental evidence collected during the last few years has strongly supported the view that the α particle is a charged helium atom, but it has been found exceedingly difficult to give a decisive proof of the relation. In recent papers, Rutherford and Geiger † have supplied still further evidence of the correctness of this point of view. The number of α particles from one gram of radium have been counted, and the charge carried by each determined. The values of several radioactive quantities, calculated on the assumption that the α particle is a helium atom carrying two unit charges, have been shown to be in good agreement with the experimental numbers. In particular, the good agreement between the calculated rate of production of helium by radium and the rate experimentally determined by Sir James Dewar ‡, is strong evidence in favour of the identity of the α particle with the helium atom.

The methods of attack on this problem have been largely indirect, involving considerations of the charge carried by the helium atom and the value of e/m of the α particle. The proof of the identity of the α particle with the helium atom is incomplete until it can be shown that the α particles, accumulated quite independently of the matter from which they are expelled, consist of helium. For example, it might be argued that

* Communicated by the Authors.

† Proc. Roy. Soc. A. lxxxi. pp. 141–173 (1908).

‡ Proc. Roy. Soc. A. lxxxi. p. 280 (1908).

the appearance of helium in the radium emanation was a result of the expulsion of the α particle, in the same way that the appearance of radium A is a consequence of the expulsion

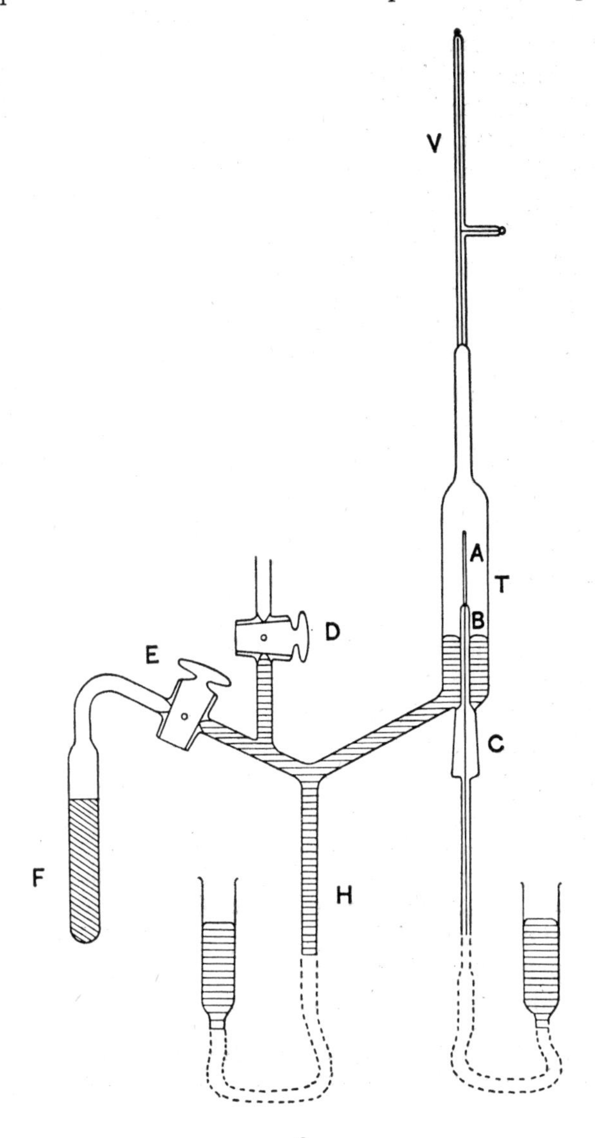

of an α particle from the emanation. If one atom of helium appeared for each α particle expelled, calculation and experiment might still agree, and yet the α particle itself might be an atom of hydrogen or of some other substance.

We have recently made experiments to test whether helium appears in a vessel into which the α particles have been fired, the active matter itself being enclosed in a vessel sufficiently thin to allow the α particles to escape, but impervious to the passage of helium or other radioactive products.

The experimental arrangement is clearly seen in the figure. The equilibrium quantity of emanation from about 140 milligrams of radium was purified and compressed by means of a mercury-column into a fine glass tube A about 1·5 cms. long. This fine tube, which was sealed on a larger capillary tube B, was sufficiently thin to allow the α particles from the emanation and its products to escape, but sufficiently strong to withstand atmospheric pressure. After some trials, Mr. Baumbach succeeded in blowing such fine tubes very uniform in thickness. The thickness of the wall of the tube employed in most of the experiments was less than $\frac{1}{100}$ mm., and was equivalent in stopping power of the α particle to about 2 cms. of air. Since the ranges of the α particles from the emanation and its products radium A and radium C are 4·3, 4·8, and 7 cms. respectively, it is seen that the great majority * of the α particles expelled by the active matter escape through the walls of the tube. The ranges of the α particles after passing through the glass were determined with the aid of a zinc-sulphide screen. Immediately after the introduction of the emanation the phosphorescence showed brilliantly when the screen was close to the tube, but practically disappeared at a distance of 3 cms. After an hour, bright phosphorescence was observable at a distance of 5 cms. Such a result is to be expected. The phosphorescence initially observed was due mainly to the α particles of the emanation and its product radium A (period 3 mins.). In the course of time the amount of radium C, initially zero, gradually

* The α particles fired at a very oblique angle to the tube would be stopped in the glass. The fraction stopped in this way would be small under the experimental conditions.

increased, and the α radiations from it of range 7 cms. were able to cause phosphorescence at a greater distance.

The glass tube A was surrounded by a cylindrical glass tube T, 7·5 cms. long and 1·5 cms. diameter, by means of a ground-glass joint C. A small vacuum-tube V was attached to the upper end of T. The outer glass tube T was exhausted by a pump through the stopcock D, and the exhaustion completed with the aid of the charcoal tube F cooled by liquid air. By means of a mercury column H attached to a reservoir, mercury was forced into the tube T until it reached the bottom of the tube A.

Part of the α particles which escaped through the walls of the fine tube were stopped by the outer glass tube and part by the mercury surface. If the α particle is a helium atom, helium should gradually diffuse from the glass and mercury into the exhausted space, and its presence could then be detected spectroscopically by raising the mercury and compressing the gases into the vacuum-tube.

In order to avoid any possible contamination of the apparatus with helium, freshly distilled mercury and entirely new glass apparatus were used. Before introducing the emanation into A, the absence of helium was confirmed experimentally. At intervals after the introduction of the emanation the mercury was raised, and the gases in the outer tube spectroscopically examined. After 24 hours no trace of the helium yellow line was seen; after 2 days the helium yellow was faintly visible; after 4 days the helium yellow and green lines were bright; and after 6 days all the stronger lines of the helium spectrum were observed. The absence of the neon spectrum shows that the helium present was not due to a leakage of air into the apparatus.

There is, however, one possible source of error in this experiment. The helium may not be due to the α particles themselves, but may have *diffused* from the emanation through the thin walls of the glass tube. In order to test this point the emanation was completely pumped out of A, and after some hours a quantity of helium, about 10 times the previous volume of the emanation, was compressed into the same tube A.

The outer tube T and the vacuum-tube were removed and a fresh apparatus substituted. Observations to detect helium in the tube T were made at intervals, in the same way as before, but no trace of the helium spectrum was observed over a period of eight days.

The helium in the tube A was then pumped out and a fresh supply of emanation substituted. Results similar to the first experiment were observed. The helium yellow and green lines showed brightly after four days.

These experiments thus show conclusively that the helium could not have diffused through the glass walls, but must have been derived from the α particles which were fired through them. In other words, the experiments give a decisive proof that the α particle after losing its charge is an atom of helium.

Other Experiments

We have seen that in the experiments above described helium was not observed in the outer tube in sufficient quantity to show the characteristic yellow line until two days had elapsed. Now the equilibrium amount of emanation from 100 milligrams of radium should produce helium at the rate of about ·03 c.mm. per day. The amount produced in one day, if present in the outer tube, should produce a bright spectrum of helium under the experimental conditions. It thus appeared probable that the helium fired into the glass must escape very slowly into the exhausted space, for if the helium escaped at once, the presence of helium should have been detected a few hours after the introduction of the emanation.

In order to examine this point more closely the experiments were repeated, with the addition that a cylinder of thin sheet lead of sufficient thickness to stop the α particles was placed over the fine emanation tube. Preliminary experiments, in the manner described later, showed that the lead-foil did not initially contain a detectable amount of helium. Twenty-four hours after the introduction into the tube A of about the same amount of emanation as before, the yellow and green lines of helium showed brightly in the vacuum-tube, and after two days the whole helium spectrum was observed. The spectrum of helium in this case after one day was of about the same intensity as that after the fourth day in the experiments without the lead screen. It was thus clear that the lead-foil gave up the helium fired into it far more readily than the glass.

In order to form an idea of the rapidity of escape of the helium from the lead some further experiments were made. The outer cylinder T was removed and a small cylinder of lead-foil placed round the thin emanation-tube surrounded the air at atmospheric pressure. After exposure for a definite time to the emanation, the lead screen was removed and tested for helium as follows. The lead-foil was placed in a glass tube between two stopcocks. In order to avoid a possible release of the helium present in the lead by pumping out the air, the air was displaced by a current of pure electrolytic oxygen *. The stopcocks were closed and the tube attached to a subsidiary apparatus similar to that employed for testing for the presence of neon and helium in the gases produced by the action of the radium emanation on water (Phil. Mag. Nov. 1908). The oxygen was absorbed by charcoal and the tube then heated beyond the melting-point of lead to allow the helium to escape. The presence of helium was then spectroscopically looked for in the usual way. Using this method, it was found possible to detect the presence of helium in the lead which had been exposed for only four hours to the α rays from the emanation. After an exposure of 24 hours the helium yellow and green lines came out brightly. These experiments were repeated several times with similar results.

A number of blank experiments were made, using samples of the lead-foil which had not been exposed to the α rays, but in no case was any helium detected. In a similar way, the presence of helium was detected in a cylinder of tinfoil exposed for a few hours over the emanation-tube.

These experiments show that the helium does not escape at once from the lead, but there is on the average a period of retardation of several hours and posssibly longer.

* That the air was completely displaced was shown by the absence of neon in the final spectrum.

The detection of helium in the lead and tin foil, as well as in the glass, removes a possible objection that the helium might have been in some way present in the glass initially, and was liberated as a consequence of its bombardment by the α particles.

The use of such thin glass tubes containing emanation affords a simple and convenient method of examining the effect on substances of an intense α radiation quite independently of the radioactive material contained in the tube.

We can conclude with certainty from these experiments that the α particle after losing its charge is a helium atom. Other evidence indicates that the charge is twice the unit charge carried by the hydrogen atom set free in the electrolysis of water.

University of Manchester,
Nov. 13, 1908.

On a Diffuse Reflection of the α-Particles

By H. Geiger, Ph.D., John Harling Fellow, and E. Marsden, Hatfield Scholar, University of Manchester

(Communicated by Prof. E. Rutherford, F.R.S. Received May 19,—Read June 17, 1909.)

Proceedings of the Royal Society, A. **82**, 495–500 (1909).

When β-particles fall on a plate, a strong radiation emerges from the same side of the plate as that on which the β-particles fall. This radiation is regarded by many observers as a secondary radiation, but more recent experiments seem to show that it consists mainly of primary β-particles, which have been scattered inside the material to such an extent that they emerge again at the same side of the plate.* For α-particles a similar effect has not previously been observed, and is perhaps not to be expected on account of the relatively small scattering which α-particles suffer in penetrating matter.†

In the following experiments, however, conclusive evidence was found of the existence of a diffuse reflection of the α-particles. A small fraction of the α-particles falling upon a metal plate have their directions changed to such an extent that they emerge again at the side of incidence. To form an idea of the way in which this effect takes place, the following three points were investigated:—

(I) The relative amount of reflection from different metals.

(II) The relative amount of reflection from a metal of varying thickness.

(III) The fraction of the incident α-particles which are reflected.

* See Schmidt, 'Jahrbuch der Radioaktivität und Electronik,' vol. 5, p. 471, 1908.

† Rutherford, 'Phil. Mag.,' vol. 12, p. 143, 1906; H. Geiger, 'Roy. Soc. Proc.,' A, vol. 81, p. 174, 1908.

For the observation of the reflected particles the scintillation method was used in all experiments. With regard to the details of the method we refer to the papers of Regener* and of Rutherford and Geiger.†

On account of the fact that the amount of reflection is very small, it was necessary to use a very intense source of α-rays. A tube was employed similar to that which has been proved to be a suitable source in the scattering experiments of one of us.‡ This source consisted of a glass tube AB (fig. 1), drawn down conically and filled with radium emanation, the end B of the tube being closed airtight by means of a mica window. The thickness of the mica was equivalent to about 1 cm. of air, so that the α-particles could easily pass through it.

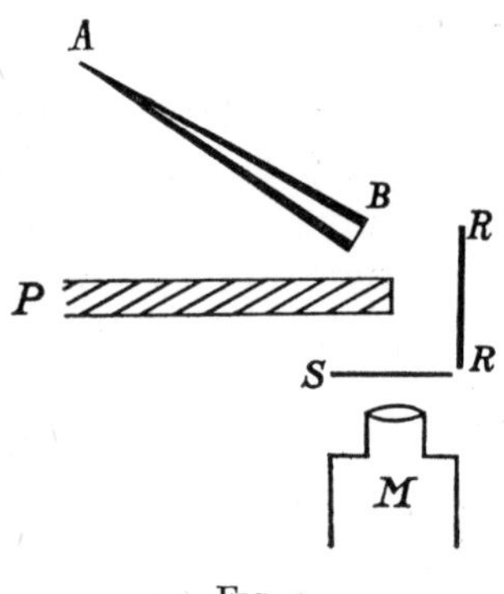

FIG. 1.

Since it is of importance that the gas pressure inside this tube should be as low as possible, the emanation was purified according to the methods developed by Prof. Rutherford.§ The tube contained an amount of emanation equivalent to about 20 milligrammes $RaBr_2$ at a pressure of a few centimetres. The number of α-particles expelled per second through the window was, therefore, very great, and, on account of the small pressure inside the tube, the different ranges of the α-particles from the three products (*i.e.* emanation, RaA, and RaC) were sharply defined.

The zinc sulphide screen S (fig. 1) was fixed behind the lead plate P, in such a position that no α-particles could strike it directly. When a reflector was placed in the position RR at about 1 cm. from the end of the tube, scintillations were at

* 'Verh. d. D. Phys. Ges.,' vol. 10, p. 78, 1908.

† 'Roy. Soc. Proc.,' A, vol. 81, p. 141, 1908.

‡ Geiger, 'Roy. Soc. Proc.,' A, vol. 81, p. 174, 1908.

§ 'Phil. Mag.,' August, p. 300, 1908.

once observed. At the same time the screen brightened up appreciably on account of the reflected β-particles.

By means of a low power microscope, the number of scintillations per minute on a definite square millimetre of the screen was counted for reflectors of different materials. Care was taken that the different reflectors were always placed in exactly the same position.

It is, of course, to be expected that the number of α-particles reflected from the plate would be different in different directions, and would also depend on the angle of incidence. In our arrangement, however, no appreciable difference was found for different angles. This is due to the fact that, owing to the necessity of having the tube very near to the reflector, the angle of incidence varied very much. An investigation of the variation of the effect with the angles of incidence and emergence would necessitate a parallel and very intense source of homogeneous α-rays, which can, however, not easily be realised.

In the following table the number of scintillations observed per minute are given in column 3; in column 4 the ratio to the atomic weight is calculated, and it can be seen that this ratio decreases with decreasing atomic weight. The case of lead appears to be an exception which may be due to slight impurities in the lead.

1. Metal.	2. Atomic weight, A.	3. Number of scintillations per minute, Z.	4. A/Z.
Lead	207	62	30
Gold	197	67	34
Platinum	195	63	33
Tin	119	34	28
Silver	108	27	25
Copper	64	14·5	23
Iron	56	10·2	18·5
Aluminium	27	3·4	12·5

Even in the absence of any reflector about one scintillation per minute was observed. It was easy to show that this was due to a reflection from the air through which the α-particles passed. The numbers on the table are corrected for this effect.

It is interesting to note here that for β-particles the number of reflected particles also decreases with the atomic weight of the reflector.* But while for β-particles the number reflected from gold is only about twice as great as for aluminium, for α-particles the same ratio amounts to about twenty.

(II) We have already pointed out that the diffuse reflection of the α-particles is a consequence of their scattering. According to this point of view, the number of particles reflected must

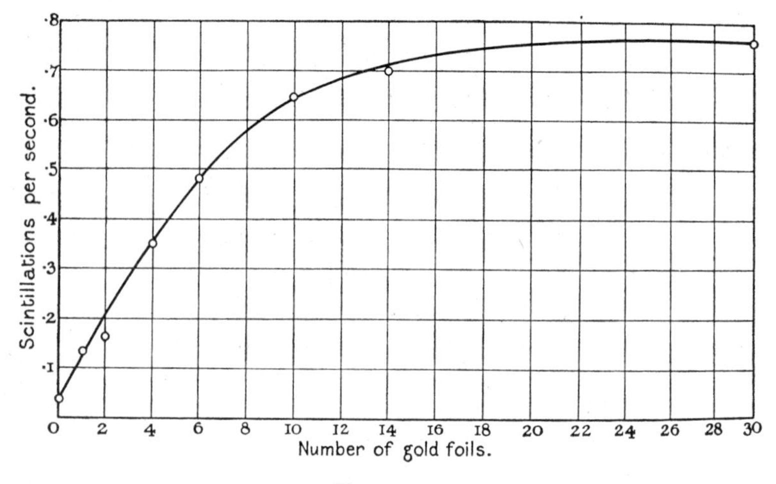

FIG. 2.

vary with the thickness of the reflecting screen. Since gold can be obtained in very thin and uniform foils, different numbers of these foils were used as reflectors. Each foil was equivalent in stopping power to about 0·4 mm. of air. It was necessary to mount the foils on glass plates, but the number reflected from the glass itself was found to be very small compared even with the number from one gold foil. The curve, fig. 2, gives the result of the measurements.

The number of scintillations which were due to the reflection from the air is subtracted from each reading. The first point on

* McClelland, 'Dublin Trans.,' vol. 9, p. 9, 1906.

the curve represents the number of scintillations observed for a glass plate alone as reflector; the last point (marked 30) gives the number of scintillations when a thick gold plate was used.

The curve is similar to those which have been obtained for the reflection of the β-particles.* It brings out clearly that the reflection is not a surface but a volume effect.

Compared, however, with the thickness of gold which an α-particle can penetrate, the effect is confined to a relatively thin layer. In our experiment, about half of the reflected particles were reflected from a layer equivalent to about 2 mm. of air. If the high velocity and mass of the α-particle be taken into account, it seems surprising that some of the α-particles, as the experiment shows, can be turned within a layer of 6×10^{-5} cm. of gold through an angle of 90°, and even more. To produce a similar effect by a magnetic field, the enormous field of 10^9 absolute units would be required.

(III) In the next experiment, an estimate of the total number of particles reflected was aimed at. For this purpose the emanation tube used in the previous experiments was unsuitable, firstly, on account of the difficulty of correctly ascertaining the number of α-particles emerging from the tube; and secondly, on account of the different ranges of the α-particles from the three products: emanation, radium A, and radium C. Consequently, as radiating source, radium C, deposited on a plate of small dimensions, was used. The arrangement, which is sketched in fig. 3, was such that the α-particles from the plate A fell upon the platinum reflector R, of about 1 square centimetre area, at an average angle of 90°. The reflected particles were counted on different points of the screen S.

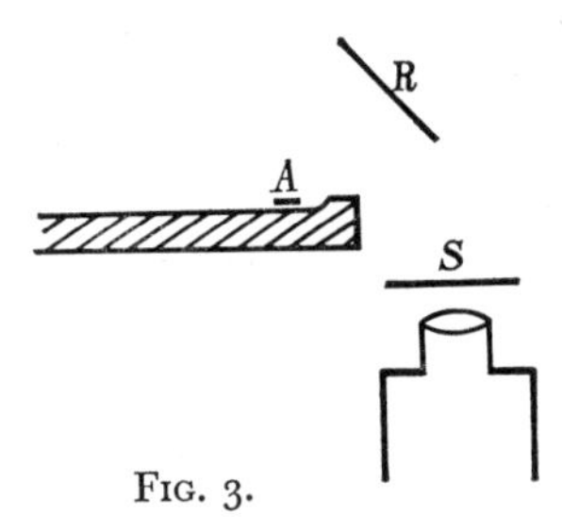

FIG. 3.

No appreciable variation of the number was found with different angles of emergence, the reason of which has already been explained above.

The amount of radium C deposited on the plate was determined

* McClelland, 'Phil. Mag.,' vol. 9, p. 230, 1905; 'Ann. d. Phys.,' vol. 18, p. 974, 1905; Schmidt, 'Ann. d. Phys.,' vol. 23, p. 671, 1907; 'Phys. Zeit.,' vol. 8, p. 737, 1907.

by its γ-ray activity. Assuming that $3{\cdot}4 \times 10^{10}$ particles are expelled per second from an amount of RaC equivalent to 1 gramme Ra,* the number of α-particles expelled per second from the active plate was determined. The number falling on the platinum reflector was then easily calculated from its known distance and area. To find the whole number of reflected particles, it was assumed that they were distributed uniformly round a half sphere with the middle of the reflector as centre.

Three different determinations showed that of the incident α-particles about 1 in 8000 was reflected, under the described conditions.

A special experiment conducted at low pressure showed that in the case of grazing incidence the number of particles reflected at a very small angle to the reflector is largely in excess of the number calculated from the above ratio. This tangential scattering is of considerable importance in some experiments; for instance, if α-particles from a radio-active source are fired along a glass tube of appreciable length the conditions are very favourable for this effect. The number of scintillations counted on a screen sealed to the other end of the tube is made up not only of the particles striking the screen directly, but also of those which have been reflected from the glass walls of the tube.

The correction for the latter effect may be appreciable, and would be still greater in the case of a metal tube. In the counting experiments of Rutherford and Geiger this effect did not influence the final result, the arrangement being such that the reflected particles were prevented from entering the opening of the ionisation vessel by the narrow constriction of a stopcock.

It appears probable that the number of reflected particles depends also upon the velocity of the α-particles falling on the reflector. In our case the particles from the radium C had to travel through a little over a centimetre of air before reaching the reflector. The reflected particles had still an appreciable velocity, since, by interposing an aluminium foil of thickness equivalent in stopping power to $\frac{1}{2}$ cm. of air, the number of scintillations counted was not changed. This might be expected

* Rutherford and Geiger, 'Roy. Soc. Proc.,' A, vol. 81, p. 162, 1908.

from Experiment (II), which showed that the α-particles are reflected from a relatively thin surface layer of the reflector.

We are indebted to Prof. Rutherford for his kind interest and advice throughout this research.

The Scattering of α and β Particles by Matter and the Structure of the Atom. By Professor E. RUTHERFORD, *F.R.S., University of Manchester**.

The *Philosophical Magazine*, Series VI, **21**, 669–688 (1911)

§ 1. IT is well known that the α and β particles suffer deflexions from their rectilinear paths by encounters with atoms of matter. This scattering is far more marked for the β than for the α particle on account of the much smaller momentum and energy of the former particle. There seems to be no doubt that such swiftly moving particles pass through the atoms in their path, and that the deflexions observed are due to the strong electric field traversed within the atomic system. It has generally been supposed that the scattering of a pencil of α or β rays in passing through a thin plate of matter is the result of a multitude of small scatterings by the atoms of matter traversed. The observations, however, of Geiger and Marsden† on the scattering of α rays indicate that some of the α particles must suffer a deflexion of more than a right angle at a single encounter. They found, for example, that a small fraction of the incident α particles, about 1 in 20,000, were turned through an average angle of 90° in passing through a layer of gold-foil about ·00004 cm. thick, which was equivalent in stopping-power of the α particle to 1·6 millimetres of air. Geiger ‡ showed later that the most probable angle of deflexion for a pencil of α particles traversing a gold-foil of this thickness was about 0°·87. A simple calculation based on the theory of probability shows that the chance of an α particle being deflected through 90° is vanishingly small. In addition, it will be seen later that the distribution of the α particles for

* Communicated by the Author. A brief account of this paper was communicated to the Manchester Literary and Philosophical Society in February, 1911.

† Proc. Roy. Soc. lxxxii, p. 495 (1909).

‡ Proc. Roy. Soc. lxxxiii, p. 492 (1910).

various angles of large deflexion does not follow the probability law to be expected if such large deflexions are made up of a large number of small deviations. It seems reasonable to suppose that the deflexion through a large angle is due to a single atomic encounter, for the chance of a second encounter of a kind to produce a large deflexion must in most cases be exceedingly small. A simple calculation shows that the atom must be a seat of an intense electric field in order to produce such a large deflexion at a single encounter.

Recently Sir J. J. Thomson * has put forward a theory to explain the scattering of electrified particles in passing through small thicknesses of matter. The atom is supposed to consist of a number N of negatively charged corpuscles, accompanied by an equal quantity of positive electricity uniformly distributed through a sphere. The deflexion of a negatively electrified particle in passing through the atom is ascribed to two causes—(1) the repulsion of the corpuscles distributed through the atom, and (2) the attraction of the positive electricity in the atom. The deflexion of the particle in passing through the atom is supposed to be small, while the average deflexion after a large number m of encounters was taken as $\sqrt{m} \, . \, \theta$, where θ is the average deflexion due to a single atom. It was shown that the number N of the electrons within the atom could be deduced from observations of the scattering of electrified particles. The accuracy of this theory of compound scattering was examined experimentally by Crowther † in a later paper. His results apparently confirmed the main conclusions of the theory, and he deduced, on the assumption that the positive electricity was continuous, that the number of electrons in an atom was about three times its atomic weight.

The theory of Sir J. J. Thomson is based on the assumption that the scattering due to a single atomic encounter is small, and the particular structure assumed for the atom does not admit of a very large deflexion of an α particle in traversing a single atom, unless it be supposed that the diameter of the

* Camb. Lit. & Phil. Soc. xv, pt. 5 (1910).

† Crowther, Proc. Roy. Soc. lxxxiv, p. 226 (1910).

sphere of positive electricity is minute compared with the diameter of the sphere of influence of the atom.

Since the α and β particles traverse the atom, it should be possible from a close study of the nature of the deflexion to form some idea of the constitution of the atom to produce the effects observed. In fact, the scattering of high-speed charged particles by the atoms of matter is one of the most promising methods of attack of this problem. The development of the scintillation method of counting single α particles affords unusual advantages of investigation, and the researches of H. Geiger by this method have already added much to our knowledge of the scattering of α rays by matter.

§ 2. We shall first examine theoretically the single encounters * with an atom of simple structure, which is able to produce large deflexions of an α particle, and then compare the deductions from the theory with the experimental data available.

Consider an atom which contains a charge $\pm Ne$ at its centre surrounded by a sphere of electrification containing a charge $\mp Ne$ supposed uniformly distributed throughout a sphere of radius R. e is the fundamental unit of charge, which in this paper is taken as $4{\cdot}65 \times 10^{-10}$ E.S. unit. We shall suppose that for distances less than 10^{-12} cm. the central charge and also the charge on the α particle may be supposed to be concentrated at a point. It will be shown that the main deductions from the theory are independent of whether the central charge is supposed to be positive or negative. For convenience, the sign will be assumed to be positive. The question of the stability of the atom proposed need not be considered at this stage, for this will obviously depend upon the minute structure of the atom, and on the motion of the constituent charged parts.

In order to form some idea of the forces required to deflect an α particle through a large angle, consider an atom containing a positive charge Ne at its centre, and surrounded by a distribution of negative electricity Ne uniformly distributed within a

* The deviation of a particle throughout a considerable angle from an encounter with a single atom will in this paper be called "single" scattering. The deviation of a particle resulting from a multitude of small deviations will be termed "compound" scattering.

sphere of radius R. The electric force X and the potential V at a distance r from the centre of an atom for a point inside the atom, are given by

$$X = Ne\left(\frac{1}{r^2} - \frac{r}{R^3}\right)$$

$$V = Ne\left(\frac{1}{r} - \frac{3}{2R} + \frac{r^2}{2R^3}\right).$$

Suppose an α particle of mass m and velocity u and charge E shot directly towards the centre of the atom. It will be brought to rest at a distance b from the centre given by

$$\tfrac{1}{2}mu^2 = NeE\left(\frac{1}{b} - \frac{3}{2R} + \frac{b^2}{2R^3}\right).$$

It will be seen that b is an important quantity in later calculations. Assuming that the central charge is 100 e, it can be calculated that the value of b for an α particle of velocity $2{\cdot}09 \times 10^9$ cms. per second is about $3{\cdot}4 \times 10^{-12}$ cm. In this calculation b is supposed to be very small compared with R. Since R is supposed to be of the order of the radius of the atom, viz. 10^{-8} cm., it is obvious that the α particle before being turned back penetrates so close to the central charge, that the field due to the uniform distribution of negative electricity may be neglected. In general, a simple calculation shows that for all deflexions greater than a degree, we may without sensible error suppose the deflexion due to the field of the central charge alone. Possible single deviations due to the negative electricity, if distributed in the form of corpuscles, are not taken into account at this stage of the theory. It will be shown later that its effect is in general small compared with that due to the central field.

Consider the passage of a positive electrified particle close to the centre of an atom. Supposing that the velocity of the particle is not appreciably changed by its passage through the atom, the path of the particle under the influence of a repulsive force varying as the square of the distance will be an hyperbola with the centre of the atom S as the external focus. Suppose the particle to enter the atom in the direction PO (fig. 1), and that the direction of motion on escaping the atom is OP′. OP and OP′ make equal angles with the line SA, where A is the apse of the hyperbola. p = SN = perpendicular distance from centre on direction of initial motion of particle.

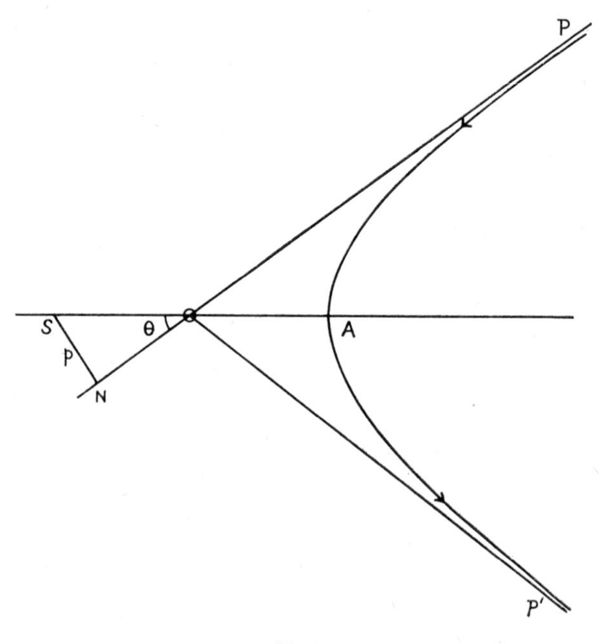

Fig. 1

Let angle POA = θ.

Let V = velocity of particle on entering the atom, v its velocity at A, then from conservation of angular momentum

$$pV = SA \, . \, v.$$

From conservation of energy

$$\tfrac{1}{2}mV^2 = \tfrac{1}{2}mv^2 - \frac{NeE}{SA},$$

$$v^2 = V^2\left(1 - \frac{b}{SA}\right).$$

Since the eccentricity is sec θ,

$$SA = SO + OA = p \operatorname{cosec} \theta(1 + \cos \theta)$$
$$= p \cot \theta/2,$$
$$p^2 = SA(SA - b) = p \cot \theta/2(p \cot \theta/2 - b),$$
$$\therefore \quad b = 2p \cot \theta.$$

The angle of deviation ϕ of the particle is $\pi - 2\theta$ and

$$\cot \phi/2 = \frac{2p^*}{b}. \qquad (1)$$

This gives the angle of deviation of the particle in terms of b, and the perpendicular distance of the direction of projection from the centre of the atom.

For illustration, the angle of deviation ϕ for different values of p/b are shown in the following table:—

p/b …………	10	5	2	1	·5	·25	·125
ϕ …………	5°·7	11°·4	28°	53°	90°	127°	152°

§ 3. *Probability of single deflexion through any angle*

Suppose a pencil of electrified particles to fall normally on a thin screen of matter of thickness t. With the exception of the few particles which are scattered through a large angle, the particles are supposed to pass nearly normally through the plate with only a small change of velocity. Let n = number of atoms in unit volume of material. Then the number of collisions of the particle with the atom of radius R is $\pi R^2 nt$ in the thickness t.

The probability m of entering an atom within a distance p of its centre is given by

$$m = \pi p^2 nt.$$

Chance dm of striking within radii p and $p + dp$ is given by

$$dm = 2\pi pnt \, . \, dp = \frac{\pi}{4} ntb^2 \cot \phi/2 \operatorname{cosec}^2 \phi/2 \, d\phi, \qquad (2)$$

* A simple consideration shows that the deflexion is unaltered if the forces are attractive instead of repulsive.

since

$$\cot \phi/2 = 2p/b.$$

The value of dm gives the *fraction* of the total number of particles which are deviated between the angles ϕ and $\phi + d\phi$.

The fraction ρ of the total number of particles which are deflected through an angle greater than ϕ is given by

$$\rho = \frac{\pi}{4} ntb^2 \cot^2 \phi/2. \quad . \quad . \quad . \quad (3)$$

The fraction ρ which is deflected between the angles ϕ_1 and ϕ_2 is given by

$$\rho = \frac{\pi}{4} ntb^2\left(\cot^2 \frac{\phi_1}{2} - \cot^2 \frac{\phi_2}{2}\right). \quad . \quad . \quad (4)$$

It is convenient to express the equation (2) in another form for comparison with experiment. In the case of the α rays, the number of scintillations appearing on a *constant* area of a zinc sulphide screen are counted for different angles with the direction of incidence of the particles. Let r = distance from point of incidence of α rays on scattering material, then if Q be the total number of particles falling on the scattering material, the number y of α particles falling on unit area which are deflected through an angle ϕ is given by

$$y = \frac{Qdm}{2\pi r^2 \sin \phi \,.\, d\phi} = \frac{ntb^2 \,.\, Q \,.\, \operatorname{cosec}^4 \phi/2}{16r^2} \quad . \quad (5)$$

Since $b = \frac{2NeE}{mu^2}$, we see from this equation that the number of α particles (scintillations) per unit area of zinc sulphide screen at a given distance r from the point of incidence of the rays is proportional to

(1) $\operatorname{cosec}^4 \phi/2$ or $1/\phi^4$ if ϕ be small;
(2) thickness of scattering material t provided this is small;
(3) magnitude of central charge Ne;
(4) and is inversely proportional to $(mu^2)^2$, or to the fourth power of the velocity if m be constant.

In these calculations, it is assumed that the α particles scattered through a large angle suffer only one large deflexion. For this to hold, it is essential that the thickness of the scattering material should be so small that the chance of a second encounter involving another large deflexion is very small. If, for example, the probability of a single deflexion ϕ in passing through a thickness t is $1/1000$, the probability of two successive deflexions each of value ϕ is $1/10^6$, and is negligibly small.

The angular distribution of the α particles scattered from a thin metal sheet affords one of the simplest methods of testing the general correctness of this theory of single scattering. This has been done recently for α rays by Dr. Geiger *, who found that the distribution for particles deflected between 30° and 150° from a thin gold-foil was in substantial agreement with the theory. A more detailed account of these and other experiments to test the validity of the theory will be published later.

§ 4. *Alteration of velocity in an atomic encounter*

It has so far been assumed that an α or β particle does not suffer an appreciable change of velocity as the result of a single atomic encounter resulting in a large deflexion of the particle. The effect of such an encounter in altering the velocity of the particle can be calculated on certain assumptions. It is supposed that only two systems are involved, viz., the swiftly moving particle and the atom which it traverses supposed initially at rest. It is supposed that the principle of conservation of momentum and of energy applies, and that there is no appreciable loss of energy or momentum by radiation.

Let m be mass of the particle,
v_1 = velocity of approach,
v_2 = velocity of recession,
M = mass of atom,
V = velocity communicated to atom as result of encounter.

Let OA (fig. 2) represent in magnitude and direction the

* Manch. Lit. & Phil. Soc. 1910.

momentum mv_1 of the entering particle, and OB the momentum of the receding particle which has been turned through an angle AOB $= \phi$. Then BA represents in magnitude and direction the momentum MV of the recoiling atom.

$$(MV)^2 = (mv_1)^2 + (mv_2)^2 - 2m^2v_1v_2 \cos \phi. \quad (1)$$

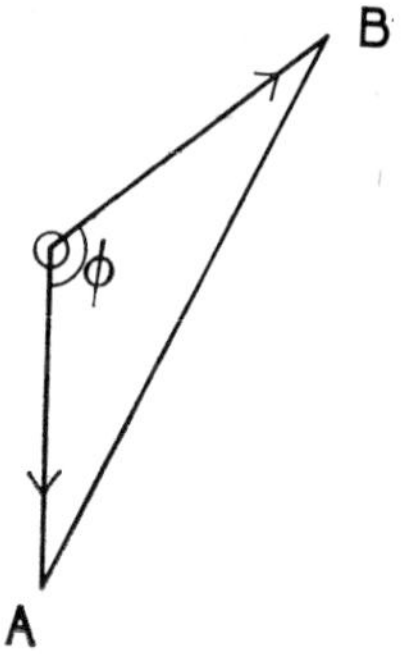

By the conservation of energy

$$MV^2 = mv_1^2 - mv_2^2. \quad . \quad (2)$$

Suppose $M/m = K$ and $v_2 = \rho v_1$, where ρ is <1.

From (1) and (2),

$$(K + 1)\rho^2 - 2\rho \cos \phi = K - 1,$$

or

$$\rho = \frac{\cos \phi}{K + 1} + \frac{1}{K + 1} \sqrt{K^2 - \sin^2 \phi}.$$

Fig. 2

Consider the case of an α particle of atomic weight 4, deflected through an angle of 90° by an encounter with an atom of gold of atomic weight 197.

Since K = 49 nearly,

$$\rho = \sqrt{\frac{K - 1}{K + 1}} = \cdot 979,$$

or the velocity of the particle is reduced only about 2 per cent. by the encounter.

In the case of aluminium $K = 27/4$ and for $\phi = 90°$ $\rho = \cdot 86$.

It is seen that the reduction of velocity of the α particle becomes marked on this theory for encounters with the lighter atoms. Since the range of an α particle in air or other matter is approximately proportional to the cube of the velocity, it follows that an α particle of range 7 cms. has its range reduced to 4·5 cms. after incurring a single deviation of 90° in traversing an aluminium atom. This is of a magnitude to be easily detected experimentally. Since the value of K is very large for an encounter of a β particle with an atom, the reduction of velocity on this formula is very small.

Some very interesting cases of the theory arise in considering the changes of velocity and the distribution of scattered particles when the α particle encounters a light atom, for example a hydrogen or helium atom. A discussion of these and similar cases is reserved until the question has been examined experimentally.

§ 5. *Comparison of single and compound scattering*

Before comparing the results of theory with experiment, it is desirable to consider the relative importance of single and compound scattering in determining the distribution of the scattered particles. Since the atom is supposed to consist of a central charge surrounded by a uniform distribution of the opposite sign through a sphere of radius R, the chance of encounters with the atom involving small deflexions is very great compared with the chance of a single large deflexion.

This question of compound scattering has been examined by Sir J. J. Thomson in the paper previously discussed (§ 1). In the notation of this paper, the average deflexion ϕ_1, due to the field of the sphere of positive electricity of radius R and quantity Ne was found by him to be

$$\phi_1 = \frac{\pi}{4} \cdot \frac{NeE}{mu^2} \cdot \frac{1}{R}.$$

The average deflexion ϕ_2 due to the N negative corpuscles supposed distributed uniformly throughout the sphere was found to be

$$\phi_2 = \frac{16}{5} \frac{eE}{mu^2} \cdot \frac{1}{R} \sqrt{\frac{3N}{2}}.$$

The mean deflexion due to both positive and negative electricity was taken as

$$(\phi_1^2 + \phi_2^2)^{1/2}.$$

In a similar way, it is not difficult to calculate the average deflexion due to the atom with a central charge discussed in this paper.

Since the radial electric field X at any distance r from the centre is given by

$$X = Ne\left(\frac{1}{r^2} - \frac{r}{R^3}\right),$$

it is not difficult to show that the deflexion (supposed small) of an electrified particle due to this field is given by

$$\theta = \frac{b}{p}\left(1 - \frac{p^2}{R^2}\right)^{3/2},$$

where p is the perpendicular from the centre on the path of the particle and b has the same value as before. It is seen that the value of θ increases with diminution of p and becomes great for small values of ϕ.

Since we have already seen that the deflexions become very large for a particle passing near the centre of the atom, it is obviously not correct to find the average value by assuming θ is small.

Taking R of the order 10^{-8} cm., the value of p for a large deflexion is for α and β particles of the order 10^{-11} cm. Since the chance of an encounter involving a large deflexion is small compared with the chance of small deflexions, a simple consideration shows that the average small deflexion is practically unaltered if the large deflexions are omitted. This is equivalent to integrating over that part of the cross section of the atom where the deflexions are small and neglecting the small central area. It can in this way be simply shown that the average small deflexion is given by

$$\phi_1 = \frac{3\pi}{8}\frac{b}{R}.$$

This value of ϕ_1 for the atom with a concentrated central charge is three times the magnitude of the average deflexion for the same value of Ne in the type of atom examined by Sir J. J. Thomson. Combining the deflexions due to the electric field and to the corpuscles, the average deflexion is

$$(\phi_1{}^2 + \phi_2{}^2)^2 \quad \text{or} \quad \frac{b}{2R}\left(5{\cdot}54 + \frac{15{\cdot}4}{N}\right)^{1/2}.$$

It will be seen later that the value of N is nearly proportional to the atomic weight, and is about 100 for gold. The effect due to scattering of the individual corpuscles expressed by the second term of the equation is consequently small for heavy atoms compared with that due to the distributed electric field.

Neglecting the second term, the average deflexion per atom is $\frac{3\pi b}{8\mathrm{R}}$. We are now in a position to consider the relative effects on the distribution of particles due to single and to compound scattering. Following J. J. Thomson's argument, the average deflexion θ_t after passing through a thickness t of matter is proportional to the square root of the number of encounters and is given by

$$\theta_t = \frac{3\pi b}{8\mathrm{R}} \sqrt{\pi \mathrm{R}^2 \,.\, n \,.\, t} = \frac{3\pi b}{8} \sqrt{\pi n t},$$

where n as before is equal to the number of atoms per unit volume.

The probability p_1 for compound scattering that the deflexion of the particle is greater than ϕ is equal to $e^{-\phi^2/\theta_t^2}$.

Consequently

$$\phi^2 = -\frac{9\pi^3}{64} b^2 nt \log p_1.$$

Next suppose that single scattering alone is operative. We have seen (§ 3) that the probability p_2 of a deflexion greater than ϕ is given by

$$p_2 = \frac{\pi}{4} b^2 \,.\, n \,.\, t \cot^2 \phi/2.$$

By comparing these two equations

$$p_2 \log p_1 = -{\cdot}181 \phi^2 \cot^2 \phi/2,$$

ϕ is sufficiently small that

$$\tan \phi/2 = \phi/2,$$
$$p_2 \log p_1 = -{\cdot}72.$$

If we suppose $p_2 = \cdot 5$, then $p_1 = \cdot 24$.

If $p_2 = \cdot 1$, $p_1 = \cdot 0004$.

It is evident from this comparison, that the probability for any given deflexion is always greater for single than for compound scattering. The difference is especially marked when only a small fraction of the particles are scattered through any given angle. It follows from this result that the distribution of particles due to encounters with the atoms is for small thicknesses mainly governed by single scattering. No doubt compound scattering produces some effect in equalizing the distribution of the scattered particles; but its effect becomes relatively smaller, the smaller the fraction of the particles scattered through a given angle.

§ 6. *Comparison of Theory with Experiments*

On the present theory, the value of the central charge Ne is an important constant, and it is desirable to determine its value for different atoms. This can be most simply done by determining the small fraction of α or β particles of known velocity falling on a thin metal screen, which are scattered between ϕ and $\phi + d\phi$ where ϕ is the angle of deflexion. The influence of compound scattering should be small when this fraction is small.

Experiments in these directions are in progress, but it is desirable at this stage to discuss in the light of the present theory the data already published on scattering of α and β particles.

The following points will be discussed:—

(*a*) The "diffuse reflexion" of α particles, *i. e.* the scattering of α particles through large angles (Geiger and Marsden).

(*b*) The variation of diffuse reflexion with atomic weight of the radiator (Geiger and Marsden).

(*c*) The average scattering of a pencil of α rays transmitted through a thin metal plate (Geiger).

(*d*) The experiments of Crowther on the scattering of β rays of different velocities by various metals.

(*a*) In the paper of Geiger and Marsden (*loc. cit.*) on the diffuse reflexion of α particles falling on various substances it was shown that about 1/8000 of the α particles from radium C falling on a thick plate of platinum are scattered back in the direction of the incidence. This fraction is deduced on the assumption that the α particles are uniformly scattered in all directions, the observations being made for a deflexion of about 90°. The form of experiment is not very suited for accurate calculation, but from the data available it can be shown that the scattering observed is about that to be expected on the theory if the atom of platinum has a central charge of about 100 e.

(*b*) In their experiments on this subject, Geiger and Marsden gave the relative number of α particles diffusely reflected from thick layers of different metals, under similar conditions. The numbers obtained by them are given in the table below, where z represents the relative number of scattered particles, measured by the number of scintillations per minute on a zinc sulphide screen.

Metal.	Atomic weight.	z.	$z/A^{3/2}$.
Lead	207	62	208
Gold	197	67	242
Platinum	195	63	232
Tin	119	34	226
Silver	108	27	241
Copper	64	14·5	225
Iron	56	10·2	250
Aluminium	27	3·4	243
		Average	233

On the theory of single scattering, the fraction of the total number of α particles scattered through any given angle in passing through a thickness t is proportional to $n \,.\, A^2t$, assuming that the central charge is proportional to the atomic weight A. In the present case, the thickness of matter from which the scattered α particles are able to emerge and affect the zinc sulphide screen depends on the metal. Since Bragg has shown that the stopping power of an atom for an α particle is proportional to the square root of its atomic weight, the value of nt for different elements is proportional to $1/\sqrt{A}$. In this case t represents the greatest depth from which the scattered α particles emerge. The number z of α particles scattered back from a thick layer is consequently proportional to $A^{3/2}$ or $z/A^{3/2}$ should be a constant.

To compare this deduction with experiment, the relative values of the latter quotient are given in the last column. Considering the difficulty of the experiments, the agreement between theory and experiment is reasonably good *.

The single large scattering of α particles will obviously affect to some extent the shape of the Bragg ionization curve for a pencil of α rays. This effect of large scattering should be marked when the α rays have traversed screens of metals of high atomic weight but should be small for atoms of light atomic weight.

(*c*) Geiger made a careful determination of the scattering of α particles passing through thin metal foils, by the scintillation method, and deduced the most probable angle through which the α particles are deflected in passing through known thicknesses of different kinds of matter.

A narrow pencil of homogeneous α rays was used as a source. After passing through the scattering foil, the total number of α particles deflected through different angles was directly measured. The angle for which the number of scattered particles was a maximum was taken as the most probable angle. The variation of the most probable angle with thickness of matter was determined, but calculation from these data is somewhat complicated by the variation of velocity of the α particles in their passage through the scattering material. A consideration of the curve of distribution of the α particles

* The effect of change of velocity in an atomic encounter is neglected in this calculation.

given in the paper (*loc. cit.* p. 496) shows that the angle through which half the particles are scattered is about 20 per cent greater than the most probable angle.

We have already seen that compound scattering may become important when about half the particles are scattered through a given angle, and it is difficult to disentangle in such cases the relative effects due to the two kinds of scattering. An approximate estimate can be made in the following way:—From (§ 5) the relation between the probabilities p_1 and p_2 for compound and single scattering respectively is given by

$$p_2 \log p_1 = -\cdot 721.$$

The probability q of the combined effects may as a first approximation be taken as

$$q = (p_1{}^2 + p_2{}^2)^{1/2}.$$

If $q = \cdot 5$, it follows that

$$p_1 = \cdot 2 \quad \text{and} \quad p_2 = \cdot 46.$$

We have seen that the probability p_2 of a single deflexion greater than ϕ is given by

$$p_2 = \frac{\pi}{4} n \,.\, t \,.\, b^2 \cot^2 \phi/2.$$

Since in the experiments considered ϕ is comparatively small

$$\frac{\phi \sqrt{p_2}}{\sqrt{\pi n t}} = b = \frac{2\text{N}e\text{E}}{mu^2}.$$

Geiger found that the most probable angle of scattering of the α rays in passing through a thickness of gold equivalent in stopping power to about ·76 cm. of air was 1° 40′. The angle ϕ through which half the α particles are turned thus corresponds to 2° nearly.

$$t = \cdot 00017 \text{ cm.}; \; n = 6{\cdot}07 \times 10^{22};$$
$$u \text{ (average value)} = 1{\cdot}8 \times 10^9.$$
$$E/m = 1{\cdot}5 \times 10^{14} \text{ . E.S. units}; \; e = 4{\cdot}65 \times 10^{-10}.$$

Taking the probability of single scattering = ·46 and

substituting the above values in the formula, the value of N for gold comes out to be 97.

For a thickness of gold equivalent in stopping power to 2·12 cms. of air, Geiger found the most probable angle to be $3° 40'$. In this case $t = \cdot 00047$, $\phi = 4°\cdot 4$, and average $u = 1\cdot 7 \times 10^9$, and N comes out to be 114.

Geiger showed that the most probable angle of deflexion for an atom was nearly proportional to its atomic weight. It consequently follows that the value of N for different atoms should be nearly proportional to their atomic weights, at any rate for atomic weights between gold and aluminium.

Since the atomic weight of platinum is nearly equal to that of gold, it follows from these considerations that the magnitude of the diffuse reflexion of α particles through more than 90° from gold and the magnitude of the average small angle scattering of a pencil of rays in passing through gold-foil are both explained on the hypothesis of single scattering by supposing the atom of gold has a central charge of about 100 e.

(*d*) *Experiments of Crowther on scattering of β rays.*—We shall now consider how far the experimental results of Crowther on scattering of β particles of different velocities by various materials can be explained on the general theory of single scattering. On this theory, the fraction of β particles p turned through an angle greater than ϕ is given by

$$p = \frac{\pi}{4} n \,.\, t \,.\, b^2 \cot^2 \phi/2.$$

In most of Crowther's experiments ϕ is sufficiently small that $\tan \phi/2$ may be put equal to $\phi/2$ without much error. Consequently

$$\phi^2 = 2\pi\, n \,.\, t \,.\, b^2 \qquad \text{if } p = 1/2.$$

On the theory of compound scattering, we have already seen that the chance p_1 that the deflexion of the particles is greater than ϕ is given by

$$\phi^2/\log p_1 = -\frac{9\pi^3}{64} n \,.\, t \,.\, b^2.$$

Since in the experiments of Crowther, the thickness t of matter was determined for which $p_1 = 1/2$,

$$\phi^2 = \cdot 96\pi\, n\, t\, b^2.$$

For a probability of 1/2, the theories of single and compound scattering are thus identical in general form, but differ by a numerical constant. It is thus clear that the main relations on the theory of compound scattering of Sir J. J. Thomson, which were verified experimentally by Crowther, hold equally well on the theory of single scattering.

For example, if t_m be the thickness for which half the particles are scattered through an angle ϕ, Crowther showed that $\phi/\sqrt{t_m}$ and also $\frac{mu^2}{E} \cdot \sqrt{t_m}$ were constants for a given material when ϕ was fixed. These relations hold also on the theory of single scattering. Notwithstanding this apparent similarity in form, the two theories are fundamentally different. In one case, the effects observed are due to cumulative effects of small deflexions, while in the other the large deflexions are supposed to result from a single encounter. The distribution of scattered particles is entirely different on the two theories when the probability of deflexion greater than ϕ is small.

We have already seen that the distribution of scattered α particles at various angles has been found by Geiger to be in substantial agreement with the theory of single scattering, but cannot be explained on the theory of compound scattering alone. Since there is every reason to believe that the laws of scattering of α and β particles are very similar, the law of distribution of scattered β particles should be the same as for α particles for small thicknesses of matter. Since the value of mu^2/E for the β particles is in most cases much smaller than the corresponding value for the α particles, the chance of large single deflexions for β particles in passing through a given thickness of matter is much greater than for α particles. Since on the theory of single scattering the fraction of the number of particles which are deflected through a given angle is proportional to kt, where t is the thickness supposed small and k a constant, the number of particles which are undeflected through this angle is proportional to $1 - kt$. From considerations based on the theory of compound scattering, Sir J. J. Thomson deduced that the probability of deflexion less than ϕ is proportional to $1 - e^{-\mu/t}$ where μ is a constant for any given value of ϕ.

The correctness of this latter formula was tested by Crowther by measuring electrically the fraction I/I_0 of the scattered β particles which passed through a circular opening subtending an angle of 36° with the scattering material. If

$$I/I_0 = 1 - e^{-\mu/t},$$

the value of I should decrease very slowly at first with increase of t. Crowther, using aluminium as scattering material, states that the variation of I/I_0 was in good accord with this theory for small values of t. On the other hand, if single scattering be present, as it undoubtedly is for α rays, the curve showing the relation between I/I_0 and t should be nearly linear in the initial stages. The experiments of Madsen * on scattering of β rays, although not made with quite so small a thickness of aluminium as that used by Crowther, certainly support such a conclusion. Considering the importance of the point at issue, further experiments on this question are desirable.

From the table given by Crowther of the value $\phi/\sqrt{t_m}$ for different elements for β rays of velocity $2{\cdot}68 \times 10^{10}$ cms. per second, the values of the central charge Ne can be calculated on the theory of single scattering. It is supposed, as in the case of the α rays, that for the given value of $\phi/\sqrt{t_m}$ the fraction of the β particles deflected by single scattering through an angle greater than ϕ is ·46 instead of ·5.

The values of N calculated from Crowther's data are given below.

Element.	Atomic weight.	$\phi/\sqrt{t_m}$.	N.
Aluminium	27	4·25	22
Copper	63·2	10·0	42
Silver	108	15·4	78
Platinum	194	29·0	138

* Phil. Mag. xviii, p. 909 (1909).

It will be remembered that the values of N for gold deduced from scattering of the α rays were in two calculations 97 and 114. These numbers are somewhat smaller than the values given above for platinum (viz. 138), whose atomic weight is not very different from gold. Taking into account the uncertainties involved in the calculation from the experimental data, the agreement is sufficiently close to indicate that the same general laws of scattering hold for the α and β particles, notwithstanding the wide differences in the relative velocity and mass of these particles.

As in the case of the α rays, the value of N should be most simply determined for any given element by measuring the small fraction of the incident β particles scattered through a large angle. In this way, possible errors due to small scattering will be avoided.

The scattering data for the β rays, as well as for the α rays, indicate that the central charge in an atom is approximately proportional to its atomic weight. This falls in with the experimental deductions of Schmidt *. In his theory of absorption of β rays, he supposed that in traversing a thin sheet of matter, a small fraction α of the particles are stopped, and a small fraction β are reflected or scattered back in the direction of incidence. From comparison of the absorption curves of different elements, he deduced that the value of the constant β for different elements is proportional to nA^2 where n is the number of atoms per unit volume and A the atomic weight of the element. This is exactly the relation to be expected on the theory of single scattering if the central charge on an atom is proportional to its atomic weight.

§ 7. *General Considerations*

In comparing the theory outlined in this paper with the experimental results, it has been supposed that the atom consists of a central charge supposed concentrated at a point, and that the large single deflexions of the α and β particles are mainly due to their passage through the strong central field.

* *Annal. d. Phys.* iv, 23, p. 671 (1907).

The effect of the equal and opposite compensating charge supposed distributed uniformly throughout a sphere has been neglected. Some of the evidence in support of these assumptions will now be briefly considered. For concreteness, consider the passage of a high speed α particle through an atom having a positive central charge Ne, and surrounded by a compensating charge of N electrons. Remembering that the mass, momentum, and kinetic energy of the α particle are very large compared with the corresponding values for an electron in rapid motion, it does not seem possible from dynamic considerations that an α particle can be deflected through a large angle by a close approach to an electron, even if the latter be in rapid motion and constrained by strong electrical forces. It seems reasonable to suppose that the chance of single deflexions through a large angle due to this cause, if not zero, must be exceedingly small compared with that due to the central charge.

It is of interest to examine how far the experimental evidence throws light on the question of the extent of the distribution of the central charge. Suppose, for example, the central charge to be composed of N unit charges distributed over such a volume that the large single deflexions are mainly due to the constituent charges and not to the external field produced by the distribution. It has been shown (§ 3) that the fraction of the α particles scattered through a large angle is proportional to $(NeE)^2$, where Ne is the central charge concentrated at a point and E the charge on the deflected particle. If, however, this charge is distributed in single units, the fraction of the α particles scattered through a given angle is proportional to Ne^2 instead of N^2e^2. In this calculation, the influence of mass of the constituent particle has been neglected, and account has only been taken of its electric field. Since it has been shown that the value of the central point charge for gold must be about 100, the value of the distributed charge required to produce the same proportion of single deflexions through a large angle should be at least 10,000. Under these conditions the mass of the constituent particle would be small compared with that of the α particle, and the difficulty arises of the production of large single deflexions at all. In addition, with such a large distributed charge, the effect of compound scattering is relatively more important than that of single scattering. For example, the probable small angle of deflexion of a pencil of α particles passing through a thin gold foil would be much greater than that experimentally observed by Geiger (§ *b–c*). The large and small angle scattering could not then be explained by the assumption of a central charge of the same value. Considering the evidence as a whole, it seems simplest to suppose that the atom contains a central charge distributed through a very small volume, and that the large single deflexions are due to the central charge as a whole, and not to its constituents. At the same time, the experimental evidence is not precise enough to negative the possibility that a small fraction of the positive charge may be carried by satellites extending some distance from the centre. Evidence on this point could be obtained by examining whether the same central charge is required to explain the large single deflexions of α and β particles; for the α particle must approach much closer to the centre of the atom than the β particle of average speed to suffer the same large deflexion.

The general data available indicate that the value of this central charge for different atoms is approximately proportional to their atomic weights, at any rate for atoms heavier than aluminium. It will be of great interest to examine experimentally whether such a simple relation holds also for the lighter atoms. In cases where the mass of the deflecting atom (for example, hydrogen, helium, lithium) is not very different from that of the α particle, the general theory of single scattering will require modification, for it is necessary to take into account the movements of the atom itself (see § 4).

It is of interest to note that Nagaoka * has mathematically considered the properties of a "Saturnian" atom which he supposed to consist of a central attracting mass surrounded by rings of rotating electrons. He showed that such a system was stable if the attractive force was large. From the point of view considered in this paper, the chance of large deflexion would practically be unaltered, whether the atom is considered to be a

* Nagaoka, Phil. Mag. vii, p. 445 (1904).

disk or a sphere. It may be remarked that the approximate value found for the central charge of the atom of gold (100 e) is about that to be expected if the atom of gold consisted of 49 atoms of helium, each carrying a charge 2 e. This may be only a coincidence, but it is certainly suggestive in view of the expulsion of helium atoms carrying two unit charges from radioactive matter.

The deductions from the theory so far considered are independent of the sign of the central charge, and it has not so far been found possible to obtain definite evidence to determine whether it be positive or negative. It may be possible to settle the question of sign by consideration of the difference of the laws of absorption of the β particle to be expected on the two hypotheses, for the effect of radiation in reducing the velocity of the β particle should be far more marked with a positive than with a negative centre. If the central charge be positive, it is easily seen that a positively charged mass if released from the centre of a heavy atom, would acquire a great velocity in moving through the electric field. It may be possible in this way to account for the high velocity of expulsion of α particles without supposing that they are initially in rapid motion within the atom.

Further consideration of the application of this theory to these and other questions will be reserved for a later paper, when the main deductions of the theory have been tested experimentally. Experiments in this direction are already in progress by Geiger and Marsden.

University of Manchester,
April 1911.

The Laws of Deflexion of α Particles through Large Angles *. *By* Dr. H. Geiger *and* E. Marsden †.

The *Philosophical Magazine*, Series VI, **25**, 604–623 (1913)

IN a former paper ‡ one of us has shown that in the passage of α particles through matter the deflexions are, on the average, small and of the order of a few degrees only. In the experiments a narrow pencil of α particles fell on a zinc-sulphide screen in vacuum, and the distribution of the scintillations on the screen was observed when different metal foils were placed in the path of the α particles. From the distribution obtained, the most probable angle of scattering could be deduced, and it was shown that the results could be explained on the assumption that the deflexion of a single α particle is the resultant of a large number of very small deflexions caused by the passage of the α particle through the successive individual atoms of the scattering substance.

In an earlier paper §, however, we pointed out that α particles are sometimes turned through very large angles. This was made evident by the fact that when α particles fall on a metal plate, a small fraction of them, about 1/8000 in the case of platinum, appears to be diffusely reflected. This amount of reflexion, although small, is, however, too large to be explained on the above simple theory of scattering. It is easy to calculate from the experimental data that the probability of a deflexion through an angle of 90° is vanishingly small, and of a different order to the value found experimentally.

Professor Rutherford ‖ has recently developed a theory to account for the scattering of α particles through these large

* Communicated to *k. d.-k. Akad. d. Wiss. Wien.*

† Communicated by Prof. E. Rutherford, F.R.S.

‡ H. Geiger, Roy. Soc. Proc. vol. lxxxiii. p. 492 (1910); vol. lxxxvi. p. 235 (1912).

§ H. Geiger and E. Marsden, Roy. Soc. Proc. vol. lxxxii. p. 495 (1909).

‖ E. Rutherford, Phil. Mag. vol. xxi. p. 669 (1911).

angles, the assumption being that the deflexions are the result of an intimate encounter of an α particle with a single atom of the matter traversed. In this theory an atom is supposed to consist of a strong positive or negative central charge concentrated within a sphere of less than about 3×10^{-12} cm. radius, and surrounded by electricity of the opposite sign distributed throughout the remainder of the atom of about 10^{-8} cm. radius. In considering the deflexion of an α particle directed against such an atom, the main deflexion-effect can be supposed to be due to the central concentrated charge which will cause the α particle to describe an hyperbola with the centre of the atom as one focus.

The angle between the directions of the α particle before and after deflexion will depend on the perpendicular distance of the initial trajectory from the centre of the atom. The fraction of the α particles whose paths are sufficiently near to the centre of the atom will, however, be small, so that the probability of an α particle suffering a large deflexion of this nature will be correspondingly small. Thus, assuming a narrow pencil of α particles directed against a thin sheet of matter containing atoms distributed at random throughout its volume, if the scattered particles are counted by the scintillations they produce on a zinc-sulphide screen distance r from the point of incidence of the pencil in a direction making an angle ϕ with it, the number of α particles falling on unit area of the screen per second is deduced to be equal to

$$\frac{Qntb^2 \operatorname{cosec}^4 \phi/2}{16r^2},$$

where Q is the number of α particles per second in the original pencil, n the number of atoms in unit volume of the material, and t the thickness of the foil. The quantity

$$b = \frac{2NeE}{mu^2},$$

where Ne is the central charge of the atom, and m, E, and u are the respective mass, charge, and velocity of the α particle.

The number of deflected α particles is thus proportional to

(1) cosec^4 $\phi/2$, (2) thickness of scattering material t if the thickness is small, (3) the square of the central charge Ne of the atoms of the particular matter employed to scatter the particles, (4) the inverse fourth power of the velocity u of the incident α particles.

At the suggestion of Prof. Rutherford, we have carried out experiments to test the main conclusions of the above theory. The following points were investigated:—

(1) Variation with angle.
(2) Variation with thickness of scattering material.
(3) Variation with atomic weight of scattering material.
(4) Variation with velocity of incident α particles.
(5) The fraction of particles scattered through a definite angle.

The main difficulty of the experiments has arisen from the necessity of using a very intense and narrow source of α particles owing to the smallness of the scattering effect. All the measurements have been carried out by observing the scintillations due to the scattered α particles on a zinc-sulphide screen, and during the course of the experiments over 100,000 scintillations have been counted. It may be mentioned in anticipation that all the results of our investigation are in good agreement with the theoretical deductions of Prof. Rutherford, and afford strong evidence of the correctness of the underlying assumption that an atom contains a strong charge at the centre of dimensions, small compared with the diameter of the atom.

(1) *Variation of Scattering with Angle*

We have already pointed out that to obtain measurable effects an intense pencil of α particles is required. It is further necessary that the path of the α particles should be in an evacuated chamber to avoid complications due to the absorption and scattering of the air. The apparatus used is shown in fig. 1, and mainly consisted of a strong cylindrical metal box B, which contained the source of α particles R, the scattering foil F, and a microscope M to which the zinc-sulphide screen S was rigidly attached. The box was fastened down to a graduated circular platform A, which could be rotated by means of a conical airtight joint C. By rotating the platform the box and microscope moved with it, whilst the scattering foil and radiating source remained in position, being attached to the tube T, which was fastened to the standard L. The box B was closed by the ground-glass plate P, and could be exhausted through the tube T.

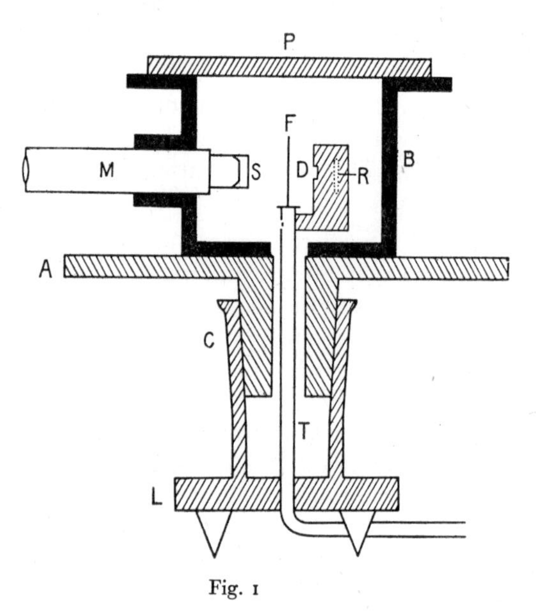

Fig. 1

The source of α particles employed was similar to that used originally by Rutherford and Royds * in their experiments on the nature of the α particle. It consisted of a small thin-walled glass tube about 1 mm. in diameter, containing a large quantity of well purified radium emanation. The α particles emitted by the emanation and its active deposit could pass through the glass walls without much reduction of range. For these experiments the unhomogeneity of the source, due to the different α particles from the emanation, Ra A and Ra C, does not interfere with the application of the law of scattering with

* E. Rutherford and T. Royds, Phil. Mag. vol. xvii. p. 281 (1909).

angle as deduced from the theory as each group of α particles is scattered according to the same law.

By means of a diaphragm placed at D, a pencil of α particles was directed normally on to the scattering foil F. By rotating the microscope the α particles scattered in different directions could be observed on the screen S. Although over 100 millicuries of radium emanation were available for the experiments, the smallness of the effect for the larger angles of deflexion necessitated short distances of screen and source from the scattering foil. In some experiments the distance between the source and scattering foil was 2·5 cm., and the screen moved in a circle of 1·6 cm radius, while in other experiments these distances were increased. Observations were taken in various experiments for angles of deflexion from 5° to 150°. When measuring the scattering through large angles the zinc-sulphide screen had to be turned very near to the source, and the β and γ rays produced a considerable luminescence on it, thus making countings of the scintillations difficult. The effect of the β rays was reduced as far as possible by enclosing the source in a lead box shown shaded in the diagram. The amount of lead was, however, limited by considerations of the space taken up by it, and consequently observations could not be made for angles of deflexion between 150° and 180°.

In the investigation of the scattering through relatively small angles the distances of source and screen from the scattering foil were increased considerably in order to obtain beams of smaller solid angle.

The number of particles scattered through different angles was found to decrease extremely rapidly with increase of angle, and as it is not possible to count with certainty more than 90 scintillations per minute or less than about 5 per minute, measurements could only be made over a relatively small range of angles at the same time. The number of α particles scattered through large angles was first measured, and as the emanation decayed it was possible to take measurements for smaller and smaller angles, and from the known decay of the emanation measurements taken at different times could be corrected for the decrease of activity.

Even when no scattering foil was used a few scintillations were always observed on the screen. They were obviously due to scattered radiation from the walls of the vessel and from the edge of the diaphragm limiting the beam. The effect was reduced as far as possible by lining the box with paper and by using a substance of low atomic weight, viz. aluminium, for the diaphragm. The number of stray α particles was determined for different positions of the microscope by removing the scattering foil so that the necessary corrections could be applied with certainty.

In order to make the best use of the emanation available, measurements were made simultaneously with different foils. These foils were attached to frames which fitted into a slot in the tube T in such a way that they could be exchanged and accurately replaced in position. Table I. gives an example of a particular set of countings, when a silver foil was used to scatter the α particles.

TABLE I.—Variation of Scattering with Angle. (Example of a set of measurements.) Silver Foil. Time elapsed since filling of emanation tube, 51 hours. Correction for decay, 0·683.

Angle ϕ.	Scintillations per minute.				$\frac{1}{\sin^4 \phi/2}$.	$N \times \sin^4 \phi/2$.
	Without foil.	With foil.	Corrected for effect without foil.	Corrected for decay, N.		
150°...	0·2	4·95	4·75	6·95	1·15	6·0
135 ...	2·6	8·3	5·7	8·35	1·38	6·1
120 ...	3·8	10·3	6·5	9·5	1·79	5·3
105 ...	0·6	10·6	10·0	14·6	2·53	5·8
75 ...	0·0	28·6	28·6	41·9	7·25	5·8
60 ...	0·3	69·2	68·9	101	16·0	6·3

In this set about 2500 scintillations were counted. After a few days had elapsed the measurements for the smaller angles were repeated and the range of angles extended. Proceeding in this way the whole range of angles was investigated in the course of a few weeks. When measuring relatively large angles of deflexion a wide beam of about 15° radius had to be used in order to obtain a suitable number of scintillations, but for the smaller angles the aperture of the diaphragm confining the beam was reduced considerably, so that the angle at which the scintillations were counted was always large compared with the angular radius of the beam. When changing over from one diaphragm to another comparative measurements for different angles were made so as to obtain an accurate value of the reduction constant.

Table II. gives the collected results for two series of experiments with foils of silver and gold. The thicknesses of the foils were in the first series equivalent to 0·45 and 0·3 cm. air, and in the second series 0·45 and 0·1 cm. air for silver and gold respectively. Col. I. gives the values of the angles ϕ between

TABLE II.

Variation of Scattering with Angle. (Collected results.)

I.	II.	III. Silver.	IV. Silver.	V. Gold.	VI Gold.
Angle of deflexion, ϕ.	$\frac{1}{\sin^4 \phi/2}$.	Number of scintillations, N.	$\frac{N}{\sin^4 \phi/2}$.	Number of scintillations, N.	$\frac{N}{\sin^4 \phi/2}$.
150°	1·15	22·2	19·3	33·1	28·8
135	1·38	27·4	19·8	43·0	31·2
120	1·79	33·0	18·4	51·9	29·0
105	2·53	47·3	18·7	69·5	27·5
75	7·25	136	18·8	211	29·1
60	16·0	320	20·0	477	29·8
45	46·6	989	21·2	1435	30·8
37·5......	93·7	1760	18·8	3300	35·3
30	223	5260	23·6	7800	35·0
22·5......	690	20300	29·4	27300	39·6
15	3445	105400	30·6	132000	38·4
30	223	5·3	0·024	3·1	0·014
22·5......	690	16·6	0·024	8·4	0·012
15	3445	93·0	0·027	48·2	0·014
10	17330	508	0·029	200	0·0115
7·5......	54650	1710	0·031	607	0·011
5	276300	...	...	3320	0·012

the direction of the beam and the direction in which the scattered α particles were counted. Col. II. gives the values of $\frac{1}{\sin^4 \phi/2}$. In Cols. III. and V. the numbers of scintillations are entered which were observed for the silver and gold respectively. Corrections are made for the decay of the emanation, for the natural effect, and for change of diaphragm. For the smaller angles corrections have been applied (in no case exceeding 20 per cent.) owing to the fact that the beam of α particles was of finite dimensions and not negligible compared with the angle of deflexion. These corrections were calculated from geometrical considerations. In Cols. IV. and VI. the ratios of the numbers of scintillations to $\frac{1}{\sin^4 \phi/2}$ are entered. It will be seen that in both sets the values are approximately constant. The deviations are somewhat systematic, the ratio increasing with decreasing angle. However, any slight asymmetry in the apparatus and other causes would affect the results in a systematic way so that, fitting on the two sets of observations and considering the enormous variation in the numbers of scattered particles, from 1 to 250,000, the deviations from constancy of the ratio are probably well within the experimental error. The experiments, therefore, prove that the number of α particles scattered in a definite direction varies as $\mathrm{cosec}^4 \phi/2$.

Variation with Thickness of Material

In investigating the variation of scattering with thickness of material, it seemed necessary to use a homogeneous source of α particles, for according to the theory the effect of the change of velocity with increasing thickness will be very appreciable for α particles of low velocity. In the experiments on "compound scattering" by one of us, a source was used consisting of Ra C deposited from radium emanation *in situ* in a small conical tube fitted with a mica window, the emanation being withdrawn when measurements were taken by expanding into a large volume connected to it. In our first experiments we used such a source, but the observations eventually showed it to be unsuitable. After expansion some emanation remains clinging to the walls of the glass tube. This emanation and the Ra A associated with it gives α particles of considerably lower velocity than the α particles of Ra C, and although the number of α particles so contributed was of the order of only a few per cent. of the number from the Ra C, yet owing to the fact that the amount of scattering increases very rapidly with decreasing velocity, the disturbances caused by the slower α particles were so large as to render the source unsuitable for the present work.

Fig. 2

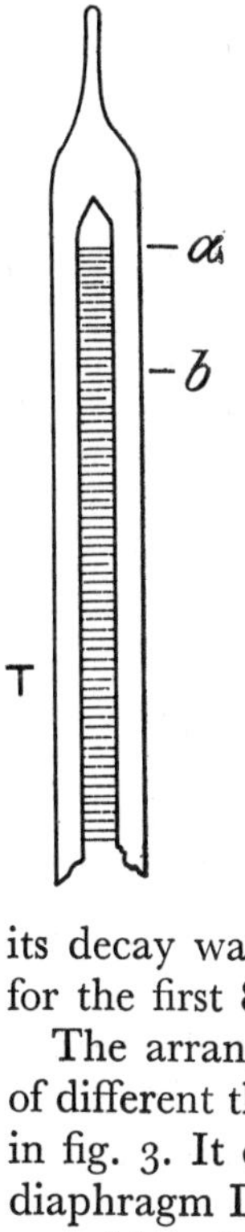

The source finally adopted was prepared as shown in fig. 2. About 80 millicuries of radium emanation were very highly purified and pressed into the conical end of the glass tube T of about 1 mm. internal diameter. After the emanation had remained in position for a sufficient time to attain equilibrium with Ra C, it was expanded into a bulb below, and a small part of the capillary tube was drawn off at *b*. About 1 mm. of the end of the tube which was coated with the Ra C was then cut off (at *a*) and freed from occluded emanation by washing with alcohol and by heating. The resulting source of Ra C was used in the experiments, and with due care its decay was found to be in agreement with theory, at least for the first 80 minutes.

The arrangement used for the comparison of the scattering of different thicknesses of metal foils is shown diagrammatically in fig. 3. It consists essentially of a source of α radiation R, a diaphragm D, a scattering foil F, and a zinc-sulphide screen Z on which the scattered α particles were observed. The main part of the apparatus was enclosed in a cylindrical brass ring A, the ends of which were planed so that they could be closed airtight by the two glass plates B and C. The depth of the ring was 3·5 cm., and its internal and external diameters 5·5 and 7·5 cm. respectively. Two holes were drilled through the glass plate B, one in the centre and the other 1·65 cm. excentric.

The source of radiation R was placed directly against a sheet of mica which was waxed over and closed the opening E. By placing the source outside the apparatus, any small amount of emanation associated with it was prevented from entering the chamber and disturbing the measurements.

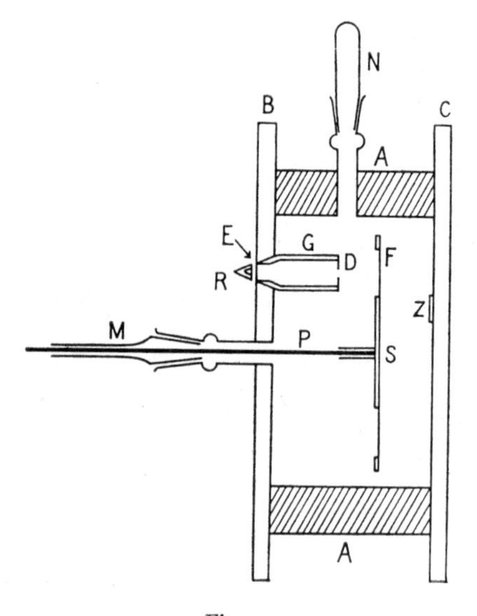

Fig. 3

By means of the diaphragm D a narrow pencil of α particles could be directed on to the scattering foil. The different foils were attached to the disk S and covered five of six holes drilled through it at equal distances from its centre. The uncovered opening was used to determine the natural effect. The disk could be fitted on to the rod P, which was fastened to the ground-glass joint M so that it could be rotated and the different foils brought in front of the diaphragm. The scattered α particles were observed by means of a microscope on the zinc-sulphide screen Z fixed inside the glass plate.

In making the observations the disk carrying the foils was placed in position about 1·2 cm. from the glass plate C. The apparatus was then completely exhausted through a tube not shown in the diagram, charcoal cooled by liquid air being used for the final exhaustion. After the source of radiation had been placed in position, the microscope was adjusted at that part of the zinc-sulphide screen where the scintillations appeared at a rate convenient for counting. With a source of 30 millicuries of Ra C this was usually the case for an angle of deflexion of from 20° to 30°. The area of the screen visible through the microscope was about 1 sq. mm., whilst the main beam of α particles covered an area of about 3 sq. mm.

As soon as the Ra A in the source had decayed completely (*i. e.* after 20 minutes) countings were commenced. Measurements were first taken with the layers of foils of smaller thickness, and as the source decayed they were extended to the thicker foils. From the known decay of the active deposit of radium the measurements could all be corrected for the variation in activity of the source, the results being verified by making observations on the same foils at different times. An experiment generally extended for about 80 minutes. After that time the decay corrections for the source were not always reliable owing to small quantities of radium emanation associated with it, as has been mentioned above. Owing to the relatively short time available in each experiment for the completion of the measurements, only about 100 to 200 scintillations could be counted with each foil.

As in the experiments on the variation of scattering with angle, some scintillations appeared on the zinc-sulphide screen even when no scattering foil was interposed. It was found that these scintillations were due to α particles which had been scattered from the edges of the diaphragm limiting the beam. Experiments were made with paper diaphragms and with aluminium diaphragms of only $\frac{1}{10}$ mm. thickness, whilst a diaphragm D′ (fig. 4) was also introduced to prevent scattering from the inside of the glass tube G carrying the main diaphragm D. Even with these precautions the effect was still so large that accurate experiments with foils of low atomic weight would have been impossible. The difficulty was, however, successfully overcome by intercepting the stray α particles by a screen K, which could be turned by means of a ground-glass joint (N in fig. 3) about a vertical axis passing through A so as to be just outside the main pencil. The adjustment was made by observation of the scintillations produced by the main beam on the zinc-sulphide screen Z, which was temporarily placed at Z′. The magnitude of the effect may be judged from the following figures obtained in a particular experiment with an aluminium diaphragm:—The number of scintillations without both the screen K and the scattering foil F was 60 per minute, whilst by bringing the screen K into position the number was reduced to 0·5 per minute. With the screen K in position and an aluminium foil equivalent to 0·5 cm. air as scattering foil, the number of scintillations was 14 per minute, or about one quarter the effect without screen or scattering foil.

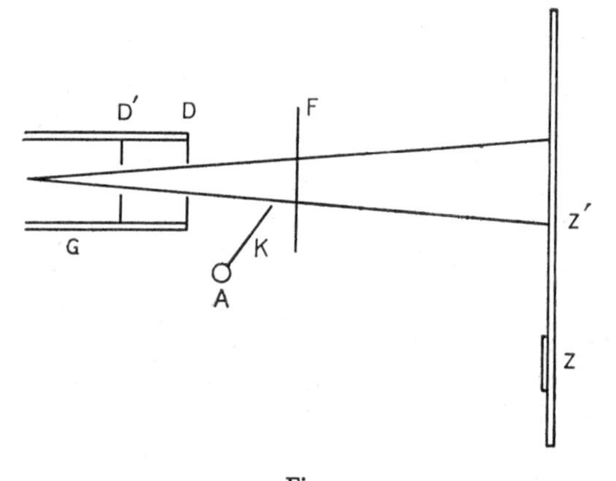

Fig. 4

In the following table the results of an experiment with gold foils are tabulated. Column I. gives the number of foils and column II. the thicknesses expressed as the stopping power of α particles in centimetres of air as determined by the scintillation method. The figures given in column III. represent the number of scintillations observed on the zinc-sulphide screen. These figures are corrected for the variation of activity with time of the source. A slight correction has been made due to the increase of scattering on account of the decrease of velocity of the α particles in passing through the foils. The magnitude of this correction could be calculated from the results given in the last section of the present paper, and amounted to 9 per cent. in this experiment for the thickest foil used. The last column of the table gives the ratio of the corrected number of scintillations to the thickness. The values are constant within the limits of the experimental error. The variations exhibited by the figures are well within the probability errors, owing to the relatively small number of scintillations which could be counted in the time available.

TABLE III.

Gold.—Variation of Scattering with Thickness.

I.	II.	III.	IV.
Number of Foils.	Air equivalent. T in cm.	Number N of scintillations per minute.	Ratio $\frac{N}{T}$.
1	0·11	21·9	200
2	0·22	38·4	175
5	0·51	84·3	165
8	0·81	121·5	150
9	0·90	145	160

Similar experiments were carried out with foils of tin, silver, copper, and aluminium. In each set about 1000 scintillations were counted. The results are plotted in fig. 5, where the abscissae represent the thickness of the scattering foil expressed in centimetres of air equivalent and the ordinates the number of scattered particles. Similar corrections to the above have been introduced in each case.

For all the metals examined the points lie on straight lines which pass through the origin. The experiments therefore prove that for small thicknesses of matter the scattering is proportional to the thickness. If there is any appreciable diminution in velocity of the α particles in passing through the foils, the number of scattered particles increases somewhat more rapidly than the thickness.

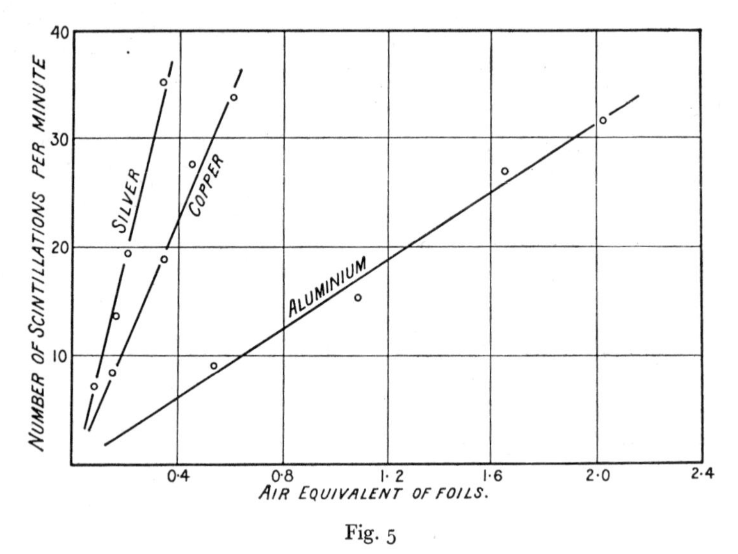

Fig. 5

Variation with Atomic Weight

Assuming that the magnitude of the central charge of the atom is proportional to the atomic weight A, Professor Rutherford has shown that the number of α particles scattered by different foils containing the same number of atoms should be proportional to A^2. With the thin foils which had to be used experimentally, it was found impracticable to calculate the number of atoms per unit area by weighing the foils. It proved much more reliable to deduce the required number of atoms from the air equivalent as found by the reduction of the range of α particles by the scintillation method. This method had the advantage that the thickness was determined at the exact part of the foil which served to scatter the α particles, thus eliminating any errors due to variations in the thickness of the foils. Bragg and others have given numbers connecting the thicknesses of foils of various materials and their stopping power, and it has been shown that for different foils of the same air equivalent the numbers of atoms per unit area are inversely proportional to the square roots of the atomic weights. Consequently if the scattering per atom of atomic weight A is proportional to A^2, the scattering per centimetre air equivalent will be proportional to $A^2 \times A^{-\frac{1}{2}}$, *i. e.* to $A^{3/2}$.

In the experimental investigation the same apparatus was used as in the previous experiments on the variation of scattering with thickness of material. The openings in the disk S were covered with thin foils of different materials, and their thicknesses chosen in such a way that they gave approximately the same effect of scattering. A number of different sets of experiments were made, the foils being varied in each experiment. The results in a particular experiment are given in Table IV. Columns I. and II. give the foils used and their respective atomic weights. In column III. the air equivalents of the foils are entered. Column IV. gives the number of scintillations observed after correction for the variation in activity of the source and the loss of velocity of the α particles in the foil. Column V. gives the number of scintillations per unit air equivalent of material. In column VI. the values of $A^{3/2}$ are given, and in column VII. the ratios of the numbers of scintillations to $A^{3/2}$ are calculated. The figures are constant within the experimental error.

TABLE IV.

Variation of Scattering with Atomic Weight. (Example of a set of measurements.)

I.	II.	III.	IV.	V.	VI.	VII.
Substance.	Atomic weight. A.	Air equivalent in cm.	Number of scintillations per minute corrected for decay.	Number N of scintillations per cm. air equivalent.	$A^{3/2}$.	$N \times A^{2/3}$.
Gold	197	·229	133	581	2770	0·21
Tin	119	·441	119	270	1300	0·21
Silver	107·9	·262	51·7	198	1120	0·18
Copper	63·6	·616	71	115	507	0·23
Aluminium...	27·1	2·05	71	34·6	141	0·24

The combined results of four experiments are given in Table V. In the last column are given the ratios of the numbers of scintillations per centimetre equivalent to $A^{3/2}$. This ratio should be constant according to theory. The experimental values show a slight increase with decreasing atomic weight.

TABLE V.

Variation of Scattering with Atomic Weight. (Collected results using Ra C.)

Substance.	Total number of scintillations counted for each material.	$A^{3/2}$.	Ratio of scintillations per cm. air equivalent to $A^{3/2}$ *.
Gold	850	2770	95
Platinum	200	2730	99
Tin	700	1300	96
Silver	800	1120	98
Copper	600	507	104
Aluminium	700	144	110

* *Note* 1.—Since these experiments were carried out, Richardson and one of us (Phil. Mag. vol. xxv. p. 184 (1913)) have determined the masses per unit area per cm. air equivalent for different metals, using the scintillation method. Introducing the results, and calculating the values of the ratio of the scattering per atom divided by A^2, the following are obtained:—Au 3·4, Pt 3·2, Sn 3·3, Ag 3·6, Cu 3·7, Al 3·6. These numbers show better agreement than those in the last column above, which are calculated on the assumption of Bragg's law.

On account of the importance of these experiments further measurements were made under somewhat different conditions. The main difficulty in the previous experiments arose from the fact, that owing to the rapid decay of the source it was impossible to count in each case a sufficient number of scintillations to obtain a true average value. In the following set of measurements radium emanation in equilibrium with its active deposit was used as source of radiation. The source consisted of a conical glass tube (fig. 6) of about $1\frac{1}{2}$ mm. internal diameter at its widest part, the height of the cone being about 2·5 mm. The end of the tube was closed airtight by a sheet of mica of 0·62 cm. air equivalent. This tube was filled with about 30 millicuries of highly purified emanation and placed at R (fig. 3, p. 214) directly against the mica window E, the air equivalent of which was also 0·62 cm.

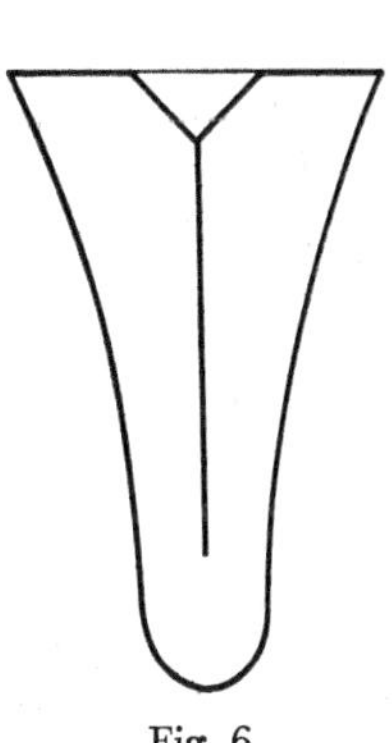

Fig. 6

The difficulty introduced by the employment of α particles of different velocities (emanation, Ra A, and Ra C) was eliminated by using foils of approximately the same air equivalent. The α particles therefore suffered the same reduction in velocity in each foil, and the numbers of scattered particles were therefore directly comparable. It was of course impossible to obtain foils of exactly the same air equivalent, but this difficulty was easily overcome by determining the scattering for two foils of the same material, one slightly smaller and the other slightly larger than a standard thickness of 0·6 cm. air equivalent.

Owing to the large variation with atomic weight of the amount of scattering, the foils could not be all directly compared with each other at the same angle. They were therefore compared in sets, the angle being chosen smaller for the sets of lower atomic weight. Column VI. in the following table gives the mean results of the ratio of the number of scattered particles to $A^{3/2}$.

The scattering of carbon was obtained by using thin sheets of paraffin wax which contained about 85·2 per cent. carbon and 14·8 per cent. hydrogen. The air equivalent of the carbon was calculated from Bragg's law to be about 78 per cent. of the whole stopping power, and on account of the low atomic weight of hydrogen all the scattering effect was assumed due to the carbon. The measurements of the scattering were made by comparison with that due to aluminium foils of the same air equivalent.

TABLE VI.

Variation of Scattering with Atomic Weight. (Collected results using Radium emanation.)

I. Substance.	II. Air equivalents of foils used.	III. Total number of scintillations counted for each substance.	IV. Number N of scintillations at same angle and for same air equivalent.	V. $A^{3/2}$.	VI $N \times A^{2/3}$.
Gold	·52, ·68	1200	2400	2770	·85
Platinum ...	·54, ·625	1000	2900	2730	1·05
Tin	·51, 1·15	1400	1290	1300	·99
Silver	·38, ·435	600	1060	1120	·95
Copper	·495, ·61	1300	570	507	1·12
Aluminium	·45, ·52, 1·06	1600	151	144	1·05
Carbon ...	·55, ·57	400	57	41·6	1·37

Note 2.—Introducing the new data for the mass per unit area of foils of the same air equivalent, as in note 1, the following are the values for the ratio of the scattering per atom divided by A^2:—Au 3·1, Pt 3·4, Sn 3·4, Ag 3·4, Cu 3·95, Al 3·4.

It will be seen from the table that, although the experimental conditions were very different from those in the previous experiments, the results are similar, and indicate the essential correctness of the assumption that the scattering per atom is proportional to the square of the atomic weight. The deviations from constancy of the ratio (see notes 1 and 2) are nearly within the experimental error.

The measurements have not so far been extended to substances of lower atomic weight than carbon. When the atomic weight is small and comparable with the mass of the α particle, the laws of scattering will require some modification to take into account the relative motion of the atom itself when a collision occurs.

Variation of Scattering with Velocity

In order to determine the variation of scattering with velocity the apparatus was somewhat modified. A conical glass tube coated with active deposit was again used as source of radiation. This source was placed about 1 mm. from the mica window (E, fig. 3), so that it was possible to insert additional sheets of mica between the source and the window to reduce the velocity of the α particles. Mica sheets were used for this purpose on account of their uniformity of thickness in comparison with metal foils. The micas were attached to a cardboard disk which could be rotated to bring the different sheets successively in position. The α particles were scattered by a foil of gold or silver, of stopping power about 3 mm. of air, which was attached to a rod passing through the ground glass N. This made it possible to turn the foil away from the main beam during an experiment in order to test the natural effect. The disk S, in this case, rotated in a plane very close to the glass plate C and carried sheets of mica of different thicknesses. By rotating the ground-glass joint the micas could be placed directly in front of the zinc-sulphide screen, making it possible to test the homogeneity of the α particles after they had been scattered.

The results are given in Table VII. Column I. gives the number of mica sheets which were interposed in addition to the mica window, and column II. the ranges of the α particles

TABLE VII.

Variation of Scattering with Velocity.

I. Number of sheets of mica.	II. Range R of α particles after leaving mica.	III. Relative values of $1/v^4$.	IV. Number N of scintillations per minute.	V. Nv^4.
0	5·5	1·0	24·7	25
1	4·76	1·21	29·0	24
2	4·05	1·50	33·4	22
3	3·32	1·91	44	23
4	2·51	2·84	81	28
5	1·84	4·32	101	23
6	1·04	9·22	255	28

incident on the scattering foil. The values of the velocities v were calculated from these ranges R by use of the formula $v^3 = a\mathrm{R}$ previously found by one of us *. The relative values of $1/v^4$ are given in column III. The number of scintillations per minute N are entered in column IV., and in column V. relative values of $\mathrm{N} \times v^4$ are given. Over the range examined the number of scintillations varies in the ratio 1 : 10, while it will be seen that the product $\mathrm{N}v^4$ remains sensibly constant. Several experiments were made, and in every case the scattering was found to vary at a rate more nearly proportional to the inverse fourth power of the velocity than to any other integral power. Owing to the comparative uncertainty of the values of the velocity for small ranges, however, the error of experiment may be somewhat greater than appears from column V. of the table.

In these experiments it proved essential to use a source possessing a high degree of homogeneity. In earlier experiments, where we were not able to fulfil this condition, the scattering apparently increased much more rapidly than the inverse fourth power of the velocity of the Ra C α particles. Even with a source of Ra C with which only a small quantity of emanation was associated, the amount of scattering first rapidly increased on interposing the sheets of mica, then showed a slight decrease, and finally increased again. This irregularity was due to the α particles of the emanation and Ra A, which are of shorter range than those of Ra C, and therefore more easily scattered.

The measurements could not easily be extended to α particles of lower velocity than corresponds to a range of about 1 centimetre, owing to the difficulty of observing the faint scintillations at lower ranges. However, in one particular experiment, by adding sheets of mica to cut down the velocity the number of scattered α particles appearing on the screen was increased 25 times, showing how easily the α particles of low velocity are scattered.

The results of the examination of the homogeneity of the scattered α particles showed that at least in the case of gold they remained practically homogeneous after the scattering.

* H. Geiger, Roy. Soc. Proc. A. vol. lxxxiii. p. 506 (1910).

Experiments of this nature in the case of scattering foils of low atomic weight would be very interesting, but are somewhat difficult.

Determination of Absolute Number of Scattered α Particles

In the previous sections we have completely verified the theory given by Prof. Rutherford. Since, according to this theory, the large deflexion of an α particle is the result of a close encounter with a single atom of matter, it is possible to calculate the magnitude of the central charge of the atom when the fraction of α particles scattered under definite conditions is determined. We have made several attempts under different conditions to obtain a quantitative estimate of the scattered particles, but the results so far have only given us an approximate value. The main difficulty arises from the fact that the scattered particles consist of such a small fraction of the original beam that different methods of measurement have to be employed in the two cases. The number of scattered α particles was determined from the number of scintillations observed on the zinc-sulphide screen, a correction being necessary owing to the fact that with the particular screens used only about 85 per cent. of the incident α particles produce scintillations. The number of α particles in the main beam was in one case in which an emanation tube was used (as shown in fig. 1, p. 208) determined directly by the scintillation method, several weeks being allowed to elapse, so that the emanation had decayed to a small value. In other experiments Ra C deposited on the inside of a conical glass tube (as in fig. 2, p. 213) was used, and the number of α particles was calculated from its γ-ray activity and the distance and area of the diaphragm determining the beam.

The results showed that, using a gold foil of air equivalent 1 mm. (actual thickness $2{\cdot}1 \times 10^{-5}$ cm.), the fraction of incident Ra C α particles ($v = 2{\cdot}06 \times 10^9$ cm./sec.) scattered through an angle of $45°$ and observed on an area of 1 sq. mm. placed normally at a distance of 1 cm. from the point of incidence of the beam, was $3{\cdot}7 \times 10^{-7}$. Substituting this value in the equation given at the commencement of this paper, it can be calculated that the value of the number of elementary electric charges composing the central charge of the gold atom is about half the atomic weight. This result is probably correct to 20 per cent., and agrees with the deduction of Prof. Rutherford from the less definite data given in our previous paper.

From the results of this and the previous sections it is possible to calculate the probability of an α particle being scattered through any angle under any specified conditions. For materials of atomic weight greater than that of aluminium, it is sufficiently accurate to put N equal to half the atomic weight in the equation given at the commencement of the paper.

It will be seen that the laws of "single scattering" found in this paper are quite distinct from the laws of "compound scattering" previously deduced by Geiger. It must be remembered, however, that the experiments are not directly comparable. In the present paper we are dealing with very thin sheets of matter, and are measuring the very small fraction of α particles which are deflected by single collisions through relatively large angles. The experiments of Geiger, however, deal with larger thicknesses of scattering foils and angles of deflexion of a few degrees only. Under these conditions the scattering is due to the combination of a large number of deflexions not only by the central charges of the atoms, but probably also by the electronic charges distributed throughout the remainder of their volumes.

Summary

The experiments described in the foregoing paper were carried out to test a theory of the atom proposed by Prof. Rutherford, the main feature of which is that there exists at the centre of the atom an intense highly concentrated electrical charge. The verification is based on the laws of scattering which were deduced from this theory. The following relations have been verified experimentally:—

(1) The number of α particles emerging from a scattering foil at an angle ϕ with the original beam varies as $1/\sin^4 \phi/2$, when the α particles are counted on a definite area at a constant

distance from the foil. This relation has been tested for angles varying from $5°$ to $150°$, and over this range the number of α particles varied from 1 to 250,000 in good agreement with the theory.

(2) The number of α particles scattered in a definite direction is directly proportional to the thickness of the scattering foil for small thicknesses. For larger thicknesses the decrease of velocity of the α particles in the foil causes a somewhat more rapid increase in the amount of scattering.

(3) The scattering per atom of foils of different materials varies approximately as the square of the atomic weight. This relation was tested for foils of atomic weight from that of carbon to that of gold.

(4) The amount of scattering by a given foil is approximately proportional to the inverse fourth power of the velocity of the incident α particles. This relation was tested over a range of velocities such that the number of scattered particles varied as 1 : 10.

(5) Quantitative experiments show that the fraction of α particles of Ra C, which is scattered through an angle of $45°$ by a gold foil of 1 mm. air equivalent ($2{\cdot}1 \times 10^{-5}$ cm.), is $3{\cdot}7 \times 10^{-7}$ when the scattered particles are counted on a screen of 1 sq. mm. area placed at a distance of 1 cm. from the scattering foil. From this figure and the foregoing results, it can be calculated that the number of elementary charges composing the centre of the atom is equal to half the atomic weight.

We are indebted to Prof. Rutherford for his kind interest in these experiments, and for placing at our disposal the large quantities of radium emanation necessary. We are also indebted to the Government Grant Committee of the Royal Society for a grant to one of us, out of which part of the expenses has been paid.

On the Constitution of Atoms and Molecules. By N. BOHR, *Dr. phil. Copenhagen* *.

The *Philosophical Magazine*, Series VI, **26**, 1–25 (1913)

Introduction

IN order to explain the results of experiments on scattering of α rays by matter Prof. Rutherford † has given a theory of the structure of atoms. According to this theory, the atoms consist of a positively charged nucleus surrounded by a system of electrons kept together by attractive forces from the nucleus; the total negative charge of the electrons is equal to the positive charge of the nucleus. Further, the nucleus is assumed to be the seat of the essential part of the mass of the atom, and to have linear dimensions exceedingly small compared with the linear dimensions of the whole atom. The number of electrons in an atom is deduced to be approximately equal to half the atomic weight. Great interest is to be attributed to this atom-model; for, as Rutherford has shown, the assumption of the existence of nuclei, as those in question, seems to be necessary in order to account for the results of the experiments on large angle scattering of the α rays ‡.

In an attempt to explain some of the properties of matter on the basis of this atom-model we meet, however, with difficulties of a serious nature arising from the apparent instability of the system of electrons: difficulties purposely avoided in atom-models previously considered, for instance, in the one proposed by Sir J. J. Thomson §. According to the theory of the latter the atom consists of a sphere of uniform positive electrification, inside which the electrons move in circular orbits.

* Communicated by Prof. E. Rutherford, F.R.S.

† E. Rutherford, Phil. Mag. xxi. p. 669 (1911).

‡ See also Geiger and Marsden, Phil. Mag. April 1913.

§ J. J. Thomson, Phil. Mag. vii. p. 237 (1904).

The principal difference between the atom-models proposed by Thomson and Rutherford consists in the circumstance that the forces acting on the electrons in the atom-model of Thomson allow for certain configurations and motions of the electrons for which the system is in a stable equilibrium; such configurations, however, apparently do not exist for the second atom-model. The nature of the difference in question will perhaps be most clearly seen by noticing that among the quantities characterizing the first atom a quantity appears—the radius of the positive sphere—of dimensions of a length and of the same order of magnitude as the linear extension of the atom, while such a length does not appear among the quantities characterizing the second atom, viz., the charges and masses of the electrons and the positive nucleus; nor can it be determined solely by help of the latter quantities.

The way of considering a problem of this kind has, however, undergone essential alterations in recent years owing to the development of the theory of the energy radiation, and the direct affirmation of the new assumptions introduced in this theory, found by experiments on very different phenomena such as specific heats, photoelectric effect, Röntgen-rays, &c. The result of the discussion of these questions seems to be a general acknowledgment of the inadequacy of the classical electrodynamics in describing the behaviour of systems of atomic size *. Whatever the alteration in the laws of motion of the electrons may be, it seems necessary to introduce in the laws in question a quantity foreign to the classical electrodynamics, *i. e.* Planck's constant, or as it often is called the elementary quantum of action. By the introduction of this quantity the question of the stable configuration of the electrons in the atoms is essentially changed, as this constant is of such dimensions and magnitude that it, together with the mass and charge of the particles, can determine a length of the order of magnitude required.

This paper is an attempt to show that the application of the above ideas to Rutherford's atom-model affords a basis for a

* See f. inst., 'Théorie du rayonnement et les quanta.' Rapports de la réunion à Bruxelles, Nov. 1911. Paris, 1912.

theory of the constitution of atoms. It will further be shown that from this theory we are led to a theory of the constitution of molecules.

In the present first part of the paper the mechanism of the binding of electrons by a positive nucleus is discussed in relation to Planck's theory. It will be shown that it is possible from the point of view taken to account in a simple way for the law of the line spectrum of hydrogen. Further, reasons are given for a principal hypothesis on which the considerations contained in the following parts are based.

I wish here to express my thanks to Prof. Rutherford for his kind and encouraging interest in this work.

PART I.—BINDING OF ELECTRONS BY POSITIVE NUCLEI

§ 1. *General Considerations*

The inadequacy of the classical electrodynamics in accounting for the properties of atoms from an atom-model as Rutherford's, will appear very clearly if we consider a simple system consisting of a positively charged nucleus of very small dimensions and an electron describing closed orbits around it. For simplicity, let us assume that the mass of the electron is negligibly small in comparison with that of the nucleus, and further, that the velocity of the electron is small compared with that of light.

Let us at first assume that there is no energy radiation. In this case the electron will describe stationary elliptical orbits. The frequency of revolution ω and the major-axis of the orbit $2a$ will depend on the amount of energy W which must be transferred to the system in order to remove the electron to an infinitely great distance apart from the nucleus. Denoting the charge of the electron and of the nucleus by $-e$ and E respectively and the mass of the electron by m, we thus get

$$\omega = \frac{\sqrt{2}}{\pi} \frac{W^{\frac{3}{2}}}{eE\sqrt{m}}, \quad 2a = \frac{eE}{W}. \qquad (1)$$

Further, it can easily be shown that the mean value of the kinetic energy of the electron taken for a whole revolution is equal to W. We see that if the value of W is not given, there will be no values of ω and a characteristic for the system in question.

Let us now, however, take the effect of the energy radiation into account, calculated in the ordinary way from the acceleration of the electron. In this case the electron will no longer describe stationary orbits. W will continuously increase, and the electron will approach the nucleus describing orbits of smaller and smaller dimensions, and with greater and greater frequency; the electron on the average gaining in kinetic energy at the same time as the whole system loses energy. This process will go on until the dimensions of the orbit are of the same order of magnitude as the dimensions of the electron or those of the nucleus. A simple calculation shows that the energy radiated out during the process considered will be enormously great compared with that radiated out by ordinary molecular processes.

It is obvious that the behaviour of such a system will be very different from that of an atomic system occurring in nature. In the first place, the actual atoms in their permanent state seem to have absolutely fixed dimensions and frequencies. Further, if we consider any molecular process, the result seems always to be that after a certain amount of energy characteristic for the systems in question is radiated out, the systems will again settle down in a stable state of equilibrium, in which the distances apart of the particles are of the same order of magnitude as before the process.

Now the essential point in Planck's theory of radiation is that the energy radiation from an atomic system does not take place in the continuous way assumed in the ordinary electrodynamics, but that it, on the contrary, takes place in distinctly separated emissions, the amount of energy radiated out from an atomic vibrator of frequency ν in a single emission being equal to $\tau h\nu$, where τ is an entire number, and h is a universal constant *.

Returning to the simple case of an electron and a positive

* See f. inst., M. Planck, *Ann. d. Phys.* xxxi. p. 758 (1910); xxxvii. p. 642 (1912); *Verh. deutsch. Phys. Ges.* 1911, p. 138.

nucleus considered above, let us assume that the electron at the beginning of the interaction with the nucleus was at a great distance apart from the nucleus, and had no sensible velocity relative to the latter. Let us further assume that the electron after the interaction has taken place has settled down in a stationary orbit around the nucleus. We shall, for reasons referred to later, assume that the orbit in question is circular; this assumption will, however, make no alteration in the calculations for systems containing only a single electron.

Let us now assume that, during the binding of the electron, a homogeneous radiation is emitted of a frequency ν, equal to half the frequency of revolution of the electron in its final orbit; then, from Planck's theory, we might expect that the amount of energy emitted by the process considered is equal to $\tau h\nu$, where h is Planck's constant and τ an entire number. If we assume that the radiation emitted is homogeneous, the second assumption concerning the frequency of the radiation suggests itself, since the frequency of revolution of the electron at the beginning of the emission is 0. The question, however, of the rigorous validity of both assumptions, and also of the application made of Planck's theory, will be more closely discussed in § 3.

Putting

$$W = \tau h \frac{\omega}{2}, \quad . \quad . \quad . \quad (2)$$

we get by help of the formula (1)

$$W = \frac{2\pi^2 m e^2 E^2}{\tau^2 h^2}, \quad \omega = \frac{4\pi^2 m e^2 E^2}{\tau^3 h^3}, \quad 2a = \frac{\tau^2 h^2}{2\pi^2 m e E}. \quad (3)$$

If in these expressions we give τ different values, we get a series of values for W, ω, and a corresponding to a series of configurations of the system. According to the above considerations, we are led to assume that these configurations will correspond to states of the system in which there is no radiation of energy; states which consequently will be stationary as long as the system is not disturbed from outside. We see that the value of W is greatest if τ has its smallest value 1. This case will therefore correspond to the most stable state of the system, *i. e.* will correspond to the binding of the electron for the breaking up of which the greatest amount of energy is required.

Putting in the above expressions $\tau = 1$ and $E = e$, and introducing the experimental values

$$e = 4{\cdot}7 \,.\, 10^{-10}, \quad \frac{e}{m} = 5{\cdot}31 \,.\, 10^{17}, \quad h = 6{\cdot}5 \,.\, 10^{-27},$$

we get

$$2a = 1{\cdot}1 \,.\, 10^{-8} \text{ cm.}, \quad \omega = 6{\cdot}2 \,.\, 10^{15} \frac{1}{\text{sec.}}, \quad \frac{W}{e} = 13 \text{ volt.}$$

We see that these values are of the same order of magnitude as the linear dimensions of the atoms, the optical frequencies, and the ionization-potentials.

The general importance of Planck's theory for the discussion of the behaviour of atomic systems was originally pointed out by Einstein *. The considerations of Einstein have been developed and applied on a number of different phenomena, especially by Stark, Nernst, and Sommerfield. The agreement as to the order of magnitude between values observed for the frequencies and dimensions of the atoms, and values for these quantities calculated by considerations similar to those given above, has been the subject of much discussion. It was first pointed out by Haas †, in an attempt to explain the meaning and the value of Planck's constant on the basis of J. J. Thomson's atom-model, by help of the linear dimensions and frequency of a hydrogen atom.

Systems of the kind considered in this paper, in which the forces between the particles vary inversely as the square of the distance, are discussed in relation to Planck's theory by J. W. Nicholson ‡. In a series of papers this author has shown that

* A. Einstein, *Ann. d. Phys.* xvii. p. 132 (1905); xx. p. 199 (1906); xxii. p. 180 (1907).

† A. E. Haas, *Jahrb. d. Rad. u. El.* vii. p. 261 (1910). See further, A. Schidlof, *Ann. d. Phys.* xxxv. p. 90 (1911); E. Wertheimer, *Phys. Zeitschr.* xii. p. 409 (1911), *Verh. deutsch. Phys. Ges.* 1912, p. 431; F. A. Lindemann, *Verh. deutsch. Phys. Ges.* 1911, pp. 482, 1107; F. Haber, *Verh. deutsch. Phys. Ges.* 1911, p. 1117.

‡ J. W. Nicholson, Month. Not. Roy. Astr. Soc. lxxii. pp. 49, 130, 677, 693, 729 (1912).

it seems to be possible to account for lines of hitherto unknown origin in the spectra of the stellar nebulae and that of the solar corona, by assuming the presence in these bodies of certain hypothetical elements of exactly indicated constitution. The atoms of these elements are supposed to consist simply of a ring of a few electrons surrounding a positive nucleus of negligibly small dimensions. The ratios between the frequencies corresponding to the lines in question are compared with the ratios between the frequencies corresponding to different modes of vibration of the ring of electrons. Nicholson has obtained a relation to Planck's theory showing that the ratios between the wave-length of different sets of lines of the coronal spectrum can be accounted for with great accuracy by assuming that the ratio between the energy of the system and the frequency of rotation of the ring is equal to an entire multiple of Planck's constant. The quantity Nicholson refers to as the energy is equal to twice the quantity which we have denoted above by W. In the latest paper cited Nicholson has found it necessary to give the theory a more complicated form, still, however, representing the ratio of energy to frequency by a simple function of whole numbers.

The excellent agreement between the calculated and observed values of the ratios between the wave-lengths in question seems a strong argument in favour of the validity of the foundation of Nicholson's calculations. Serious objections, however, may be raised against the theory. These objections are intimately connected with the problem of the homogeneity of the radiation emitted. In Nicholson's calculations the frequency of lines in a line-spectrum is identified with the frequency of vibration of a mechanical system in a distinctly indicated state of equilibrium. As a relation from Planck's theory is used, we might expect that the radiation is sent out in quanta; but systems like those considered, in which the frequency is a function of the energy, cannot emit a finite amount of a homogeneous radiation; for, as soon as the emission of radiation is started, the energy and also the frequency of the system are altered. Further, according to the calculation of Nicholson, the systems are unstable for some modes of vibration.

Apart from such objections—which may be only formal (see p. 254)—it must be remarked, that the theory in the form given does not seem to be able to account for the well-known laws of Balmer and Rydberg connecting the frequencies of the lines in the line-spectra of the ordinary elements.

It will now be attempted to show that the difficulties in question disappear if we consider the problems from the point of view taken in this paper. Before proceeding it may be useful to restate briefly the ideas characterizing the calculations on p. 232. The principal assumptions used are:

(1) That the dynamical equilibrium of the systems in the stationary states can be discussed by help of the ordinary mechanics, while the passing of the systems between different stationary states cannot be treated on that basis.

(2) That the latter process is followed by the emission of a *homogeneous* radiation, for which the relation between the frequency and the amount of energy emitted is the one given by Planck's theory.

The first assumption seems to present itself; for it is known that the ordinary mechanics cannot have an absolute validity, but will only hold in calculations of certain mean values of the motion of the electrons. On the other hand, in the calculations of the dynamical equilibrium in a stationary state in which there is no relative displacement of the particles, we need not distinguish between the actual motions and their mean values. The second assumption is in obvious contrast to the ordinary ideas of electrodynamics, but appears to be necessary in order to account for experimental facts.

In the calculations on page 232 we have further made use of the more special assumptions, viz. that the different stationary states correspond to the emission of a different number of Planck's energy-quanta, and that the frequency of the radiation emitted during the passing of the system from a state in which no energy is yet radiated out to one of the stationary states, is equal to half the frequency of revolution of the electron in the latter state. We can, however (see § 3), also arrive at the expressions (3) for the stationary states by using assumptions of somewhat different form. We shall, therefore, postpone the discussion of the special assumptions, and first show how by the help of the above principal assumptions, and of the expressions (3) for the stationary states, we can account for the line-spectrum of hydrogen.

§ 2. *Emission of Line-spectra*

Spectrum of Hydrogen.—General evidence indicates that an atom of hydrogen consists simply of a single electron rotating round a positive nucleus of charge e *. The reformation of a hydrogen atom, when the electron has been removed to great distances away from the nucleus—*e. g.* by the effect of electrical discharge in a vacuum tube—will accordingly correspond to the binding of an electron by a positive nucleus considered on p. 232. If in (3) we put $E = e$, we get for the total amount of energy radiated out by the formation of one of the stationary states,

$$W_\tau = \frac{2\pi^2 me^4}{h^2\tau^2}.$$

The amount of energy emitted by the passing of the system from a state corresponding to $\tau = \tau_1$ to one corresponding to $\tau = \tau_2$, is consequently

$$W_{\tau_2} - W_{\tau_1} = \frac{2\pi^2 me^4}{h^2}\left(\frac{1}{\tau_2^2} - \frac{1}{\tau_1^2}\right).$$

If now we suppose that the radiation in question is homogeneous, and that the amount of energy emitted is equal to $h\nu$, where ν is the frequency of the radiation, we get

$$W_{\tau_2} - W_{\tau_1} = h\nu,$$

and from this

$$\nu = \frac{2\pi^2 me^4}{h^3}\left(\frac{1}{\tau_2^2} - \frac{1}{\tau_1^2}\right). \quad . \quad . \quad (4)$$

* See f. inst. N. Bohr, Phil. Mag. xxv, p. 24 (1913). The conclusion drawn in the paper cited is strongly supported by the fact that hydrogen, in the experiments on positive rays of Sir J. J. Thomson, is the only element which never occurs with a positive charge corresponding to the loss of more than one electron (comp. Phil. Mag. xxiv, p. 672 (1912)).

We see that this expression accounts for the law connecting the lines in the spectrum of hydrogen. If we put $\tau_2 = 2$ and let τ_1 vary, we get the ordinary Balmer series. If we put $\tau_2 = 3$, we get the series in the ultra-red observed by Paschen* and previously suspected by Ritz. If we put $\tau_2 = 1$ and $\tau_2 = 4, 5, ..,$ we get series respectively in the extreme ultra-violet and the extreme ultra-red, which are not observed, but the existence of which may be expected.

The agreement in question is quantitative as well as qualitative. Putting

$$e = 4{\cdot}7 \,.\, 10^{-10}, \quad \frac{e}{m} = 5{\cdot}31 \,.\, 10^{17}, \quad \text{and} \quad h = 6{\cdot}5 \,.\, 10^{-27},$$

we get

$$\frac{2\pi^2 me^4}{h^3} = 3{\cdot}1 \,.\, 10^{15}.$$

The observed value for the factor outside the bracket in the formula (4) is

$$3{\cdot}290 \,.\, 10^{15}.$$

The agreement between the theoretical and observed values is inside the uncertainty due to experimental errors in the constants entering in the expression for the theoretical value. We shall in § 3 return to consider the possible importance of the agreement in question.

It may be remarked that the fact, that it has not been possible to observe more than 12 lines of the Balmer series in experiments with vacuum tubes, while 33 lines are observed in the spectra of some celestial bodies, is just what we should expect from the above theory. According to the equation (3) the diameter of the orbit of the electron in the different stationary states is proportional to τ^2. For $\tau = 12$ the diameter is equal to $1{\cdot}6 \,.\, 10^{-6}$ cm., or equal to the mean distance between the molecules in a gas at a pressure of about 7 mm. mercury; for $\tau = 33$ the diameter is equal to $1{\cdot}2 \,.\, 10^{-5}$ cm., corresponding to the mean distance of the molecules at a pressure of about 0·02 mm. mercury. According to the theory the necessary

* F. Paschen, *Ann. d. Phys.* xxvii. p. 565 (1908).

condition for the appearance of a great number of lines is therefore a very small density of the gas; for simultaneously to obtain an intensity sufficient for observation the space filled with the gas must be very great. If the theory is right, we may therefore never expect to be able in experiments with vacuum tubes to observe the lines corresponding to high numbers of the Balmer series of the emission spectrum of hydrogen; it might, however, be possible to observe the lines by investigation of the absorption spectrum of this gas (see § 4).

It will be observed that we in the above way do not obtain other series of lines, generally ascribed to hydrogen; for instance, the series first observed by Pickering* in the spectrum of the star ζ Puppis, and the set of series recently found by Fowler † by experiments with vacuum tubes containing a mixture of hydrogen and helium. We shall, however, see that, by help of the above theory, we can account naturally for these series of lines if we ascribe them to helium.

A neutral atom of the latter element consists, according to Rutherford's theory, of a positive nucleus of charge $2e$ and two electrons. Now considering the binding of a single electron by a helium nucleus, we get, putting $E = 2e$ in the expressions (3) on page 232, and proceeding in exactly the same way as above,

$$\nu = \frac{8\pi^2 me^4}{h^3}\left(\frac{1}{\tau_2^2} - \frac{1}{\tau_1^2}\right) = \frac{2\pi^2 me^4}{h^3}\left(\frac{1}{\left(\frac{\tau_2}{2}\right)^2} - \frac{1}{\left(\frac{\tau_1}{2}\right)^2}\right).$$

If we in this formula put $\tau_2 = 1$ or $\tau_2 = 2$, we get series of lines in the extreme ultra-violet. If we put $\tau_2 = 3$, and let τ_1 vary, we get a series which includes 2 of the series observed by Fowler, and denoted by him as the first and second principal series of the hydrogen spectrum. If we put $\tau_2 = 4$, we get the series observed by Pickering in the spectrum of ζ Puppis. Every second of the lines in this series is identical with a line in the Balmer series of the hydrogen spectrum; the presence of hydrogen in the star in question may therefore account for the

* E. C. Pickering, Astrophys. J. iv. p. 369 (1896); v. p. 92 (1897).

† A. Fowler, Month. Not. Roy. Astr. Soc. lxxiii. Dec. 1912.

fact that these lines are of a greater intensity than the rest of the lines in the series. The series is also observed in the experiments of Fowler, and denoted in his paper as the Sharp series of the hydrogen spectrum. If we finally in the above formula put $\tau_2 = 5, 6, \ldots$, we get series, the strong lines of which are to be expected in the ultra-red.

The reason why the spectrum considered is not observed in ordinary helium tubes may be that in such tubes the ionization of helium is not so complete as in the star considered or in the experiments of Fowler, where a strong discharge was sent through a mixture of hydrogen and helium. The condition for the appearance of the spectrum is, according to the above theory, that helium atoms are present in a state in which they have lost both their electrons. Now we must assume that the amount of energy to be used in removing the second electron from a helium atom is much greater than that to be used in removing the first. Further, it is known from experiments on positive rays, that hydrogen atoms can acquire a negative charge; therefore the presence of hydrogen in the experiments of Fowler may effect that more electrons are removed from some of the helium atoms than would be the case if only helium were present.

Spectra of other substances.—In case of systems containing more electrons we must—in conformity with the result of experiments—expect more complicated laws for the line-spectra than those considered. I shall try to show that the point of view taken above allows, at any rate, a certain understanding of the laws observed.

According to Rydberg's theory—with the generalization given by Ritz *—the frequency corresponding to the lines of the spectrum of an element can be expressed by

$$\nu = F_r(\tau_1) - F_s(\tau_2),$$

where τ_1 and τ_2 are entire numbers, and F_1, F_2, F_3, ... are functions of τ which approximately are equal to $\frac{K}{(\tau + a_1)^2}$, $\frac{K}{(\tau + a_2)^2}$, ... K is a universal constant, equal to the factor

* W. Ritz, *Phys. Zeitschr.* ix. p. 521 (1908).

outside the bracket in the formula (4) for the spectrum of hydrogen. The different series appear if we put τ_1 or τ_2 equal to a fixed number and let the other vary.

The circumstance that the frequency can be written as a difference between two functions of entire numbers suggests an origin of the lines in the spectra in question similar to the one we have assumed for hydrogen; *i. e.* that the lines correspond to a radiation emitted during the passing of the system between two different stationary states. For systems containing more than one electron the detailed discussion may be very complicated, as there will be many different configurations of the electrons which can be taken into consideration as stationary states. This may account for the different sets of series in the line spectra emitted from the substances in question. Here I shall only try to show how, by help of the theory, it can be simply explained that the constant K entering in Rydberg's formula is the same for all substances.

Let us assume that the spectrum in question corresponds to the radiation emitted during the binding of an electron; and let us further assume that the system including the electron considered is neutral. The force on the electron, when at a great distance apart from the nucleus and the electrons previously bound, will be very nearly the same as in the above case of the binding of an electron by a hydrogen nucleus. The energy corresponding to one of the stationary states will therefore for τ great be very nearly equal to that given by the expression (3) on p. 232, if we put $E = e$. For τ great we consequently get

$$\lim (\tau^2 \,.\, F_1(\tau)) = \lim (\tau^2 \,.\, F_2(\tau)) = \ldots\ldots = \frac{2\pi^2 me^4}{h^3},$$

in conformity with Rydberg's theory.

§ 3. *General Considerations continued*

We shall now return to the discussion (see p. 235) of the special assumptions used in deducing the expressions (3) on p. 232 for the stationary states of a system consisting of an electron rotating round a nucleus.

For one, we have assumed that the different stationary states correspond to an emission of a different number of energy-quanta. Considering systems in which the frequency is a function of the energy, this assumption, however, may be regarded as improbable, for as soon as one quantum is sent out the frequency is altered. We shall now see that we can leave the assumption used and still retain the equation (2) on p. 232, and thereby the formal analogy with Planck's theory.

Firstly, it will be observed that it has not been necessary, in order to account for the law of the spectra by help of the expressions (3) for the stationary states, to assume that in any case a radiation is sent out corresponding to more than a single energy-quantum, $h\nu$. Further information on the frequency of the radiation may be obtained by comparing calculations of the energy radiation in the region of slow vibrations based on the above assumptions with calculations based on the ordinary mechanics. As is known, calculations on the latter basis are in agreement with experiments on the energy radiation in the named region.

Let us assume that the ratio between the total amount of energy emitted and the frequency of revolution of the electron for the different stationary states is given by the equation $W = f(\tau) \cdot h\omega$, instead of by the equation (2). Proceeding in the same way as above, we get in this case instead of (3)

$$W = \frac{\pi^2 m e^2 E^2}{2h^2 f^2(\tau)}, \quad \omega = \frac{\pi^2 m e^2 E^2}{2h^3 f^3(\tau)}.$$

Assuming as above that the amount of energy emitted during the passing of the system from a state corresponding to $\tau = \tau_1$ to one for which $\tau = \tau_2$ is equal to $h\nu$, we get instead of (4)

$$\nu = \frac{\pi^2 m e^2 E^2}{2h^3} \left(\frac{1}{f^2(\tau_2)} - \frac{1}{f^2(\tau_1)} \right).$$

We see that in order to get an expression of the same form as the Balmer series we must put $f(\tau) = c\tau$.

In order to determine c let us now consider the passing of the system between two successive stationary states corresponding to $\tau = \text{N}$ and $\tau = \text{N} - 1$; introducing $f(\tau) = c\tau$, we get for the frequency of the radiation emitted

$$\nu = \frac{\pi^2 m e^2 \text{E}^2}{2c^2 h^3} \cdot \frac{2\text{N} - 1}{\text{N}^2(\text{N} - 1)^2}.$$

For the frequency of revolution of the electron before and after the emission we have

$$\omega_{\text{N}} = \frac{\pi^2 m e^2 \text{E}^2}{2c^3 h^3 \text{N}^3} \text{ and } \omega_{\text{N}-1} = \frac{\pi^2 m e^2 \text{E}^2}{2c^3 h^3 (\text{N} - 1)^3}.$$

If N is great the ratio between the frequency before and after the emission will be very near equal to 1; and according to the ordinary electrodynamics we should therefore expect that the ratio between the frequency of radiation and the frequency of revolution also is very nearly equal to 1. This condition will only be satisfied if $c = \frac{1}{2}$. Putting $f(\tau) = \frac{\tau}{2}$, we, however, again arrive at the equation (2) and consequently at the expression (3) for the stationary states.

If we consider the passing of the system between two states corresponding to $\tau = \text{N}$ and $\tau = \text{N} - n$, where n is small compared with N, we get with the same approximation as above, putting $f(\tau) = \frac{\tau}{2}$,

$$\nu = n\omega.$$

The possibility of an emission of a radiation of such a frequency may also be interpreted from analogy with the ordinary electrodynamics, as an electron rotating round a nucleus in an elliptical orbit will emit a radiation which according to Fourier's theorem can be resolved into homogeneous components, the frequencies of which are $n\omega$, if ω is the frequency of revolution of the electron.

We are thus led to assume that the interpretation of the equation (2) is not that the different stationary states correspond to an emission of different numbers of energy-quanta, but that the frequency of the energy emitted during the passing of the system from a state in which no energy is yet radiated out to one of the different stationary states, is equal to different multiples of $\frac{\omega}{2}$, where ω is the frequency of revolution of the electron in the state considered. From this assumption we get exactly the same expressions as before for the stationary states, and from these by help of the principal assumptions on p. 235 the same expression for the law of the hydrogen spectrum. Consequently we may regard our preliminary considerations on p. 232 only as a simple form of representing the results of the theory.

Before we leave the discussion of this question, we shall for a moment return to the question of the significance of the agreement between the observed and calculated values of the constant entering in the expressions (4) for the Balmer series of the hydrogen spectrum. From the above consideration it will follow that, taking the starting-point in the form of the law of the hydrogen spectrum and assuming that the different lines correspond to a homogeneous radiation emitted during the passing between different stationary states, we shall arrive at exactly the same expression for the constant in question as that given by (4), if we only assume (1) that the radiation is sent out in quanta $h\nu$, and (2) that the frequency of the radiation emitted during the passing of the system between successive stationary states will coincide with the frequency of revolution of the electron in the region of slow vibrations.

As all the assumptions used in this latter way of representing the theory are of what we may call a qualitative character, we are justified in expecting—if the whole way of considering is a sound one—an absolute agreement between the values calculated and observed for the constant in question, and not only an approximate agreement. The formula (4) may therefore be of value in the discussion of the results of experimental determinations of the constants e, m, and h.

While there obviously can be no question of a mechanical foundation of the calculations given in this paper, it is, however, possible to give a very simple interpretation of the result of the calculation on p. 232, by help of symbols taken from the ordinary mechanics. Denoting the angular momentum of the electron round the nucleus by M, we have immediately for a circular orbit $\pi M = \frac{T}{\omega}$, where ω is the frequency of revolution and T the kinetic energy of the electron; for a circular orbit we further have T = W (see p. 230) and from (2), p. 232, we consequently get

$$M = \tau M_0,$$

where

$$M_0 = \frac{h}{2\pi} = 1{\cdot}04 \times 10^{-27}.$$

If we therefore assume that the orbit of the electron in the stationary states is circular, the result of the calculation on p. 232 can be expressed by the simple condition: that the angular momentum of the electron round the nucleus in a stationary state of the system is equal to an entire multiple of a universal value, independent of the charge on the nucleus. The possible importance of the angular momentum in the discussion of atomic systems in relation to Planck's theory is emphasized by Nicholson *.

The great number of different stationary states we do not observe except by investigation of the emission and absorption of radiation. In most of the other physical phenomena, however, we only observe the atoms of the matter in a single distinct state, *i. e.* the state of the atoms at low temperature. From the preceding considerations we are immediately led to the assumption that the "permanent" state is the one among the stationary states during the formation of which the greatest amount of energy is emitted. According to the equation (3) on p. 232, this state is the one which corresponds to $\tau = 1$.

§ 4. *Absorption of Radiation*

In order to account for Kirchhoff's law it is necessary to introduce assumptions on the mechanism of absorption of radiation which correspond to those we have used considering the emission. Thus we must assume that a system consisting of a nucleus and an electron rotating round it under certain

* J. W. Nicholson, *loc. cit.* p. 679.

circumstances can absorb a radiation of a frequency equal to the frequency of the homogeneous radiation emitted during the passing of the system between different stationary states. Let us consider the radiation emitted during the passing of the system between two stationary states A_1 and A_2 corresponding to values for τ equal to τ_1 and τ_2, $\tau_1 > \tau_2$. As the necessary condition for an emission of the radiation in question was the presence of systems in the state A_1, we must assume that the necessary condition for an absorption of the radiation is the presence of systems in the state A_2.

These considerations seem to be in conformity with experiments on absorption in gases. In hydrogen gas at ordinary conditions for instance there is no absorption of a radiation of a frequency corresponding to the line-spectrum of this gas; such an absorption is only observed in hydrogen gas in a luminous state. This is what we should expect according to the above. We have on p. 236 assumed that the radiation in question was emitted during the passing of the systems between stationary states corresponding to $\tau \geqq 2$. The state of the atoms in hydrogen gas at ordinary conditions should, however, correspond to $\tau = 1$; furthermore, hydrogen atoms at ordinary conditions combine into molecules, *i. e.* into systems in which the electrons have frequencies different from those in the atoms (see Part III). From the circumstance that certain substances in a non-luminous state, as, for instance, sodium vapour, absorb radiation corresponding to lines in the line-spectra of the substances, we may, on the other hand, conclude that the lines in question are emitted during the passing of the system between two states, one of which is the permanent state.

How much the above considerations differ from an interpretation based on the ordinary electrodynamics is perhaps most clearly shown by the fact that we have been forced to assume that a system of electrons will absorb a radiation of a frequency different from the frequency of vibration of the electrons calculated in the ordinary way. It may in this connexion be of interest to mention a generalization of the considerations to which we are led by experiments on the photo-electric effect, and which may be able to throw some light on the problem in question. Let us consider a state of the system in which the electron is free, *i. e.* in which the electron possesses kinetic energy sufficient to remove to infinite distances from the nucleus. If we assume that the motion of the electron is governed by the ordinary mechanics and that there is no (sensible) energy radiation, the total energy of the system—as in the above considered stationary states—will be constant. Further, there will be perfect continuity between the two kinds of states, as the difference between frequency and dimensions of the systems in successive stationary states will diminish without limit if τ increases. In the following considerations we shall for the sake of brevity refer to the two kinds of states in question as "mechanical" states; by this notation only emphasizing the assumption that the motion of the electron in both cases can be accounted for by the ordinary mechanics.

Tracing the analogy between the two kinds of mechanical states, we might now expect the possibility of an absorption of radiation, not only corresponding to the passing of the system between two different stationary states, but also corresponding to the passing between one of the stationary states and a state in which the electron is free; and as above, we might expect that the frequency of this radiation was determined by the equation $E = h\nu$, where E is the difference between the total energy of the system in the two states. As it will be seen, such an absorption of radiation is just what is observed in experiments on ionization by ultra-violet light and by Röntgen rays. Obviously, we get in this way the same expression for the kinetic energy of an electron ejected from an atom by photo-electric effect as that deduced by Einstein *, *i. e.* $T = h\nu - W$, where T is the kinetic energy of the electron ejected, and W the total amount of energy emitted during the original binding of the electron.

The above considerations may further account for the result of some experiments of R. W. Wood † on absorption of light by sodium vapour. In these experiments, an absorption

* A. Einstein, *Ann. d. Phys.* xvii. p. 146 (1905).

† R. W. Wood, Physical Optics, p. 513 (1911).

corresponding to a very great number of lines in the principal series of the sodium spectrum is observed, and in addition a continuous absorption which begins at the head of the series and extends to the extreme ultra-violet. This is exactly what we should expect according to the analogy in question, and, as we shall see, a closer consideration of the above experiments allows us to trace the analogy still further. As mentioned on p. 237 the radii of the orbits of the electrons will for stationary states corresponding to high values for τ be very great compared with ordinary atomic dimensions. This circumstance was used as an explanation of the non-appearance in experiments with vacuum-tubes of lines corresponding to the higher numbers in the Balmer series of the hydrogen spectrum. This is also in conformity with experiments on the emission spectrum of sodium; in the principal series of the emission spectrum of this substance rather few lines are observed. Now in Wood's experiments the pressure was not very low, and the states corresponding to high values for τ could therefore not appear; yet in the absorption spectrum about 50 lines were detected. In the experiments in question we consequently observe an absorption of radiation which is not accompanied by a complete transition between two different stationary states. According to the present theory we must assume that this absorption is followed by an emission of energy during which the systems pass back to the original stationary state. If there are no collisions between the different systems this energy will be emitted as a radiation of the same frequency as that absorbed, and there will be no true absorption but only a scattering of the original radiation; a true absorption will not occur unless the energy in question is transformed by collisions into kinetic energy of free particles. In analogy we may now from the above experiments conclude that a bound electron—also in cases in which there is no ionization—will have an absorbing (scattering) influence on a homogeneous radiation, as soon as the frequency of the radiation is greater than W/h, where W is the total amount of energy emitted during the binding of the electron. This would be highly in favour of a theory of absorption as the one sketched above, as there can in such a case be no question of a coincidence of the frequency of the radiation and a characteristic frequency of vibration of the electron. It will further be seen that the assumption, that there will be an absorption (scattering) of any radiation corresponding to a transition between two different mechanical states, is in perfect analogy with the assumption generally used that a free electron will have an absorbing (scattering) influence on light of any frequency. Corresponding considerations will hold for the emission of radiation.

In analogy to the assumption used in this paper that the emission of line-spectra is due to the re-formation of atoms after one or more of the lightly bound electrons are removed, we may assume that the homogeneous Röntgen radiation is emitted during the settling down of the systems after one of the firmly bound electrons escapes, *e.g.* by impact of cathode particles *. In the next part of this paper, dealing with the constitution of atoms, we shall consider the question more closely and try to show that a calculation based on this assumption is in quantitative agreement with the results of experiments: here we shall only mention briefly a problem with which we meet in such a calculation.

Experiments on the phenomena of X-rays suggest that not only the emission and absorption of radiation cannot be treated by the help of the ordinary electrodynamics, but not even the result of a collision between two electrons of which the one is bound in an atom. This is perhaps most clearly shown by some very instructive calculations on the energy of β-particles emitted from radioactive substances recently published by Rutherford †. These calculations strongly suggest that an electron of great velocity in passing through an atom and colliding with the electrons bound will lose energy in distinct finite quanta. As is immediately seen, this is very different from what we might expect if the result of the collisions was governed by the usual mechanical laws. The failure of the classical mechanics in such a problem might also be expected

* Compare J. J. Thomson, Phil. Mag. xxiii. p. 456 (1912).

† E. Rutherford, Phil. Mag. xxiv. pp. 453 & 893 (1912).

beforehand from the absence of anything like equipartition of kinetic energy between free electrons and electrons bound in atoms. From the point of view of the "mechanical" states we see, however, that the following assumption—which is in accord with the above analogy—might be able to account for the result of Rutherford's calculation and for the absence of equipartition of kinetic energy: two colliding electrons, bound or free, will, after the collision as well as before, be in mechanical states. Obviously the introduction of such an assumption would not make any alteration necessary in the classical treatment of a collision between two free particles. But, considering a collision between a free and a bound electron, it would follow that the bound electron by the collision could not acquire a less amount of energy than the difference in energy corresponding to successive stationary states, and consequently that the free electron which collides with it could not lose a less amount.

The preliminary and hypothetical character of the above considerations needs not to be emphasized. The intention, however, has been to show that the sketched generalization of the theory of the stationary states possibly may afford a simple basis of representing a number of experimental facts which cannot be explained by help of the ordinary electro-dynamics and that the assumptions used do not seem to be inconsistent with experiments on phenomena for which a satisfactory explanation has been given by the classical dynamics and the wave theory of light.

§ 5. *The permanent State of an Atomic System.*

We shall now return to the main object of this paper—the discussion of the "permanent" state of a system consisting of nuclei and bound electrons. For a system consisting of a nucleus and an electron rotating round it, this state is, according to the above, determined by the condition that the angular momentum of the electron round the nucleus is equal to $\frac{h}{2\pi}$.

On the theory of this paper the only neutral atom which

contains a single electron is the hydrogen atom. The permanent state of this atom should correspond to the values of a and ω calculated on p. 232. Unfortunately, however, we know very little of the behaviour of hydrogen atoms on account of the small dissociation of hydrogen molecules at ordinary temperatures. In order to get a closer comparison with experiments, it is necessary to consider more complicated systems.

Considering systems in which more electrons are bound by a positive nucleus, a configuration of the electrons which presents itself as a permanent state is one in which the electrons are arranged in a ring round the nucleus. In the discussion of this problem on the basis of the ordinary electrodynamics, we meet—apart from the question of the energy radiation—with new difficulties due to the question of the stability of the ring. Disregarding for a moment this latter difficulty, we shall first consider the dimensions and frequency of the systems in relation to Planck's theory of radiation.

Let us consider a ring consisting of n electrons rotating round a nucleus of charge E, the electrons being arranged at equal angular intervals around the circumference of a circle of radius a.

The total potential energy of the system consisting of the electrons and the nucleus is

$$P = -\frac{ne}{a}(E - es_n),$$

where

$$s_n = \frac{1}{4}\sum_{s=1}^{s=n-1} \operatorname{cosec}\frac{s\pi}{n}.$$

For the radial force exerted on an electron by the nucleus and the other electrons we get

$$F = -\frac{1}{n}\frac{dP}{da} = -\frac{e}{a^2}(E - es_n).$$

Denoting the kinetic energy of an electron by T and neglecting the electromagnetic forces due to the motion of the electrons (see Part II.), we get, putting the centrifugal force on an electron equal to the radial force,

$$\frac{2T}{a} = \frac{e}{a^2}(E - es_n),$$

or

$$T = \frac{e}{2a}(E - es_n).$$

From this we get for the frequency of revolution

$$\omega = \frac{1}{2\pi}\sqrt{\frac{e(E - es_n)}{ma^3}}.$$

The total amount of energy W necessary transferred to the system in order to remove the electrons to infinite distances apart from the nucleus and from each other is

$$W = -P - nT = \frac{ne}{2a}(E - es_n) = nT,$$

equal to the total kinetic energy of the electrons.

We see that the only difference in the above formula and those holding for the motion of a single electron in a circular orbit round a nucleus is the exchange of E for $E - es_n$. It is also immediately seen that corresponding to the motion of an electron in an elliptical orbit round a nucleus, there will be a motion of the n electrons in which each rotates in an elliptical orbit with the nucleus in the focus, and the n electrons at any moment are situated at equal angular intervals on a circle with the nucleus as the centre. The major axis and frequency of the orbit of the single electrons will for this motion be given by the expressions (1) on p. 230 if we replace E by $E - es_n$, and W by $\frac{W}{n}$. Let us now suppose that the system of n electrons rotating in a ring round a nucleus is formed in a way analogous to the one assumed for a single electron rotating round a nucleus. It will thus be assumed that the electrons, before the binding by the nucleus, were at a great distance apart from the latter and possessed no sensible velocities, and also that during the binding a homogeneous radiation is emitted. As in the case of a single electron, we have here that the total amount of energy emitted during the formation of the system is equal to the final kinetic energy of the electrons. If we now suppose that during the formation of the system the electrons at any moment are situated at equal angular intervals on the circumference of a circle with the nucleus in the centre, from analogy with the considerations on p. 232 we are here led to assume the existence of a series of stationary configurations in which the kinetic energy per electron is equal to $\tau h \frac{\omega}{2}$, where τ is an entire number, h Planck's constant, and ω the frequency of revolution. The configuration in which the greatest amount of energy is emitted is, as before, the one in which $\tau = 1$. This configuration we shall assume to be the permanent state of the system if the electrons in this state are arranged in a single ring. As for the case of a single electron we get that the angular momentum of each of the electrons is equal to $\frac{h}{2\pi}$. It may be remarked that instead of considering the single electrons we might have considered the ring as an entity. This would, however, lead to the same result, for in this case the frequency of revolution ω will be replaced by the frequency $n\omega$ of the radiation from the whole ring calculated from the ordinary electrodynamics, and T by the total kinetic energy nT.

There may be many other stationary states corresponding to other ways of forming the system. The assumption of the existence of such states seems necessary in order to account for the line-spectra of systems containing more than one electron (p. 239); it is also suggested by the theory of Nicholson mentioned on p. 233, to which we shall return in a moment. The consideration of the spectra, however, gives, as far as I can see, no indication of the existence of stationary states in which all the electrons are arranged in a ring and which correspond to greater values for the total energy emitted than the one we above have assumed to be the permanent state.

Further, there may be stationary configurations of a system of n electrons and a nucleus of charge E in which all the electrons are not arranged in a single ring. The question, however, of the existence of such stationary configurations is not essential for our determination of the permanent state, as long as we assume that the electrons in this state of the system are arranged in a single ring. Systems corresponding to more complicated configurations will be discussed on p. 254.

Using the relation $T = h\frac{\omega}{2}$, we get, by help of the above expressions for T and ω, values for a and ω corresponding to the permanent state of the system which only differ from those given by the equations (3) on p. 232, by exchange of E for $E - es_n$.

The question of stability of a ring of electrons rotating round a positive charge is discussed in great detail by Sir J. J. Thomson *. An adaption of Thomson's analysis for the case here considered of a ring rotating round a nucleus of negligibly small linear dimensions is given by Nicholson †. The investigation of the problem in question naturally divides in two parts: one concerning the stability for displacements of the electrons in the plane of the ring; one concerning displacements perpendicular to this plane. As Nicholson's calculations show, the answer to the question of stability differs very much in the two cases in question. While the ring for the latter displacements in general is stable if the number of electrons is not great; the ring is in no case considered by Nicholson stable for displacements of the first kind.

According, however, to the point of view taken in this paper, the question of stability for displacements of the electrons in the plane of the ring is most intimately connected with the question of the mechanism of the binding of the electrons, and like the latter cannot be treated on the basis of the ordinary dynamics. The hypothesis of which we shall make use in the following is that the stability of a ring of electrons rotating round a nucleus is secured through the above condition of the universal constancy of the angular momentum, together with the further condition that the configuration of the particles is the one by the formation of which the greatest amount of energy is emitted. As will be shown, this hypothesis is, concerning

* *Loc. cit.*

† *Loc. cit.*

the question of stability for a displacement of the electrons perpendicular to the plane of the ring, equivalent to that used in ordinary mechanical calculations.

Returning to the theory of Nicholson on the origin of lines observed in the spectrum of the solar corona, we shall now see that the difficulties mentioned on p. 234 may be only formal. In the first place, from the point of view considered above the objection as to the instability of the systems for displacements of the electrons in the plane of the ring may not be valid. Further, the objection as to the emission of the radiation in quanta will not have reference to the calculations in question, if we assume that in the coronal spectrum we are not dealing with a true emission but only with a scattering of radiation. This assumption seems probable if we consider the conditions in the celestial body in question; for on account of the enormous rarefaction of the matter there may be comparatively few collisions to disturb the stationary states and to cause a true emission of light corresponding to the transition between different stationary states; on the other hand there will in the solar corona be intense illumination of light of all frequencies which may excite the natural vibrations of the systems in the different stationary states. If the above assumption is correct, we immediately understand the entirely different form for the laws connecting the lines discussed by Nicholson and those connecting the ordinary line-spectra considered in this paper.

Proceeding to consider systems of a more complicated constitution, we shall make use of the following theorem, which can be very simply proved:—

"In every system consisting of electrons and positive nuclei, in which the nuclei are at rest and the electrons move in circular orbits with a velocity small compared with the velocity of light, the kinetic energy will be numerically equal to half the potential energy."

By help of this theorem we get—as in the previous cases of a single electron or of a ring rotating round a nucleus—that the total amount of energy emitted, by the formation of the systems from a configuration in which the distances apart of the particles are infinitely great and in which the particles have no velocities relative to each other, is equal to the kinetic energy of the electrons in the final configuration.

In analogy with the case of a single ring we are here led to assume that corresponding to any configuration of equilibrium a series of geometrically similar, stationary configurations of the system will exist in which the kinetic energy of every electron is equal to the frequency of revolution multiplied by $\frac{\tau}{2}h$ where τ is an entire number and h Planck's constant. In any such series of stationary configurations the one corresponding to the greatest amount of energy emitted will be the one in which τ for every electron is equal to 1. Considering that the ratio of kinetic energy to frequency for a particle rotating in a circular orbit is equal to π times the angular momentum round the centre of the orbit, we are therefore led to the following simple generalization of the hypotheses mentioned on pp. 244 and 252.

"*In any molecular system consisting of positive nuclei and electrons in which the nuclei are at rest relative to each other and the electrons move in circular orbits, the angular momentum of every electron round the centre of its orbit will in the permanent state of the system be equal to* $\frac{h}{2\pi}$, *where h is Planck's constant*" *.

In analogy with the consideration on p. 253 we shall assume that a configuration satisfying this condition is stable if the total energy of the system is less than in any neighbouring configuration satisfying the same condition of the angular momentum of the electrons.

As mentioned in the introduction, the above hypothesis will be used in a following communication as a basis for a theory of the constitution of atoms and molecules. It will be shown that it leads to results which seem to be in conformity with experiments on a number of different phenomena.

The foundation of the hypothesis has been sought entirely in its relation with Planck's theory of radiation; by help of

* In the considerations leading to this hypothesis we have assumed that the velocity of the electrons is small compared with the velocity of light. The limits of the validity of this assumption will be discussed in Part II.

considerations given later it will be attempted to throw some further light on the foundation of it from another point of view.

April 5, 1913.

The High-Frequency Spectra of the Elements. By H. G. J. MOSELEY, *M.A.**

The *Philosophical Magazine*, Series VI, **26**, 1024–1034 (1913)

IN the absence of any available method of spectrum analysis, the characteristic types of X radiation, which an atom emits when suitably excited, have hitherto been described in terms of their absorption in aluminium †. The interference phenomena exhibited by X rays when scattered by a crystal have now, however, made possible the accurate determination of the frequencies of the various types of radiation. This was shown by W. H. and W. L. Bragg ‡, who by this method analysed the line spectrum emitted by the platinum target of an X-ray tube. C. G. Darwin and the author § extended this analysis and also examined the continuous spectrum, which in this case constitutes the greater part of the radiation. Recently Prof. Bragg ‖ has also determined the wave-lengths of the strongest lines in the spectra of nickel, tungsten, and rhodium. The electrical methods which have hitherto been employed are, however, only successful where a constant source of radiation is available. The present paper contains a description of a method of photographing these spectra, which makes the analysis of the X rays as simple as any other branch of spectroscopy. The author intends first to make a general survey of the principal types of high-frequency radiation, and then to examine the spectra of a few elements in greater detail and with greater accuracy. The results already obtained show that such data have an important bearing on the question of the

* Communicated by Prof. E. Rutherford, F.R.S.

† *Cf.* Barkla, Phil. Mag. xxii. p. 396 (1911).

‡ Proc. Roy. Soc. A. lxxxviii. p. 428 (1913).

§ Phil. Mag. xxvi. p. 210 (1913).

‖ Proc. Roy. Soc. A. lxxxix. p. 246 (1913).

internal structure of the atom, and strongly support the views of Rutherford * and of Bohr †.

Kaye ‡ has shown that an element excited by a stream of sufficiently fast cathode rays emits its characteristic X radiation. He used as targets a number of substances mounted on a truck inside an exhausted tube. A magnetic device enabled each target to be brought in turn into the line of fire. This apparatus was modified to suit the present work. The cathode stream was concentrated on to a small area of the target, and a platinum plate furnished with a fine vertical slit placed immediately in front of the part bombarded. The tube was exhausted by a Gaede mercury pump, charcoal in liquid air being also sometimes used to remove water vapour. The X rays,

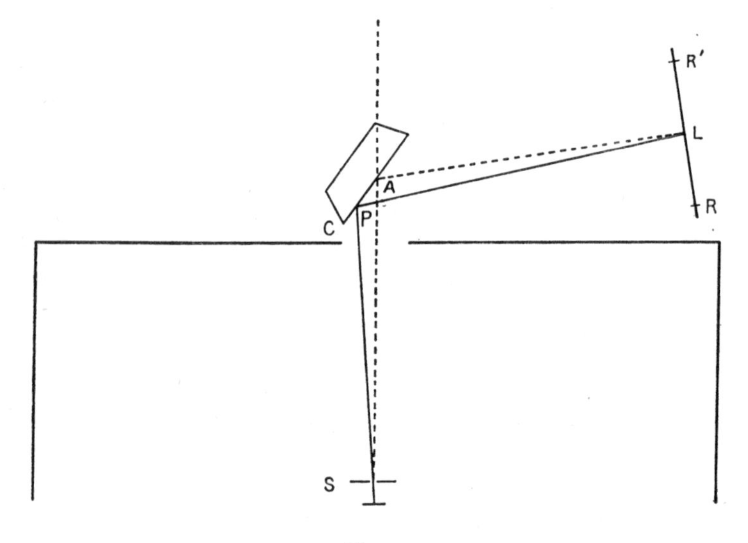

Fig. 1

after passing through the slit marked S in fig. 1, emerged through an aluminium window ·02 mm. thick. The rest of the radiation was shut off by a lead box which surrounded the

* Phil. Mag. xxi. p. 669 (1911).

† Phil. Mag. xxvi. pp. 1, 476, & 857 (1913).

‡ Phil. Trans. Roy. Soc. A. ccix. p. 123 (1909).

tube. The rays fell on the cleavage face, C, of a crystal of potassium ferrocyanide which was mounted on the prism-table of a spectrometer. The surface of the crystal was vertical and contained the geometrical axis of the spectrometer.

Now it is known * that X rays consist in general of two types, the heterogeneous radiation and characteristic radiations of definite frequency. The former of these is reflected from such a surface at all angles of incidence, but at the large angles used in the present work the reflexion is of very little intensity. The radiations of definite frequency, on the other hand, are reflected only when they strike the surface at definite angles, the glancing angle of incidence θ, the wave-length λ, and the "grating constant" d of the crystal being connected by the relation

$$n\lambda = 2d \sin \theta, \quad . \quad . \quad . \quad (1)$$

where n, an integer, may be called the "order" in which the reflexion occurs. The particular crystal used, which was a fine specimen with face 6 cm. square, was known to give strong reflexions in the first three orders, the third order being the most prominent.

If then a radiation of definite wave-length happens to strike any part P of the crystal at a suitable angle, a small part of it is reflected. Assuming for the moment that the source of the radiation is a point, the locus of P is obviously the arc of a circle, and the reflected rays will travel along the generating lines of a cone with apex at the image of the source. The effect on a photographic plate L will take the form of the arc of an hyperbola, curving away from the direction of the direct beam. With a fine slit at S, the arc becomes a fine line which is slightly curved in the direction indicated.

The photographic plate was mounted on the spectrometer arm, and both the plate and the slit were 17 cm. from the axis. The importance of this arrangement lies in a geometrical property, for when these two distances are equal the point L at which a beam reflected at a definite angle strikes the plate is independent of the position of P on the crystal surface. The

* Moseley and Darwin, *loc. cit.*

angle at which the crystal is set is then immaterial so long as a ray can strike some part of the surface at the required angle. The angle θ can be obtained from the relation

$$2\theta = 180^\circ - \mathrm{SPL} = 180^\circ - \mathrm{SAL}.$$

The following method was used for measuring the angle SAL. Before taking a photograph a reference line R was made at both ends of the plate by replacing the crystal by a lead screen furnished with a fine slit which coincided with the axis of the spectrometer. A few seconds' exposure to the X rays then gave a line R on the plate, and so defined on it the line joining S and A. A second line R′ was made in the same way after turning the spectrometer arm through a definite angle. The arm was then turned to the position required to catch the reflected beam and the angles LAP for any lines which were subsequently found on the plate deduced from the known values of RAP and the position of the lines on the plate. The angle LAR was measured with an error of not more than $0^\circ{\cdot}1$, by superposing on the negative a plate on which reference lines had been marked in the same way at intervals of 1°. In finding from this the glancing angle of reflexion two small corrections were necessary in practice, since neither the face of the crystal nor the lead slit coincided accurately with the axis of the spectrometer. Wave-lengths varying over a range of about 30 per cent. could be reflected for a given position of the crystal.

In almost all cases the time of exposure was five minutes. Ilford X-ray plates were used and were developed with rodinal. The plates were mounted in a plate-holder, the front of which was covered with black paper. In order to determine the wave-length from the reflexion angle θ it is necessary to know both the order n in which the reflexion occurs and the grating constant d. n was determined by photographing every spectrum both in the second order and the third. This also gave a useful check on the accuracy of the measurements; d cannot be calculated directly for the complicated crystal potassium ferrocyanide. The grating constant of this particular crystal had, however, previously * been accurately compared with d', the constant of a specimen of rocksalt. It was found that

$$d = 3d' \frac{\cdot 1988}{\cdot 1985}.$$

Now W. L. Bragg † has shown that the atoms in a rocksalt crystal are in simple cubical array. Hence the number of atoms per c.c.

$$2 \frac{N\sigma}{M} = \frac{1}{(d')^3}.$$

N, the number of molecules in a gram-mol., $= 6{\cdot}05 \times 10^{23}$, assuming the charge on an electron to be $4{\cdot}89 \times 10^{-10}$; σ, the density of this crystal of rocksalt, was 2·167, and M the molecular weight $= 58{\cdot}46$.

This gives $d' = 2{\cdot}814 \times 10^{-8}$ and $d = 8{\cdot}454 \times 10^{-8}$ cm. It is seen that the determination of wave-length depends on $e^{\frac{1}{3}}$, so that the effect of uncertainty in the value of this quantity will not be serious. Lack of homogeneity in the crystal is a more likely source of error, as minute inclusions of water would make the true density greater than that found experimentally.

Twelve elements have so far been examined. The ten given in Table I. were chosen as forming a continuous series with only one gap. It was hoped in this way to bring out clearly any systematic results. The inclusion of nickel was of special interest owing to its anomalous position in the periodic system. Radiations from these substances are readily excited, and the large angles of reflexion make it easy to measure the wave-lengths with accuracy. Calcium alone gave any trouble. In this case, owing to the high absorption coefficient of the principal radiation—about 1200 cm.$^{-1}$ in aluminium—the X-ray tube was provided with a window of goldbeaters' skin and the air between the crystal and the photographic plate displaced by hydrogen. The layer of lime which covered the surface of the

* Moseley & Darwin, *loc. cit.*

† Proc. Roy. Soc. A. lxxxix. p. 248 (1913).

metal gave off such a quantity of gas that the X rays could only be excited for a second or two at a time. Brass was substituted for zinc to avoid volatilization by the intense heat generated at the point struck by the cathode rays. Ferro-vanadium (35 per cent. V) and ferro-titanium (23 per cent.

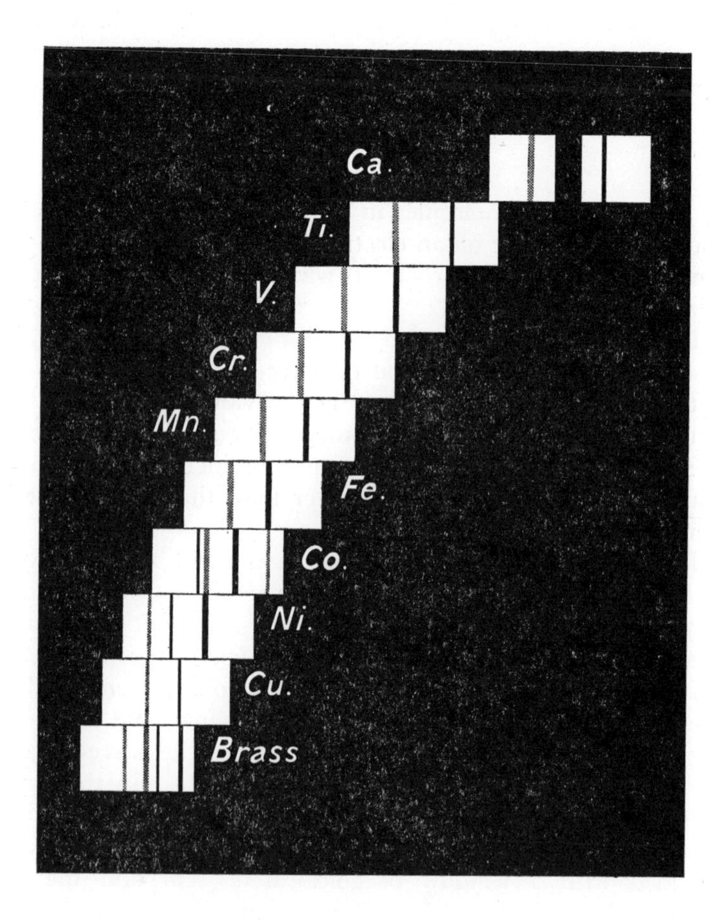

Ti), for which I am indebted to the International Vanadium Co., proved convenient substitutes for the pure elements, which are not easily obtained in the solid form.

The Plate shows the spectra in the third order placed approximately in register. Those parts of the photographs which represent the same angle of reflexion are in the same vertical line. The actual angles can be taken from Table I. It is to be seen that the spectrum of each element consists of two lines. Of these the stronger has been called α in the table, and the weaker β. The lines found on any of the plates besides α and β were almost certainly all due to impurities. Thus in both the third and second order the cobalt spectrum shows Ni α very strongly and Fe α faintly. In the third order the nickel spectrum shows Mn α_2 faintly. The brass spectra naturally show α and β both of Cu and of Zn, but Zn β_2 has not yet been found. In the second order the ferro-vanadium and ferro-titanium spectra show very intense third-order Fe lines, and the former also shows Cu α_3 faintly. The Co contained Ni and 0·8 per cent. Fe, the Ni 2·2 per cent. Mn, and the V only a trace of Cu. No other lines have been found; but a search over a wide range of wave-lengths has been made only for one or two elements, and perhaps prolonged exposures, which have not yet been attempted, will show more complex spectra. The prevalence of lines due to impurities suggests that this may prove a powerful method of chemical analysis. Its advantage over ordinary spectroscopic methods lies in the simplicity of the spectra and the impossibility of one substance masking the radiation from another. It may even lead to the discovery of missing elements, as it will be possible to predict the position of their characteristic lines.

It will be seen from Table I. that the wave-lengths calculated from the two orders are in good agreement. The third order gives the stronger reflexion, and as the angles dealt with are the larger these results are the more accurate. The similarity of the different spectra is shown by the fact that the two lines α and β remain approximately constant, not only in relative intensity but also in relative wave-length. The frequency of β increases, however, slightly faster than that of α. The same two lines α strong and β weak constitute the rhodium spectrum examined by Bragg *, and they are obviously in some way

* Proc. Roy. Soc. A. lxxxix. p. 277 (1913).

TABLE I.

Element.	Line.	θ_2.	λ.	θ_3.	λ.	$\lambda_\alpha/\lambda_\beta$.	$Q=(\nu/\frac{3}{4}\nu_0)^{\frac{1}{2}}$.	N atomic number.	Atomic weight.
CALCIUM.	α ... β ...	23·4° 21·4	3·357 × 10⁻⁸ 3·085	36·7° 33·3	3·368 × 10⁻⁸ 3·094	1·089	19·00	20	40·09
SCANDIUM.	...	...	...	...	...	...	...	21	44·1
TITANIUM.	α ... β ...	19·1 17·4	2·766 2·528	29·3 26·6	2·758 2·524	1·093	20·99	22	48·1
VANADIUM.	α ... β ...	17·35 15·8	2·521 2·302	26·55 24·05	2·519 2·297	1·097	21·96	23	51·06
CHROMIUM.	α ... β ...	15·75 14·3	2·295 2·088	24·1 21·8	2·301 2·093	1·100	22·98	24	52·0
MANGANESE.	α ... β ...	14·5 13·15	2·117 1·923	22·0 19·9	2·111 1·918	1·101	23·99	25	54·93
IRON.	α ... β ...	13·3 12·05	1·945 1·765	20·2 18·25	1·946 1·765	1·103	24·99	26	55·85
COBALT.	α ... β ...	12·25 11·15	1·794 1·635	18·6 16·8	1·798 1·629	1·104	26·00	27	58·97
NICKEL.	α ... β ...	11·35 10·25	1·664 1·504	17·15 15·5	1·662 1·506	1·104	27·04	28	58·68
COPPER.	α ... β ...	10·55 9·55	1·548 1·403	15·95 14·4	1·549 1·402	1·105	28·01	29	63·57
ZINC.	α ... β ...	9·85 not	1·446 found	14·85 13·4	1·445 1·306	1·106	29·01	30	65·37

closely related. One or two photographs taken with the radiation from platinum gave results in good agreement with those obtained by the electrical method, and no trace of the elaborate system of bands described by de Broglie * in the reflexion from rock-salt was encountered. The three lines found by Herveg † in the reflexion from selenite doubtless represent part of the Pt spectrum in the second order. The actual breadth of the lines and certain minute details in their structure will not be considered here, as discussion would take too much space and more experiments are needed. The only other element examined was tantalum. In this case the radiation belongs to the L series, and the spectrum consists of a strong line of wavelength $1{\cdot}525 \times 10^{-8}$ cm., two others of less intensity at $1{\cdot}330$ and $1{\cdot}287 \times 10^{-8}$ cm., and probably some very faint lines also.

A discussion will now be given of the meaning of the wavelengths found for the principal spectrum-line α. In Table I. the values are given of the quantity

$$Q = \sqrt{\frac{\nu}{\frac{3}{4}\nu_0}},$$

ν being the frequency of the radiation α, and ν_0 the fundamental frequency of ordinary line spectra. The latter is obtained from Rydberg's wave-number, $N_0 = \frac{\nu}{c} = 109{,}720$. The reason for introducing this particular constant will be given later. It is at once evident that Q increases by a constant amount as we pass from one element to the next, using the chemical order of the elements in the periodic system. Except in the case of nickel and cobalt ‡, this is also the order of the atomic weights. While, however, Q increases uniformly the atomic weights vary in an apparently arbitrary manner, so that an exception in their order does not come as a surprise. We have here a proof that there is in the atom a fundamental quantity, which increases by regular steps as we pass from one element to the next. This quantity can only be the charge on the central positive

* *Le Radium*, x. pp. 186 & 245 (1913).

† *Deutsch. Phys. Ges. Verh.* xv. 13, p. 555 (1913).

‡ *Cf.* Barkla, Phil. Mag. xiv. p. 408 (1907).

nucleus, of the existence of which we already have definite proof. Rutherford has shown, from the magnitude of the scattering of α particles by matter, that this nucleus carries a + charge approximately equal to that of $\frac{A}{2}$ electrons, where A is the atomic weight. Barkla, from the scattering of X rays by matter, has shown that the number of electrons in an atom is roughly $\frac{A}{2}$, which for an electrically neutral atom comes to the same thing. Now atomic weights increase on the average by about 2 units at a time, and this strongly suggests the view that N increases from atom to atom always by a single electronic unit. We are therefore led by experiment to the view that N is the same as the number of the place occupied by the element in the periodic system. This atomic number is then for H 1 for He 2 for Li 3 . . . for Ca 20 . . . for Zn 30, &c. This theory was originated by Broek * and since used by Bohr †. We can confidently predict that in the few cases in which the order of the atomic weights A clashes with the chemical order of the periodic system, the chemical properties are governed by N; while A is itself probably a complicated function of N. The very close similarity between the X-ray spectra of the different elements shows that these radiations originate inside the atom, and have no direct connexion with the complicated light-spectra and chemical properties which are governed by the structure of its surface.

We will now examine the relation

$$Q = \sqrt{\frac{\nu}{\frac{3}{4}\nu_0}}$$

more closely. So far the argument has relied on the fact that Q is a quantity which increases from atom to atom by equal steps. Now Q has been obtained by multiplying $\nu^{\frac{1}{2}}$ by a constant factor so chosen as to make the steps equal to unity. We have, therefore,

$$Q = N - k,$$

* *Phys. Zeit.* xiv. p. 32 (1913).

† *Loc. cit.*

where k is a constant. Hence the frequency ν varies as $(\mathrm{N} - k)^2$. If N for calcium is really 20 then $k = 1$.

There is good reason to believe that the X-ray spectra with which we are now dealing come from the innermost ring of electrons *. If these electrons are held in equilibrium by mechanical forces, the angular velocity ω with which they are rotating and the radius r of their orbit are connected by

$$m\omega^2 r = \frac{e^2}{r^2}(\mathrm{N} - \sigma_n),$$

where σ_n is a small term arising from the influence of the n electrons in the ring on each other, and $\sigma_2 = 0{\cdot}25$, $\sigma_4 = 0{\cdot}96$, $\sigma_6 = 1{\cdot}83$, $\sigma_8 = 2{\cdot}81$. In obtaining this simple expression the very small effect of other outside rings has been neglected. If then, as we pass from atom to atom, the number of electrons in the central ring remains unaltered,

$$(\omega^2 r^3)_{\mathrm{N}+1} - (\omega^2 r^3)_{\mathrm{N}} \text{ remains constant;}$$

but these experiments have shown that

$$\nu^{\frac{1}{2}}_{\mathrm{N}+1} - \nu^{\frac{1}{2}}_{\mathrm{N}} \text{ is also constant,}$$

and therefore

$$\frac{\omega^2 r^3}{\nu^{\frac{1}{2}}} \text{ is constant.}$$

For the types of radiation considered by Bohr, provided the ring moves from one stationary state to another as a whole, and for the ordinary transverse vibrations of the ring, provided the influence of outer rings can be neglected, ν is proportional to ω.

This gives $\omega^{\frac{3}{2}} r^3$ and therefore $m\omega r^2$, the angular momentum of an electron, the same for all the different atoms. Thus we have an experimental verification of the principle of the constancy of angular momentum which was first used by Nicholson †, and is the basis of Bohr's theory of the atom.

It is evident that $k = \sigma_n$. If then $k = 1$, it is suggested that the ring contains 4 electrons, for $\sigma_4 = 0{\cdot}96$.

* J. J. Thomson, Phil. Mag. xxiii. p. 456 (1912).

† Monthly Notes Roy. Astr. Soc. June 1912.

We are now justified in making a quantitative comparison between the frequency of α and that of the fundamental radiation from such a ring calculated from the theory of Bohr.

We have obtained the experimental result,

$$\nu = \tfrac{3}{4}\nu_0(\mathrm{N} - \sigma_n)^2.$$

On his theory, making the assumption that the ring moves as a whole from stationary state 2 to state 1, the frequency of the principal radiation emitted is

$$\nu = \left(\frac{1}{1^2} - \frac{1}{2^2}\right) \frac{2\pi^2 e^4 m}{h^3} (\mathrm{N} - \sigma_n)^2,$$

where e is the charge on an electron, m its mass, and h Planck's constant.

The numerical agreement between these two constants ν_0 and $\frac{2\pi^2 e^4 m}{h^3}$ is known to be very close, while Bohr's explanation of the Balmer series for hydrogen assumes them to be identical. This numerical agreement between the experimental values and those calculated from a theory designed to explain the ordinary hydrogen spectrum is remarkable, as the wave-lengths dealt with in the two cases differ by a factor of about 2000. The assumption that the whole ring takes part in the radiation introduces, however, a grave difficulty from energy considerations, while no explanation of the faint line β has been forthcoming. Probably further experiments will show that the theory needs some modification.

The results hitherto obtained for the radiations of the L series are too meagre to justify any explanation. As before, the line of longest wave-length is the most prominent, a result similar to that found in ordinary light-spectra. The wave-lengths found for this line in the case of tantalum and platinum suggest that possibly the frequency is here

$$\nu = \left(\frac{1}{2^2} - \frac{1}{3^2}\right) \nu_0(\mathrm{N} - \sigma_n)^2.$$

Here N and σ_n are unknown, but it is evident from the periodic system that $\mathrm{N}_{\mathrm{Pt}} - \mathrm{N}_{\mathrm{Ta}} = 5$, while probably σ_n remains the same for all elements in the same column. The actual value found for $\nu^{\frac{1}{2}}_{Pt} - \nu^{\frac{1}{2}}_{Ta}$ is $1{\cdot}08 \times 10^8$, and the calculated value is $1{\cdot}07 \times 10^8$. Whether this relation really holds good can only be decided by further experiment.

In conclusion I wish to express my warm thanks to Prof. Rutherford for the kind interest which he has taken in this work.

Physical Laboratory,
University of Manchester.

The High-Frequency Spectra of the Elements. Part II. *By* H. G. J. Moseley, *M.A.**

The *Philosophical Magazine*, Series VI, **27**, 703–713 (1914)

THE first part † of this paper dealt with a method of photographing X-ray spectra, and included the spectra of a dozen elements. More than thirty other elements have now been investigated, and simple laws have been found which govern the results, and make it possible to predict with confidence the position of the principal lines in the spectrum of any element from aluminium to gold. The present contribution is a general preliminary survey, which claims neither to be complete nor very accurate.

A somewhat different method of photographing these spectra has been developed independently by de Broglie ‡ and by Herveg §. The latter closely confirms the angles given by Moseley and Darwin || for reflexion of Pt rays from selenite. De Broglie finds less satisfactory agreement for the reflexion from rocksalt. De Broglie has also examined the spectra of W and Au, and has obtained for Cu and Fe results similar to those given in Part I.

The general experimental method has remained unaltered, and need not be again described. The same crystal of potassium ferrocyanide has been used as analyser throughout. The sharpness of the lines of short wave-length has been much improved by reducing the breadth of the defining slit to about 0·2 mm. The most convenient type of X-ray tube is drawn to scale in fig. 1. The aluminium trolley which carries the targets can be drawn to and fro by means of silk fishing-line wound on brass

* Communicated by the Author.

† Moseley, Phil. Mag. xxvi. p. 1024 (1913).

‡ De Broglie, *C. R.* 17 Nov., 22 Dec., 1913, 19 Jan., 2 Feb., 2 March, 1914.

§ Herveg, *Verh. d. D. Phys. Ges.* xvi, p. 73, Jan. 1914.

|| Moseley & Darwin, Phil. Mag. xxvi, p. 210 (1913).

bobbins. An iron screen S fastened to the rails is furnished with a fine vertical slit which defines the X-ray beam. The slit should be fixed exactly opposite the focus-spot of the cathode-stream, though a slight error can be remedied by deflecting the cathode rays with a magnet. The X-rays escape by a side-tube $2\frac{1}{2}$ cm. diameter closed by an aluminium window 0·022 mm. thick. The X-ray tube, which has a capacity of over 3 litres, was exhausted with a Gaede mercury-pump, for the loan of which I am indebted to Balliol College.

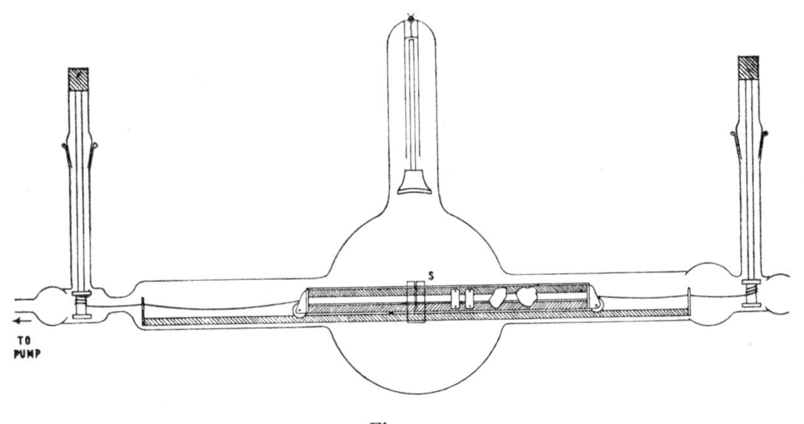

Fig. 1

The radiations of long wave-length cannot penetrate an aluminium window or more than a centimetre or two of air. The photographs had therefore in this case to be taken inside an exhausted spectrometer. Fig. 2 gives a vertical section to scale of the X-ray tube and spectrometer. The former consists of a bulb containing the cathode, joined by a very large glass T-piece to a long tube of 4 cm. diameter, in which are the rails R and the carriage C. S is the defining-slit and W a window of goldbeaters' skin which separates the tube from the spectrometer. This material, which is usually air-tight, though sometimes it may require varnishing, is extremely transparent to X-rays. A circular window of 2 cm. diameter will easily withstand the pressure of the atmosphere if left undisturbed.

In these experiments, however, the pressure was relieved every time the spectrometer was exhausted, and under such conditions the goldbeaters' skin had frequently to be renewed. The spectrometer, which was specially designed for this work, consists of a strong circular iron box of 30 cm. inside diameter and 8 cm. high, closed by a lid which, when the flange is greased, makes an air-tight joint. Two concentric grooves are cut in the floor of the box. The table A, which carries the plate-holder, rests on three steel balls, of which two run in the

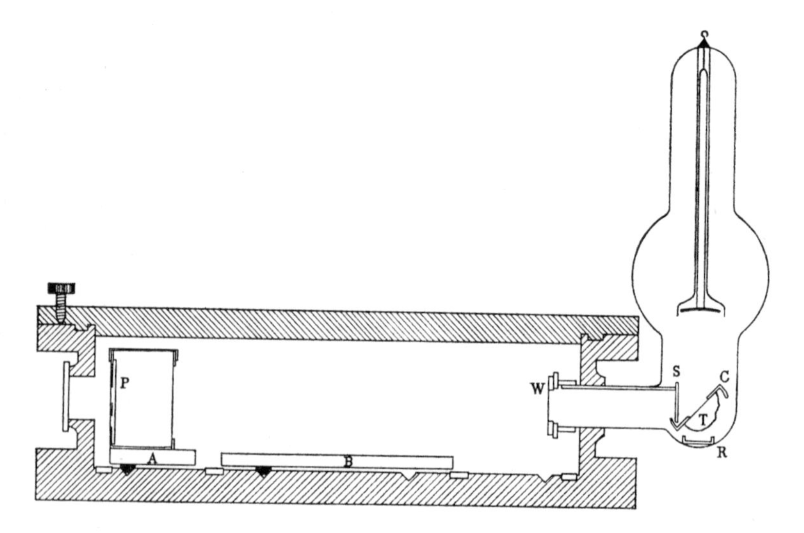

Fig. 2

outer groove, while the third rests on the floor of the box. The position of the crystal-table B is controlled in like manner by the inner groove. This geometrical construction for a spectrometer is well known. The scales are fixed to the box and the verniers to the tables. For these very soft rays the absorption by the black paper front of the plate-holder became serious, and two sheets of black tissue-paper were used instead. Lumps of the pure elements, usually several millimetres thick, were used as targets in the case of Mg, Al, Si, Mo, Ru, Pd, Ag, Sb, Ta. Foils such as Rh, W, Au were either silver-soldered or brazed onto copper. Os was used in the form of a thin chemical deposit on copper. The alloys used were ZrNi (70 per cent.), WFe (50 per cent.), NbTa (50 per cent.), and SnMn (50 per cent.). KCl and the oxides of the rare-earth elements were rubbed onto the surface of nickel plates roughened with coarse emery-powder. The only serious difficulty in the experiments is caused by the heat produced by the cathode ray bombardment, and the consequent liberation of gas and destruction of the surface of the target. This makes it necessary to use the element in a form which is not too volatile and prevents the employment of a very powerful discharge. The total time of an exposure, including rests, varied from three minutes for a substance such as ruthenium, which could safely be heated, to thirty minutes for the rare earth oxides. The importance of using an efficient high-tension valve may again be mentioned.

The oxides of Sa, Eu, Gd, Er were given me by Sir William Crookes, O.M., to whom I wish to express my sincere gratitude. For the loan of the Os and a button of Ru I am indebted to Messrs. Johnson Matthey. The alloys were obtained from the Metallic Compositions Co., and the oxides of La, Ce, Pr, Nd, and Er from Dr. Schuchardt, of Görlitz.

Almost every line was photographed in two different orders, and the double angles of reflexion measured as before to within $0^\circ\cdot1$ and sometimes $0^\circ\cdot05$. In some sets of experiments a small error caused by the crystal surface not being exactly on the spectrometer-axis gave rise to a systematic discrepancy in the results obtained from reflexion in different orders. It was found that this error, which never changed the reflexion-angle by more than $0^\circ\cdot05$, could be measured more accurately from the amount of the discrepancy than from direct observation of the crystal. A more serious correction was necessary when using the long wave-length apparatus. In this case the slit and photograph are not equidistant from the crystal, and the position of the spectrum-lines on the plate is no longer independent of the angle at which the crystal is set. The necessary corrections were calculated geometrically, and verified by photographing the same line for both right-handed and left-handed reflexions and with the crystal set at various angles.

In the work on the very short wave-lengths, the reflexion of the general heterogeneous radiation gave some trouble. This is always an important part of the radiation from an X-ray tube, but with a hard tube it is analysed by reflexion mainly into constituents of very short wave-length, and so usually does not interfere with the line-spectra. It is only with an extremely soft tube, combined with precautions against absorption by the air, that constituents reflected at large angles become prominent. When examining such a spectrum as that of Ag in the K series, the general reflexion cannot be avoided. Unfortunately, when photographed it takes the form of irregular fringes, which effectually hide faint spectrum-lines. A change of target, with the position of slit and crystal unaltered, does not affect the appearance of the fringes, a fact which proves that they are due to the general heterogeneous radiation. It is easy to show that the fringes are merely a very foreshortened pattern of patches on the crystal surface which reflect exceptionally well. The way in which they move and spread out laterally as the crystal is turned provides a proof of this, and so does Barkla's * observation that when the crystal is moved sideways the fringes move with it. It is easy to devise methods for getting rid of the fringes. In the first place, narrowing the slit or increasing the distance from the crystal will diminish their intensity compared with that of the line-spectrum. In the second place, turning the crystal will move and blur the fringes, but leave the sharpness of the lines unaffected provided the slit and photograph are equidistant from the reflecting surface †. The quantitative measurements of Moseley and Darwin ‡ on the reflexion of the general radiation must have been little affected by these fringes, as the incident beam was restricted to a very narrow pencil which always impinged on the same part of the crystal.

The results obtained for radiations belonging to Barkla's K series are given in Table I., and for convenience the figures

* Barkla and Martyn, Proc. Phys. Soc. London (1913).

† Moseley, *loc. cit.* p. 1025. See also W. H. and W. L. Bragg, Proc. Roy. Soc. A, lxxxix. p. 428 (1913).

‡ Moseley and Darwin, *loc. cit.*

already given in Part I. are included. The wave-length λ has been calculated from the glancing angle of reflexion θ by means of the relation $n\lambda = 2d \sin \theta$, where d has been taken to be $8 \cdot 454 \times 10^{-8}$ cm. As before, the strongest line is called α and the next line β. The square root of the frequency of each line is plotted in fig. 3, and the wave-lengths can be read off with the help of the scale at the top of the diagram.

The spectrum of Al was photographed in the first order only. The very light elements give several other fainter lines, which have not yet been fully investigated, while the results for Mg and Na are quite complicated, and apparently depart from the simple relations which connect the spectra of the other elements. In the spectra from yttrium onwards only the α line has so far been measured, and further results in these directions will be given in a later paper. The spectra both of K and of Cl were obtained by means of a target of KCl, but it is very improbable

TABLE I.

	α line. $\lambda \times 10^8$ cm.	Q_K.	N. Atomic Number.	β line. $\lambda \times 10^8$.
Aluminium	8·364	12·05	**13**	7·912
Silicon	7·142	13·04	14	6·729
Chlorine	4·750	16·00	17	......
Potassium	3·759	17·98	19	3·463
Calcium	3·368	19·00	20	3·094
Titanium	2·758	20·99	22	2·524
Vanadium	2·519	21·96	23	2·297
Chromium	2·301	22·98	24	2·093
Manganese	2·111	23·99	25	1·818
Iron	1·946	24·99	26	1·765
Cobalt	1·798	26·00	27	1·629
Nickel	1·662	27·04	28	1·506
Copper	1·549	28·01	29	1·402
Zinc	1·445	29·01	30	1·306
Yttrium	0·838	38·1	39	......
Zirconium.........	0·794	39·1	40	......
Niobium	0·750	40·2	41	......
Molybdenum ...	0·721	41·2	42	......
Ruthenium	0·638	43·6	44	......
Palladium	0·584	45·6	46	......
Silver	0·560	46·6	47	......

that the observed lines have been attributed to the wrong elements. The α line for elements from Y onwards appeared to consist of a very close doublet, an effect previously observed by Bragg * in the case of rhodium.

The results obtained for the spectra of the L series are given in Table II. and plotted in fig. 3. These spectra contain five lines, α, β, γ, δ, ϵ, reckoned in order of decreasing wave-length and decreasing intensity. There is also always a faint companion α' on the long wave-length side of α, a rather faint line ϕ between β and γ for the rare earth elements at least, and a number of very faint lines of wave-length greater than α.

TABLE II.

	α line. $\lambda \times 10^8$ cm.	Q_L.	N. Atomic Number.	β line. $\lambda \times 10^8$.	ϕ line. $\lambda \times 10^8$.	γ line. $\lambda \times 10^8$.
Zirconium	6·091	32·8	40	......	......	......
Niobium	5·749	33·8	41	5·507	......	......
Molybdenum	5·423	34·8	42	5·187	......	......
Ruthenium	4·861	36·7	44	4·660	......	......
Rhodium	4·622	37·7	45	......	......	......
Palladium	4·385	38·7	46	4·168	......	3·928
Silver	4·170	39·6	47	......	......	......
Tin	3·619	42·6	50	......	......	......
Antimony	3·458	43·6	51	3·245	......	......
Lanthanum	2·676	49·5	57	2·471	2·424	2·313
Cerium	2·567	50·6	58	2·360	2·315	2·209
Praseodymium	(2·471)	51·5	59	2·265	......	......
Neodymium	2·382	52·5	60	2·175	......	......
Samarium	2·208	54·5	62	2·008	1·972	1·893
Europium	2·130	55·5	63	1·925	1·888	1·814
Gadolinium	2·057	56·5	64	1·853	1·818	......
Holmium	1·914	58·6	66	1·711	......	......
Erbium	1·790	60·6	68	1·591	1·563	......
Tantalum	1·525	65·6	73	1·330	......	1·287
Tungsten	1·486	66·5	74	......	......	......
Osmium	1·397	68·5	76	1·201	......	1·172
Iridium	1·354	69·6	77	1·155	......	1·138
Platinum	1·316	70·6	78	1·121	......	1·104
Gold	1·287	71·4	79	1·092	......	1·078

* Bragg, 'Nature,' March 12, 1914.

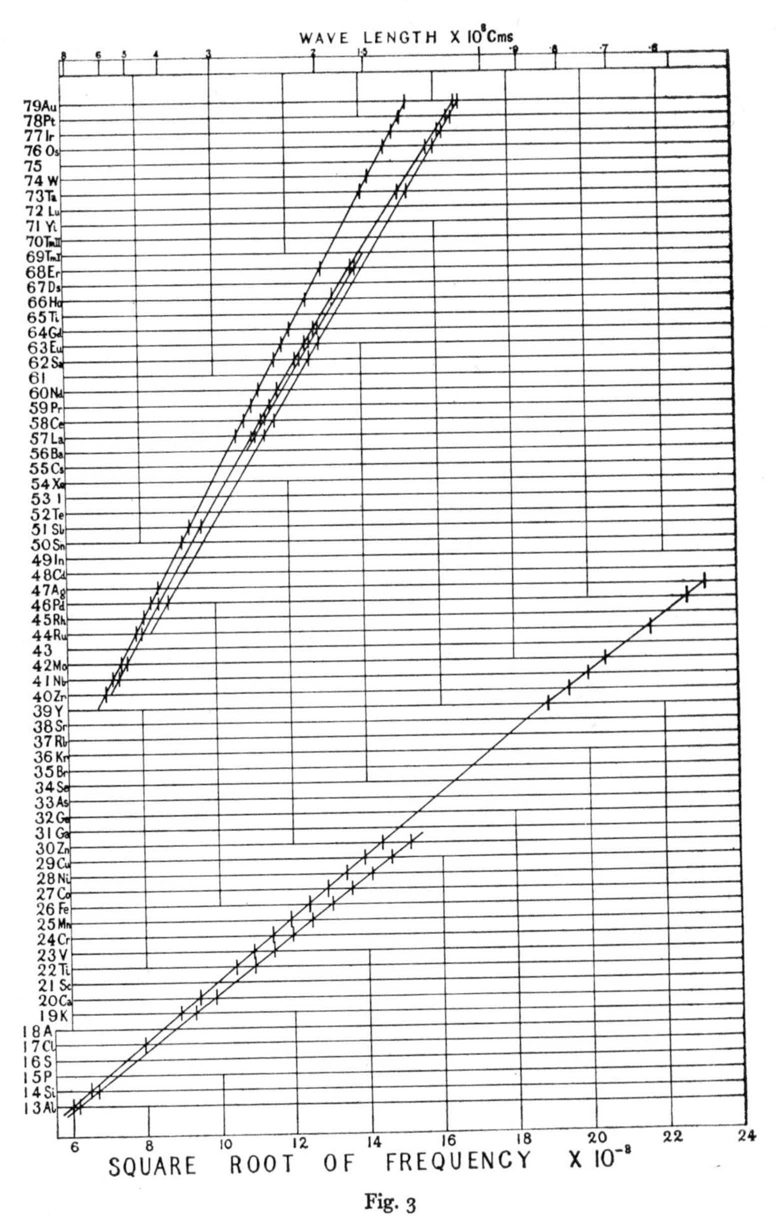
WAVE LENGTH X 10⁸ Cms
79 Au
78 Pt
77 Ir
76 Os
75
74 W
73 Ta
72 Lu
71 Yt
70 Tm II
69 Tm I
68 Er
67 Ds
66 Ho
65 Tb
64 Gd
63 Eu
62 Sa
61
60 Nd
59 Pr
58 Ce
57 La
56 Ba
55 Cs
54 Xe
53 I
52 Te
51 Sb
50 Sn
49 In
48 Cd
47 Ag
46 Pd
45 Rh
44 Ru
43
42 Mo
41 Nb
40 Zr
39 Y
38 Sr
37 Rb
36 Kr
35 Br
34 Se
33 As
32 Ge
31 Ga
30 Zn
29 Cu
28 Ni
27 Co
26 Fe
25 Mn
24 Cr
23 V
22 Ti
21 Sc
20 Ca
19 K
18 A
17 Cl
16 S
15 P
14 Si
13 Al
6
8
10
12
14
16
18
20
22
24
SQUARE ROOT OF FREQUENCY X 10⁻⁸

Fig. 3

Of these, α, β, ϕ, and γ have been systematically measured with the object of finding out how the spectrum alters from one element to another. The fact that often values are not given for all these lines merely indicates the incompleteness of the work. The spectra, so far as they have been examined, are so entirely similar that without doubt α, β, and γ at least always exist. Often γ was not included in the limited range of wave-lengths which can be photographed on one plate. Sometimes lines have not been measured, either on account of faintness or of the confusing proximity of lines due to impurities.

Lines due to impurities were frequently present, but caused little trouble except in the rare earth group. Here two extreme cases occurred. The X-ray spectrum of the praseodymia showed that it consisted roughly of 50 per cent. La, 35 per cent. Ce, and 15 per cent. Pr. Unfortunately the position expected for the α line of Pr coincides with the known position of the β line of La, but the β line of Pr was quite conspicuous, and had precisely the wave-length anticipated. Two specimens of erbia were used. The specimen purchased contained 50 per cent. Er and 50 per cent. of another element, of which the X-ray spectrum coincides with the spectrum calculated for Ho. The erbia given by Sir William Crookes was evidently nearly pure, but showed the α and β lines of Ho quite faintly, and also faint lines agreeing with α and β of Ds and α of Tm I and of Tm II. The Nd was free from La, Ce, and Pr, but contained a fair proportion of Sm. The Sm, Eu, and Gd appeared to be pure. I hope soon to complete the examination of the spectra of this group.

Conclusions

In fig. 3 the spectra of the elements are arranged on horizontal lines spaced at equal distances. The order chosen for the elements is the order of the atomic weights, except in the cases of A, Co, and Te, where this clashes with the order of the chemical properties. Vacant lines have been left for an element between Mo and Ru, an element between Nd and

Sa, and an element between W and Os, none of which are yet known, while Tm, which Welsbach* has separated into two constituents, is given two lines. This is equivalent to assigning to successive elements a series of successive characteristic integers. On this principle the integer N for Al, the thirteenth element, has been taken to be 13, and the values of N then assumed by the other elements are given on the left-hand side of fig. 3. This proceeding is justified by the fact that it introduces perfect regularity into the X-ray spectra. Examination of fig. 3 shows that the values of $\nu^{\frac{1}{2}}$ for all the lines examined both in the K and the L series now fall on regular curves which approximate to straight lines. The same thing is shown more clearly by comparing the values of N in Table I with those of

$$Q_K = \sqrt{\frac{\nu}{\frac{3}{4}\nu_0}},$$

ν being the frequency of the α line and ν_0 the fundamental Rydberg frequency. It is here plain that $Q_K = N - 1$ very approximately, except for the radiations of very short wavelength which gradually diverge from this relation. Again, in Table II, a comparison of N with

$$Q_L = \sqrt{\frac{\nu}{\frac{5}{36}\nu_0}},$$

where ν is the frequency of the L α line, shows that

$$Q_L = N - 7{\cdot}4$$

approximately, although a systematic deviation clearly shows that the relation is not accurately linear in this case.

Now if either the elements were not characterized by these integers, or any mistake had been made in the order chosen or in the number of places left for unknown elements, these regularities would at once disappear. We can therefore conclude from the evidence of the X-ray spectra alone, without using any theory of atomic structure, that these integers are really characteristic of the elements. Further, as it is improbable

* Welsbach, *Monatsh.* xxxii. p. 373 (1911).

that two different stable elements should have the same integer, three, and only three, more elements are likely to exist between Al and Au. As the X-ray spectra of these elements can be confidently predicted, they should not be difficult to find. The examination of keltium * would be of exceptional interest, as no place has been assigned to this element.

Now Rutherford † has proved that the most important constituent of an atom is its central positively charged nucleus, and van den Broek ‡ has put forward the view that the charge carried by this nucleus is in all cases an integral multiple of the charge on the hydrogen nucleus. There is every reason to suppose that the integer which controls the X-ray spectrum is the same as the number of electrical units in the nucleus, and these experiments therefore give the strongest possible support to the hypothesis of van den Broek. Soddy § has pointed out that the chemical properties of the radio-elements are strong evidence that this hypothesis is true for the elements from thallium to uranium, so that its general validity would now seem to be established.

From the approximate linear relation between $\nu^{\frac{1}{2}}$ and N for each line we obtain the general equation

$$\nu = A\,(N - b)^2,$$

where A and b are constants characteristic of each line. For the K α line

$$A = \left(\frac{1}{1^2} - \frac{1}{2^2}\right)\nu_0 \quad \text{and} \quad b = 1.$$

For the L α line approximately

$$A = \left(\frac{1}{2^2} - \frac{1}{3^2}\right)\nu_0 \quad \text{and} \quad b = 7{\cdot}4.$$

* Urbain, *C.R.* clii. p. 141 (1911).

† Rutherford, Phil. Mag. xxi. p. 669 (1911), and xxvii. p. 488 (1914).

‡ Van den Broek, *Phys. Zeit.* xiv. p. 32 (1913), and 'Nature,' Nov. 27, Dec. 25, 1913, March 5, 1914.

§ Soddy, *Jahrbuch Rad. und. Elect.* x. p. 193 (1913); 'Nature,' Dec. 4, Dec. 18 (1913).

The fact that the numbers and arrangement of the lines in the K and the L spectra are quite different, strongly suggests that they come from distinct vibrating systems, while the fact that b is much larger for the L lines than for the K lines suggests that the L system is situated the further from the nucleus.

It was shown in Part I. * that the linear relation between $\nu^{\frac{1}{2}}$ and $N - b$ was most naturally explained if the vibrating system was a ring of electrons rotating round the central nucleus with an angular momentum which was the same for the different elements. This view has been analysed and put in a more generalised form in a letter to 'Nature' †, written in answer to criticisms made by Lindemann ‡.

Summary

1. Every element from aluminium to gold is characterized by an integer N which determines its X-ray spectrum. Every detail in the spectrum of an element can therefore be predicted from the spectra of its neighbours.
2. This integer N, the atomic number of the element, is identified with the number of positive units of electricity contained in the atomic nulceus.
3. The atomic numbers for all elements from Al to Au have been tabulated on the assumption that N for Al is 13.
4. The order of the atomic numbers is the same as that of the atomic weights, except where the latter disagrees with the order of the chemical properties.
5. Known elements correspond with all the numbers between 13 and 79 except three. There are here three possible elements still undiscovered.
6. The frequency of any line in the X-ray spectrum is approximately proportional to $A(N - b)^2$, where A and b are constants.

I wish to thank Prof. J. S. Townsend, F.R.S., for providing

* *Loc. cit.* p. 1032.

† Moseley, 'Nature,' Jan. 15 (1914).

‡ F. A. Lindemann, 'Nature' Jan 1, Feb. 5, 1914.

me with every facility for carrying on this work, which has been greatly assisted by a grant from the Institut International de Physique Solvay.

Electrical Laboratory,
Oxford.

On the Quantum Theory of Radiation and the Structure of the Atom.
By N. BOHR, *Dr. phil. Copenhagen*; *p.t. Reader in Mathematical Physics at the University of Manchester* *.

The *Philosophical Magazine*, Series VI, **30**, 394–415 (1915)

IN a series of papers in this periodical † the present writer has attempted to give the outlines of a theory of the constitution of atoms and molecules by help of a certain application of the Quantum theory of radiation to the theory of the nucleus atom. As the theory has been made a subject of criticism, and as experimental evidence of importance bearing on these questions has been obtained in the meantime, an attempt will be made in this paper to consider some points more closely.

§ 1. *General assumptions*

According to the theory proposed by Sir Ernest Rutherford, in order to account for the phenomena of scattering of α-rays, the atom consists of a central positively charged nucleus surrounded by a cluster of electrons. The nucleus is the seat of the essential part of the mass of the atom, and has linear dimensions exceedingly small compared with the distances apart of the electrons in the surrounding cluster. From the results of experiments on scattering of alpha rays, Rutherford concluded that the charge on the nucleus corresponds to a number of electrons per atom approximately equal to half the atomic weight. Concordant evidence from a large number of very different phenomena has led to the more definite assumption that the number of electrons per atom is exactly equal to the atomic number, *i. e.*, the number of the corresponding element in the periodic table. This view was first proposed by

* Communicated by Sir Ernest Rutherford, F.R.S.

† Phil. Mag. xxvi, pp. 1, 476, 857 (1913) and xxvii. p. 506 (1914). These papers will be referred to as I., II., III., & IV. respectively.

van den Broek *. While the nucleus theory has been of great utility in explaining many important properties of the atom †, on the other hand it is evident that it is impossible by its aid to explain many other fundamental properties if we base our considerations on the ordinary electrodynamical theory; but this can hardly be considered as a valid objection at the present time. It does not seem that there is any escape from the conclusion that it is impossible to account for the phenomena of temperature radiation on ordinary electrodynamics, and that the modification to be introduced in this theory must be essentially equivalent with the assumptions first used by Planck in the deduction of his radiation formula ‡. These assumptions are known as the Quantum theory. In my previous paper it was attempted to apply the main principles of this theory by introducing the following general assumptions:—

A. An atomic system possesses a number of states in which no emission of energy radiation takes place, even if the particles are in motion relative to each other, and such an emission is to be expected on ordinary electrodynamics. The states are denoted as the "stationary" states of the system under consideration.

B. Any emission or absorption of energy radiation will correspond to the transition between two stationary states. The radiation emitted during such a transition is homogeneous and the frequency ν is determined by the relation

$$h\nu = A_1 - A_2, \quad . \quad . \quad . \quad (1)$$

where h is Planck's constant and A_1 and A_2 are the energies of the system in the two stationary states.

C. That the dynamical equilibrium of the systems in the stationary states is governed by the ordinary laws of mechanics, while these laws do not hold for the transition from one state to another.

* van den Broek, *Phys. Zeit.* xiv. p. 32 (1913).

† See Rutherford, Phil. Mag. xxvii. p. 488 (1914).

‡ See J. H. Jeans, "Report on Radiation and the Quantum Theory," Phys. Soc. London, 1914.

D. That the various possible stationary states of a system consisting of an electron rotating round a positive nucleus are determined by the relation

$$T = \tfrac{1}{2}nh\omega, \quad . \quad . \quad . \quad (2)$$

where T is the mean value of the kinetic energy of the system, ω the frequency of rotation, and n a whole number.

It will be seen that these assumptions are closely analogous to those originally used by Planck about the emission of radiation in quanta, and about the relation between the frequency of an atomic resonator (of constant frequency) and its energy. It can be shown that, for any system containing one electron rotating in a closed orbit, the assumption C and the relation (2) will secure a connexion between the frequency calculated by (1) and that to be expected from ordinary electrodynamics, in the limit where the difference between the frequency of the rotation of the electron in successive stationary states is very small compared with the absolute value of the frequency (see IV. p. 310). On the nucleus theory this occurs in the region of very slow vibrations. If the orbit of the electron is circular, the assumption D is equivalent to the condition that the angular momentum of the system in the stationary states is an integral multiple of $h/2\pi$. The possible importance of the angular momentum in the discussion of atomic systems in relation to Planck's theory was first pointed out by J. W. Nicholson *.

In paper I. it was shown that the above assumptions lead to an interpretation of the Balmer formula for the hydrogen spectrum, and to a determination of the Rydberg constant which was in close agreement with the measurements. In these considerations it is not necessary to make any assumption about the degree of excentricity of the orbit of the electron, and we shall see in the next section that it cannot be assumed that the orbit is always circular.

So far we have considered systems which contain only one electron, but the general validity of the assumptions A and B

* Nicholson, Month. Not. Roy. Astr. Soc. lxxii, p. 679 (1912).

seems strongly supported by the fact that they offer a simple interpretation of the general principle of combination of spectral lines (see IV, p. 507). This principle was originally discovered by Ritz to hold for the ordinary series spectra of the elements. It has recently acquired increased interest by Fowler's work on the series spectra of enhanced lines emitted from many elements when subject to a powerful electric discharge. Fowler showed that the principle of combination holds for these spectra although the laws governing the numerical relation between the lines at an important point (see section 3) differed from those of the ordinary series spectra. There is also, as we shall see in section 4, some indication that the principle holds for the high frequency spectra revealed by interference in crystals. In this connexion it may also be remarked that the assumption A recently has obtained direct support by experiments of A. Einstein and J. W. de Haas *, who have succeeded in detecting and measuring a rotational mechanical effect produced when an iron bar is magnetized. Their results agree very closely with those to be expected on the assumption that the magnetism of iron is due to rotating electrons, and as pointed out by Einstein and Haas, these experiments therefore indicate very strongly that electrons can rotate in atoms without emission of energy radiation.

When we try to apply assumptions, analogous with C and D, to systems containing more than one electron, we meet with difficulties, since in this case the application of ordinary mechanics in general does not lead to periodic orbits. An exception to this, however, occurs if the electrons are arranged in rings and rotate in circular orbits, and from simple considerations of analogy the following assumption was proposed (see I. p. 24).

E. In any atomic or molecular system consisting of positive nuclei and electrons in which the nuclei are at rest

* Einstein and Haas, *Verh. d. D. Phys. Ges.* xvii. p. 152 (1915). That such a mechanical rotational effect was to be expected on the electron theory of magnetism was pointed out several years ago by O. W. Richardson, Phys. Review, xxvi. p. 248 (1908). Richardson tried to detect this effect but without decisive results.

relative to each other, and the electrons move in circular orbits, the angular momentum of each electron round the centre of its orbit will be equal to $h/2\pi$ in the "normal" state of the system, *i. e.* the state in which the total energy is a minimum.

It was shown that in a number of different cases this assumption led to results in approximate agreement with experimental facts. In general, no stable configuration in which the electrons rotate in circular orbits can exist if the problem of stability is discussed on ordinary mechanics. This is no objection, however, since it is assumed already that the mechanics do not hold for the transition between two stationary states. Simple considerations led to the following condition of stability.

F. A configuration satisfying the condition E is stable if the total energy of the system is less than in any neighbouring configuration satisfying the same condition of angular momentum of the electrons.

As already mentioned, the foundation for the hypothesis E was sought in analogy with the simple system consisting of one electron and one nucleus. Additional support, however, was obtained from a closer consideration of the formation of the systems. It was shown how simple processes could be imagined by which the confluence of different rings of electrons could be effected without any change in the angular momentum of the electrons, if the angular momentum of each electron before the process was the same. Such considerations led to a theory of formation of molecules.

It must be emphasized that only in the case of circular orbits has the angular momentum any connexion with the principles of the Quantum theory. If, therefore, the application of ordinary mechanics to the stationary states of the system does not lead to strictly circular orbits, the assumption E cannot be applied. This case occurs if we consider configurations in which the electrons are arranged in different rings which do not rotate with the same frequency. Such configurations, however, are apparently necessary in order to explain many characteristic properties of the atoms. In my previous papers an attempt was made in certain cases to overcome this difficulty by assuming, that if a very small alteration of the forces would make circular orbits possible on ordinary mechanics, the configuration and energy of the actual system would only differ very little from that calculated for the altered system. It will be seen that this assumption is most intimately connected with the hypothesis F on the stability of the configurations. Such considerations were used to explain the general appearance of the Rydberg constant in the spectra of the elements, and were also applied in discussing possible configurations of the electrons in the atoms suggested by the observed chemical properties. These calculations have been criticised by Nicholson *, who has attempted to show that the configurations chosen for the electrons in the atoms are inconsistent with the main principles of the theory, and has also attempted to prove the impossibility of accounting for other spectra by help of assumptions similar to those used in the interpretation of the hydrogen spectrum.

Although I am quite ready to admit that these points involve great and unsolved difficulties, I am unable to agree with Nicholson's conclusions. In the first place, his calculations rest upon a particular application to non-circular orbits of the principle of constancy of angular momentum for each electron, which it does not seem possible to justify either on the Quantum theory or on the ordinary mechanics, and which has no direct connexion with the assumptions used in my papers. It has not been proved that the configurations proposed are inconsistent with the assumption C. But even if it were possible to prove that the unrestricted use of ordinary mechanics to the stationary states is inconsistent with the configurations of the electrons, apparently necessary to explain the observed properties of the elements, this would not constitute a serious objection to the deductions in my papers. It must be remarked that all the applications of ordinary mechanics are essentially connected with the assumption of periodic orbits. As far as the applications are concerned, the first part of the assumption C might

* Nicholson, Phil. Mag. xxvii. p. 541 and xxviii. p. 90 (1914).

just as well have been given the following more cautious form:—

"The relation between the frequency and energy of the particles in the stationary states can be determined by means of the ordinary laws of mechanics if these laws lead to periodic orbits."

The possible necessity for an alteration of this kind in assumption C may perhaps not seem unlikely when it is remembered that the laws of mechanics are only known to hold for certain mean values of the motion of the electrons. In this connexion it should also be remarked that when considering periodic orbits only mean values are essential (comp. I. p. 7). The preliminary and tentative character of the formulation of the general assumptions cannot be too strongly emphasized, and admittedly they are made to suit certain simple applications. For example, it has been already shown in paper IV. that the assumption B needs modification in order to account for the effect of a magnetic field on spectral lines. In the following sections some of the recent experimental evidence on line spectra and characteristic Röntgen rays will be considered, and I shall endeavour to show that it seems to give strong support to the main principles of the theory.

2. *Spectra emitted from systems containing only one electron*

In the former papers it was shown that the general assumptions led to the following formula for the spectrum emitted by an electron rotating round a positive nucleus

$$\nu = N^2 \frac{2\pi^2 e^4 Mm}{h^3(M+m)} \left(\frac{1}{n_1^2} - \frac{1}{n_2^2}\right) \quad . \quad . \quad (3)$$

Ne, $-e$, M, m are the electric charges and the masses of the nucleus and the electron respectively. The frequency of rotation and the major axis of the relative orbit of the particles in the stationary states are given by

$$\omega_n = N^2 \frac{4\pi^2 e^4 Mm}{h^3(M+m)} \frac{1}{n^3}, \quad 2a_n = \frac{1}{N} \frac{h^2(M+m)}{2\pi^2 e^2 Mm} n^2 \quad . \quad (4)$$

The energy necessary to remove the electron to infinite distance from the nucleus is

$$W_n = N^2 \frac{2\pi^2 e^4 Mm}{h^2(M + m)} \frac{1}{n^2}. \quad . \quad . \quad (5)$$

This expression is also equal to the mean value of the kinetic energy of the system. Since $-W_n$ is equal to the total energy A_n of the system we get from (4) and (5)

$$\frac{dA_n}{dn} = h\omega_n. \quad . \quad . \quad . \quad (6)$$

If we compare (6) with the relation (1), we see that the connexion with ordinary mechanics in the region of slow vibration, mentioned in the former section, is satisfied.

Putting $N = 1$ in (3) we get the ordinary series spectrum of hydrogen. Putting $N = 2$ we get a spectrum which, on the theory, should be expected to be emitted by an electron rotating round a helium nucleus. The formula is found very closely to represent some series of lines observed by Fowler * and Evans †. These series correspond to $n_1 = 3$ and $n_1 = 4$ ‡. The theoretical value for the ratio between the second factor in (3) for this spectrum and for the hydrogen spectrum is 1·000409; the value calculated from Fowler's measurements is 1·000408 §. Some of the lines under consideration have been observed earlier in star spectra, and have been ascribed to hydrogen not only on account of the close numerical relation with the lines of the Balmer series, but also on account of the fact that the lines observed, together with the lines of the Balmer series, constitutes a spectrum which shows a marked analogy with the spectra of the alkali metals. This analogy, however, has been completely disturbed by Fowler's and Evans' observations, that the two new series contain twice as many lines as is

* Fowler, Month. Not. Roy. Astr. Soc. lxxiii. Dec. 1912.

† Evans, Nature, xcii. p. 5 (1913); Phil. Mag. xxix. p. 284 (1915).

‡ For $n_1 = 2$ we get a series in the extreme ultraviolet of which some lines have recently been observed by Lyman (Nature, xcv. p. 343, 1915).

§ See Nature, xcii. p. 231 (1913).

to be expected on this analogy. In addition, Evans has succeeded in obtaining the lines in such pure helium that no trace of the ordinary hydrogen lines could be observed *. The great difference between the conditions for the production of the Balmer series and the series under consideration is also brought out very strikingly by some recent experiments of Rau † on the minimum voltage necessary for the production of spectral lines. While about 13 volts was sufficient to excite the lines of the Balmer series, about 80 volts was found necessary to excite the other series. These values agree closely with the values calculated from the assumption E for the energies necessary to remove the electron from the hydrogen atom and to remove both electrons from the helium atom, viz. 13·6 and 81·3 volts repectively. It has recently been argued ‡ that the lines are not so sharp as should be expected from the atomic weight of helium on Lord Rayleigh's theory of the width of spectral lines. This might, however, be explained by the fact that the systems emitting the spectrum, in contrast to those emitting the hydrogen spectrum, are supposed to carry an excess positive charge, and therefore must be expected to acquire great velocities in the electric field in the discharge-tube.

In paper IV. an attempt was made on the basis of the present theory to explain the characteristic effect of an electric field on the hydrogen spectrum recently discovered by Stark. This author observed that if luminous hydrogen is placed in an intense electric field, each of the lines of the Balmer series is split up into a number of homogeneous components. These components are situated symmetrically with regard to the original lines, and their distance apart is proportional to the intensity of the external electric field. By spectroscopic observation in a direction perpendicular to the field, the components are linearly polarized, some parallel and some perpendicular to the field. Further experiments have shown that the phenomenon is even more complex than was at first expected. By

* See also Stark, *Verh. d. D. Phys. Ges.* xvi. p. 468 (1914).

† Rau, *Sitz. Ber. d. Phys. Med. Ges. Würzburg* (1914).

‡ Merton, Nature, xcv, p. 65 (1915); Proc. Roy. Soc. A. xci. p. 389 (1915).

applying greater dispersion, the number of components observed has been greatly increased, and the numbers as well as the intensities of the components are found to vary in a complex manner from line to line *. Although the present development of the theory does not allow us to account in detail for the observations, it seems that the considerations in paper IV. offer a simple interpretation of several characteristic features of the phenomenon.

The calculation can be made considerably simpler than in the former paper by an application of Hamilton's principle. Consider a particle moving in a closed orbit in a stationary field. Let ω be the frequency of revolution, T the mean value of the kinetic energy during the revolution, and W the mean value of the sum of the kinetic energy and the potential energy of the particle relative to the stationary field. We have then for a small arbitrary variation of the orbit

$$\delta W = -2\omega\delta\left(\frac{T}{\omega}\right) \quad . \quad . \quad . \quad (7)$$

This equation was used in paper IV. to prove the equivalence of the formulæ (2) and (6) for any system governed by ordinary mechanics. The equation (7) further shows that if the relations (2) and (6) hold for a system of orbits, they will hold also for any small variation of these orbits for which the value of W is unaltered. If a hydrogen atom in one of its stationary states is placed in an external electric field and the electron rotates in a closed orbit, we shall therefore expect that W is not altered by the introduction of the atom in the field, and that the only variation of the total energy of the system will be due to the variation of the mean value of the potential energy relative to the external field.

In the former paper it was pointed out that the orbit of the electron will be deformed by the external field. This deformation will in course of time be considerable even if the external electric force is very small compared with the force of attraction between the particles. The orbit of the electron may at any

*Stark, *Elektrische Spektralanalyse chemischer Atome*, Leipzig, 1914.

moment be considered as an ellipse with the nucleus in the focus, and the length of the major axis will approximately remain constant, but the effect of the field will consist in a gradual variation of the direction of the major axis as well as the excentricity of the orbit. A detailed investigation of the very complicated motion of the electron was not attempted, but it was simply pointed out that the problem allows of two stationary orbits of the electron, and that these may be taken as representing two possible stationary states. In these orbits the excentricity is equal to 1, and the major axis parallel to the external force; the orbits simply consisting of a straight line through the nucleus parallel to the axis of the field, one on each side of it. It can very simply be shown that the mean value of the potential energy relative to the field for these rectilinear orbits is equal to $\mp 3/2\, aeE$, where E is the external electric force and $2a$ the major axis of the orbit, and the two signs correspond to orbits in which the direction of the major axis from the nucleus is the same or opposite to that of the electric force respectively. Using the formulæ (4) and (5) and neglecting the mass of the electron compared with that of the nucleus, we get, therefore, for the energy of the system in the two states

$$A_n = -N^2 \frac{2\pi^2 e^4 m}{h^2} \frac{1}{n^2} \mp E \frac{3h^2}{8\pi^2 Nem} n^2 \quad . \quad (8)$$

respectively. This expression is the same as that deduced in paper IV. by an application of (6) to the expressions for the energy and frequency of the system. Applying the relation (1) and using the same arguments as in paper IV. p. 515, we are therefore led to expect that the hydrogen spectrum in an electric field will contain two components polarized parallel to the field and of a frequency given by

$$\nu = \frac{1}{h}(A_{n_2} - A_{n_1}) = N^2 \frac{2\pi^2 e^4 m}{h^3} \left(\frac{1}{n_1^2} - \frac{1}{n_2^2}\right)$$
$$\mp E \frac{3h}{8\pi^2 Nem}(n_2^2 - n_1^2). \quad . \quad (9)$$

The table below contains Stark's recent measurements of the frequency difference between the two strong outer components polarized parallel to the field for the five first lines in the Balmer series *. The first column gives the values for the numbers n_1 and n_2. The second and fourth columns give the frequency difference $\Delta\nu$ corresponding to a field of 28500 and 74000 volts per cm. respectively. The third and fifth columns give the values of

$$\alpha = \Delta\nu \frac{4\pi^2 em}{3Eh(n_2^2 - n_1^2)},$$

where α should be a constant for all the lines and equal to unity.

		28500 volts. per cm.		74000 volts. per cm.	
n_1	n_2	$\Delta\nu \,.\, 10^{-12}$	a	$\Delta\nu \,.\, 10^{-12}$	a
2	3	0·46	0·83	...	...
2	4	1·04	0·79	2·86	0·83
2	5	2·06	0·89	5·41	0·90
2	6	3·16	0·90	7·81	0·85
2	7	4·47	0·90	...	...

Considering the difficulties of accurate measurement of the quantities involved, it will be seen that the agreement with regard to the variation of the frequency differences from line to line is very good. The fact that all the observed values are a little smaller than the calculated may be due to a slight over-estimate of the intensity of the fields used in the experiments (see Stark, *loc. cit.* pp. 38 and 118). Besides the two strong outer components polarized parallel to the field, Stark's experiments have revealed a large number of inner weaker components polarized in the same way, and also a number of components polarized perpendicular to the field. This complexity of the phenomenon, however, cannot be considered as

* Stark, *loc. cit.* pp. 51, 54, 55, & 56.

inconsistent with the theory. The above simple calculations deal only with the two extreme cases, and we may expect to find a number of stationary states corresponding to orbits of smaller excentricity. In a discussion of such non-periodic orbits, however, the general principles applied are no longer sufficient guidance.

Apart from the agreement with the calculations, Stark's experiments seem to give strong support to the interpretation of the origin of the two outer components. It was found that the two outer components have not always equal intensities; when the spectrum is produced by positive rays, it was found that the component of highest frequency is the stronger if the rays travel against the electric field, while if it travels in the direction of the field the component of smallest frequency is the stronger (*loc. cit.* p. 40). This indicates that the components are produced independently of each other—a result to be expected if they correspond to quite different orbits of the electron. That the orbit of the electron in general need not be circular is also very strongly indicated by the observation that the hydrogen lines emitted from positive rays under certain conditions are partly polarized without the presence of a strong external field (*loc. cit.* p. 12). This polarization, as well as the observed intensity differences of the two components, would be explained if we can assume that for some reason, when the atom is in rapid motion, there is a greater probability for the orbit of the electron to lie behind the nucleus rather than in front of it.

§ 3. *Spectra emitted from systems containing more than one electron*

According to Rydberg and Ritz, the frequency of the lines in the ordinary spectrum of an element is given by

$$\nu = f_r(n_1) - f_s(n_2), \quad . \quad . \quad . \quad (11)$$

where n_1 and n_2 are whole numbers and $f_1, f_2, \ldots$ are a series of functions of n which can be expressed by

$$f_r(n) = \frac{K}{n^2}\phi_r(n), \quad . \quad . \quad . \quad (12)$$

where K is a universal constant and ϕ a function which for large values of n approaches unity. The complete spectrum is obtained by combining the numbers n_1 and n_2 as well as the functions $f_1, f_2 \ldots$ in every possible way.

On the present theory, this indicates that the system which emits the spectrum possesses a number of series of stationary states for which the energy in the nth state in the rth series is given by (see IV. p. 511)

$$A_{n,r} = C - \frac{hK}{n^2}\phi_r(n), \quad . \quad . \quad (13)$$

where C is an arbitrary constant, the same for the whole system of stationary states. The first factor in the second term is equal to the expression (5) if $N = 1$.

In the present state of the theory it is not possible to account in detail for the formula (13), but it was pointed out in my previous papers that a simple interpretation can be given of the fact that in every series $\phi(n)$ approaches unity for large values of n. It was assumed that in the stationary states corresponding to such values of n, one of the electrons in the atom moves at a distance from the nucleus large compared with the distance of the other electrons. If the atom is neutral, the outer electron will be subject to very nearly the same forces as the electron in the hydrogen atom, and the formula (13) indicates the presence of a number of series of stationary states of the atom in which the configuration of the inner electrons is very nearly the same for all states in one series, while the configuration of the outer electron changes from state to state in the series approximately in the same way as the electron in the hydrogen atom. From the considerations in the former sections it will therefore appear that the frequency calculated from the relations (1) and (13) for the radiation emitted during the transition between successive stationary states within each series will approach that to be expected on ordinary electrodynamics in the region of slow vibrations *.

From (13) it follows that for high values of n the configuration of the inner electrons possesses the same energy in all the series of stationary states corresponding to the same spectrum (11). The different series of stationary states must therefore correspond to different types of orbits of the outer electron, involving different relations between energy and frequency. In order to fix our ideas, let us for a moment consider the helium atom. This atom contains only two electrons, and in the previous papers it was assumed that in the normal state of the atom the electrons rotate in a circular ring round a nucleus. Now the helium spectrum contains two complete systems of series given by formulæ of the type (11) and the measurements of Rau mentioned below indicate that the configuration of the inner electron in the two corresponding systems of stationary states possesses the same energy. A simple assumption is therefore that in one of the two systems the orbit of the electron is circular and in the other very flat. For high values of n the inner electron in the two configurations will act on the outer electron very nearly as a ring of uniformly distributed charge with the nucleus in the centre or as a line charge extending from the nucleus, respectively. In both cases several different types of orbit for the outer electron present themselves, for instance, circular orbits perpendicular to the axis of the system or very flat orbits parallel to this axis. The different configurations of the inner electrons might be due to

* On this view we should expect the Rydberg constant in (13) to be not exactly the same for all elements, since the expression (5) depends to a certain extent on the mass of the nucleus. The correction is very small; the difference in passing from hydrogen to an element of high atomic weight being only 0·05 per cent. (see IV. p. 512). In a recent paper (Proc. Roy. Soc. A. xci. p. 255, 1915), Nicholson has concluded that this consequence of the theory is inconsistent with the measurements of the ordinary helium spectrum. It seems doubtful, however, if the measurements are accurate enough for such a conclusion. It must be remembered that it is only for high values of n that the theory indicates values of ϕ very nearly unity; but for such values of n, the terms in question are very small, and the relative accuracy in the experimental determination not very high. The only spectra for which a sufficiently accurate determination of K seems possible at present are the ordinary hydrogen spectrum and the helium spectrum considered in the former section, and in these cases the measurements agree very closely with calculation.

different ways of removing the electron from the neutral atom: thus, if it is removed by impact perpendicular to the plane of the ring, we might expect the orbit of the remaining electron to be circular, if it is removed by an impact in the plane of the ring we might expect the orbit to be flat. Such considerations may offer a simple explanation of the fact that in contrast with the helium spectrum the lithium spectrum contains only one system of series of the type (11). The neutral lithium atom contains three electrons, and according to the configuration proposed in paper II. the two electrons move in an inner ring and the other electron in an outer orbit; for such a configuration we should expect that the mode of removal of the outer electron would be of no influence on the configuration of the inner electrons. It is unnecessary to point out the hypothetical nature of these considerations, but the intention is only to show that it does not seem impossible to obtain simple interpretations of the spectra observed on the general principles of the theory. However, in a quantitative comparison with the measurements we meet with the difficulties mentioned in the first section of applying assumptions analogous with C and D to systems for which ordinary mechanics do not lead to periodic orbits.

The above interpretation of the formulæ (11) and (12) has recently obtained very strong support by Fowler's work on series of enhanced lines on spark spectra *. Fowler showed that the frequency of the lines in these spectra, as of the lines in the ordinary spectra, can be represented by the formula (11). The only difference is that the Rydberg constant K in (12) is replaced by a constant 4K. It will be seen that this is just what we should expect on the present theory if the spectra are emitted by atoms which have lost two electrons and are regaining one of them. In this case, the outer electron will rotate round a system of double charge, and we must assume that in the stationary states it will have configurations approximately the same as an electron rotating round a helium nucleus. This view seems in conformity with the general evidence as to the conditions of the excitation of the ordinary spectra and the

* Fowler, Phil. Trans. Roy. Soc. A. 214. p. 225 (1914).

spectra of enhanced lines. From Fowler's results, it will appear that the helium spectrum given by (3) for N = 2 has exactly the same relation to the spectra of enhanced lines of other elements as the hydrogen spectrum has to the ordinary spectra. It may be expected that it will be possible to observe spectra of a new class corresponding to a loss of 3 electrons from the atom, and in which the Rydberg constant K is replaced by 9K. No definite evidence, however, has so far been obtained of the existence of such spectra *.

Additional evidence of the essential validity of the interpretation of formula (13) seems also to be derived from the result of Stark's experiments on the effect of electric fields on spectral lines. For other spectra, this effect is even more complex than for the hydrogen spectrum, in some cases not only are a great number of components observed, but the components are generally not symmetrical with regard to the original line, and their distance apart varies from line to line in the same series in a far more irregular way than for the hydrogen lines †. Without attempting to account in detail for any of the electrical effects observed, we shall see that a simple interpretation can be given of the general way in which the magnitude of the effect varies from series to series.

In the theory of the electrical effect on the hydrogen spectrum given in the former section, it was supposed that this effect was due to an alteration of the energy of the systems in the external field, and that this alteration was intimately connected with a considerable deformation of the orbit of the electron. The possibility of this deformation is due to the fact that without the external field every elliptical orbit of the electron in the hydrogen atom is stationary. This condition will only be strictly satisfied if the forces which act upon the electron vary exactly as the inverse square of the distance from the nucleus but this will not be the case for the outer electron in an atom containing more than one electron. It was pointed out in paper IV. that the deviation of the function $\phi(n)$ from unity gives us

* Fowler, *loc. cit.* p. 262, see also II. p. 490.

† Stark, *loc. cit.* pp. 67–75.

an estimate for the deviation of the forces from the inverse square, and that on the theory we can only expect a Stark effect of the same order of magnitude as for the hydrogen lines for those series in which ϕ differs very little from unity.

This conclusion was consistent with Stark's original measurements of the electric effect on the different series in the helium spectrum, and it has since been found to be in complete agreement with the later measurements for a great number of other spectral series. An electric effect of the same order of magnitude as that for hydrogen lines has been observed only for the lines in the two diffuse series of the helium spectrum and the diffuse series of lithium. This corresponds to the observation that for these three series ϕ is very much nearer to unity than for any other series; even for $n = 5$ the deviation of ϕ from 1 is less than one part in a thousand. The distance between the outer components for all three series is smaller than that observed for the hydrogen line corresponding to the same value of n, but the ratio between this distance and that of the hydrogen lines approaches rapidly to unity as n increases. This is just what would be expected on the above considerations. The series for which the effect, although much smaller, comes next in magnitude to the three series mentioned, is the principal single line series in the helium spectrum. This corresponds to the fact that the deviation of ϕ from unity, although several times greater than for the three first series, is much smaller for this series than for any other of the series examined by Stark. For all the other series the effect was very small, and in most cases even difficult of detection.

Quite apart from the question of the detailed theoretical interpretation of the formula (13), it seems that it may be possible to test the validity of this formula by direct measurements of the minimum voltages necessary to produce spectral lines. Such measurements have recently been made by Rau * for the lines in the ordinary helium spectrum. This author found that the different lines within each series appeared for slightly different voltages, higher voltages being necessary to produce the lines corresponding to higher values of n, and he

* Rau, *loc. cit.*

pointed out that the differences between the voltages observed were of the magnitude to be expected from the differences in the energies of the different stationary states calculated by (13). In addition Rau found that the lines corresponding to high values of n appeared for very nearly the same voltages for all the different series in both helium spectra. The absolute values for the voltages could not be determined very accurately with the experimental arrangement, but apparently nearly 30 volts was necessary to produce the lines corresponding to high values of n. This agrees very closely with the value calculated on the present theory for the energy necessary to remove one electron from the helium atom, viz., 29·3 volts. On the other hand, the later value is considerably larger than the ionization potential in helium (20·5 volts) measured directly by Franck and Hertz *. This apparent disagreement, however, may possibly be explained by the assumption, that the ionization potential measured does not correspond to the removal of the electron from the atom but only to a transition from the normal state of the atom to some other stationary state where the one electron rotates outside the other, and that the ionization observed is produced by the radiation emitted when the electron falls back to its original position. This radiation would be of a sufficiently high frequency to ionize any impurity which may be present in the helium gas, and also to liberate electrons from the metal part of the apparatus. The frequency of the radiation would be $20{\cdot}5/300 \frac{e}{h} = 5{\cdot}0.10^{15}$, which is of the same order of magnitude as the characteristic frequency calculated from experiments on dispersion in helium, viz., $5{\cdot}9.10^{15}$ †.

Similar considerations may possibly apply also to the recent remarkable experiments of Franck and Hertz on ionization in mercury vapour ‡. These experiments show strikingly that an electron does not lose energy by collision with a mercury atom

* Franck & Hertz, *Verh. d. D. Phys. Ges.* xv. p. 34 (1913).

† Cuthbertson, Proc. Roy. Soc. A. lxxxiv. p. 13 (1910).

‡ Franck and Hertz, *Verh. d. D. Phys. Ges.* xvi. pp. 457, 512 (1914).

if its energy is smaller than a certain value corresponding to 4·9 volts, but as soon as the energy is equal to this value the electron has a great probability of losing all its energy by impact with the atom. It was further shown that the atom, as the result of such an impact, emits a radiation consisting only of the ultraviolet mercury line of wave-length 2536, and it was pointed out that if the frequency of this line is multiplied by Planck's constant, we obtain a value which, within the limit of experimental error, is equal to the energy acquired by an electron by a fall through a potential difference of 4·9 volts. Franck and Hertz assume that 4·9 volts corresponds to the energy necessary to remove an electron from the mercury atom, but it seems that their experiments may possibly be consistent with the assumption that this voltage corresponds only to the transition from the normal state to some other stationary state of the neutral atom. On the present theory we should expect that the value for the energy necessary to remove an electron from the mercury atom could be calculated from the limit of the single line series of Paschen, 1850, 1403, 1269 *. For since mercury vapour absorbs light of wavelength 1850 †, the lines of this series as well as the line 2536 must correspond to a transition from the normal state of the atom to other stationary states of the neutral atom (see I. p. 16). Such a calculation gives 10·5 volts for the ionization potential instead of 4·9 volts ‡. If the above considerations are correct it will be seen that Frank and Hertz's measurements give very strong support to the theory considered in this paper. If, on the other hand, the ionization potential of mercury should prove to be as low as assumed by Franck and Hertz, it would constitute a serious difficulty for the above interpretation of the Rydberg constant, at any rate for the mercury spectrum, since this

* Paschen, *Ann. d. Phys.* xxxv. p. 860 (1911).

† Stark, *Ann. d. Phys.* xlii. p. 239 (1913).

‡ This value is of the same order of magnitude as the value 12·5 volts recently found by McLennan and Henderson (Proc. Roy. Soc. A. xci. p. 485, 1915) to be the minimum voltage necessary to produce the usual mercury spectrum. The interesting observations of single-lined spectra of zinc and cadmium given in their paper are analogous to Franck and Hertz's results for mercury, and similar considerations may therefore possibly also hold for them.

spectrum contains lines of greater frequency than the line 2536.

It will be remarked that it is assumed that all the spectra considered in this section are essentially connected with the displacement of a single electron. This assumption—which is in contrast to the assumptions used by Nicholson in his criticism of the present theory—does not only seem supported by the measurements of the energy necessary to produce the spectra, but it is also strongly advocated by general reasons if we base our considerations on the assumption of stationary states. Thus it may happen that the atom loses several electrons by a violent impact, but the probability that the electrons will be removed to exactly the same distance from the nucleus or will fall back into the atom again at exactly the same time would appear to be very small. For molecules, *i. e.* systems containing more than one nucleus, we have further to take into consideration that if the greater part of the electrons are removed there is nothing to keep the nuclei together, and that we must assume that the molecules in such cases will split up into single atoms (comp. III. p. 858).

§ 4. *The high frequency spectra of the elements*

In paper II. it was shown that the assumption E led to an estimate of the energy necessary to remove an electron from the innermost ring of an atom which was in approximate agreement with Whiddington's measurements of the minimum kinetic energy of cathode rays required to produce the characteristic Röntgen radiation of the K type. The value calculated for this energy was equal to the expression (5) if $n = 1$. In the calculation the repulsion from the other electrons in the ring was neglected. This must result in making the value a little too large, but on account of the complexity of the problem no attempt at that time was made to obtain a more exact determination of the energy.

These considerations have obtained strong support through Moseley's important researches on the high frequency spectra of the elements *. Moseley found that the frequency of the strongest lines in these spectra varied in a remarkably simple

* Moseley, Phil. Mag. xxvi. p. 1024 (1913); and xxvii. p. 703 (1914).

way with the atomic number of the corresponding element. For the strongest line in the K radiation he found that the frequency for a great number of elements was represented with considerable accuracy by the empirical formula

$$\nu = \tfrac{3}{4}(N - 1)^2 K, \quad . \quad . \quad . \quad (14)$$

where K is the Rydberg constant in the hydrogen spectrum. It will be seen that this result is in approximate agreement with the calculation mentioned above if we assume that the radiation is emitted as a quantum $h\nu$.

Moseley pointed out the analogy between the formula (14) and the formula (3) in section 2, and remarked that the constant 3/4 was equal to the last factor in this formula, if we put $n_1 = 1$ and $n_2 = 2$. He therefore proposed the explanation of the formula (14), that the line was emitted during a transition of the innermost ring between two states in which the angular momentum of each electron was equal to $2\frac{h}{2\pi}$ and $\frac{h}{2\pi}$ respectively. From the replacement of N^2 by $(N - 1)^2$ he deduced that the number of electrons in the ring was equal to 4. This view, however, can hardly be maintained. The approximate agreement mentioned above with Whiddington's measurements for the energy necessary to produce the characteristic radiation indicates very strongly that the spectrum is due to a displacement of a single electron, and not to a whole ring. In the latter case the energy should be several times larger. It is also pointed out by Nicholson * that Moseley's explanation would imply the emission of several quanta at the same time; but this assumption is apparently not necessitated for the explanation of other phenomena. At present it seems impossible to obtain a detailed interpretation of Moseley's results, but much light seems to be thrown on the whole problem by some recent interesting considerations by W. Kossel †.

Kossel takes the view of the nucleus atom and assumes that

* Nicholson, Phil. Mag. xxvii. p. 562 (1914).

† Kossel, *Verh. d. Deutsch. Phys. Ges.* xvi. p. 953 (1914).

the electrons are arranged in rings, the one outside the other. As in the present theory, it is assumed that any radiation emitted from the atom is due to a transition of the system between two steady states, and that the frequency of the radiation is determined by the relation (1). He considers now the radiation which results from the removal of an electron from one of the rings, assuming that the radiation is emitted when the atom settles down in its original state. The latter process may take place in different ways. The vacant place in the ring may be taken by an electron coming directly from outside the whole system, but it may also be taken by an electron jumping from one of the outer rings. In the latter case a vacant place will be left in that ring to be replaced in turn by another electron, etc. For the sake of brevity, we shall refer to the innermost ring as ring 1, the next one as ring 2, and so on. Kossel now assumes that the K radiation results from the removal of an electron from ring 1, and makes the interesting suggestion that the line denoted by Moseley as K_α corresponds to the radiation emitted when an electron jumps from ring 2 to ring 1, and that the line K_β corresponds to a jump from ring 3 to ring 1. On this view, we should expect that the K radiation consists of as many lines as there are rings in the atom, the lines forming a series of rapidly increasing intensities. For the L radiation, Kossel makes assumptions analogous to those for the K radiation, with the distinction that the radiation is ascribed to the removal of an electron from ring 2 instead of ring 1. A possible M radiation is ascribed to ring 3, and so on. The interest of these considerations is that they lead to the prediction of some simple relations between the frequencies ν of the different lines. Thus it follows as an immediate consequence of the assumption used that we must have

$$\nu_{K_\beta} - \nu_{K_\alpha} = \nu_{L_\alpha}$$

$$\nu_{K_\gamma} - \nu_{K_\beta} = \nu_{L_\beta} - \nu_{L_\alpha} = \nu_{M_\alpha}.$$

It will be seen that these relations correspond exactly to the ordinary principle of combination of spectral lines. By using Moseley's measurements for K_α and K_β and extrapolating for the values of L_α by the help of Moseley's empirical formula, Kossel showed that the first relation was closely satisfied for the elements from calcium to zinc. Recently T. Malmer * has measured the wave-length of K_α and K_β for a number of elements of higher atomic weight, and it is therefore possible to test the relation over a wider range and without extrapolation. The table gives Malmer's values for $\nu_{K_\beta} - \nu_{K_\alpha}$ and Moseley's values for ν_{L_α}, all values being multiplied by 10^{17}.

N	40	42	44	46	47	50	51	57
$\nu_{K_\beta} - \nu_{K_\alpha}$	4·6	5·5	6·1	6·6	6·9	8·4	9·0	11·6
ν_{L_α}	4·93	5·53	6·17	6·84	7·19	8·29	8·67	11·21

It is seen that the agreement is close, and probably within the limits of experimental error. A comparison with the second relation is not possible at present, and we meet also here with a difficulty arising from the fact that Moseley observed a greater number of lines in the L radiation than should be expected on Kossel's simple scheme †.

There is another point in connexion with the above considerations which appears to be of interest. In a recent paper W. H. Bragg ‡ has shown that, in order to excite any line of the K radiation of an element, the frequency of the exciting radiation must be greater than the frequency of all the lines in the K radiation. This result, which is in striking contrast to the ordinary phenomena of selective absorption, can be simply explained on Kossel's view. The simple reverse of the process corresponding to the emission of, for instance, K_α would necessitate the direct transfer of an electron from ring 1 to ring 2, but this will obviously not be possible unless at the beginning of the process there was a vacant place in the latter ring. For the excitation of any line in the K radiation, it is therefore necessary that the electron should be completely removed from the atom. Another consequence of Kossel's

* Malmer, Phil. Mag. xxviii. p. 787 (1914).

† See Kossel, *loc. cit.* p. 960.

‡ Bragg, Phil. Mag. xxix. p. 407 (1915).

view is that it should be impossible to obtain the K series of an element without the simultaneous emission of the L series. This seems to be in agreement with some recent experiments of C. G. Barkla * on the energy involved in the production of characteristic Röntgen radiation. From these examples it will be seen that even if Kossel's considerations will need modification in order to account in detail for the high frequency spectra, they seem to offer a basis for a further development.

As in the former section, it is assumed that the spectra considered above are due to the displacement of a single electron. If, however, several electrons should happen to be removed from one of the rings by a violent impact, the considerations at the end of the former section would not apply, since the electrons removed in this case can be replaced by electrons in the other rings. We might therefore possibly expect that the rearrangement of the electrons, consequent to the removal of more than one electron from a ring, would give rise to spectra of still higher frequency than those considered in this section.

University of Manchester,
August 1915.

* Barkla, Nature, XCV. p. 7 (1915). In this note Barkla proposes an explanation of his experimental results which in some points has great similarity to Kossel's theory.

Collision of α Particles with Light Atoms. IV. *An Anomalous Effect in Nitrogen. By* Professor Sir E. RUTHERFORD, *F.R.S.* *

The *Philosophical Magazine*, Series VI, 37, 581–587 (1919)

IT has been shown in paper I. that a metal source, coated with a deposit of radium C, always gives rise to a number of scintillations on a zinc sulphide screen far beyond the range of the α particles. The swift atoms causing these scintillations carry a positive charge and are deflected by a magnetic field, and have about the same range and energy as the swift H atoms produced by the passage of α particles through hydrogen. These "natural" scintillations are believed to be due mainly to swift H atoms from the radioactive source, but it is difficult to decide whether they are expelled from the radioactive source itself or are due to the action of α particles on occluded hydrogen.

The apparatus employed to study these "natural" scintillations is the same as that described in paper I. The intense source of radium C was placed inside a metal box about 3 cm. from the end, and an opening in the end of the box was covered with a silver plate of stopping power equal to about 6 cm. of air. The zinc sulphide screen was mounted outside, about 1 mm. distant from the silver plate, to admit of the introduction of absorbing foils between them. The whole apparatus was placed in a strong magnetic field to deflect the β rays. The variation in the number of these "natural" scintillations with absorption in terms of cms. of air is shown in fig. 1, curve A. In this case, the air in the box was exhausted and absorbing foils of aluminium were used. When dried oxygen or carbon dioxide was admitted into the vessel, the number of scintillations diminished to about the amount to be expected from the stopping power of the column of gas.

* Communicated by the Author.

A surprising effect was noticed, however, when dried air was introduced. Instead of diminishing, the number of scintillations was increased, and for an absorption corresponding to about 19 cm. of air the number was about twice that observed when the air was exhausted. It was clear from this experiment that the α particles in their passage through air gave rise to long-range scintillations which appeared to the eye

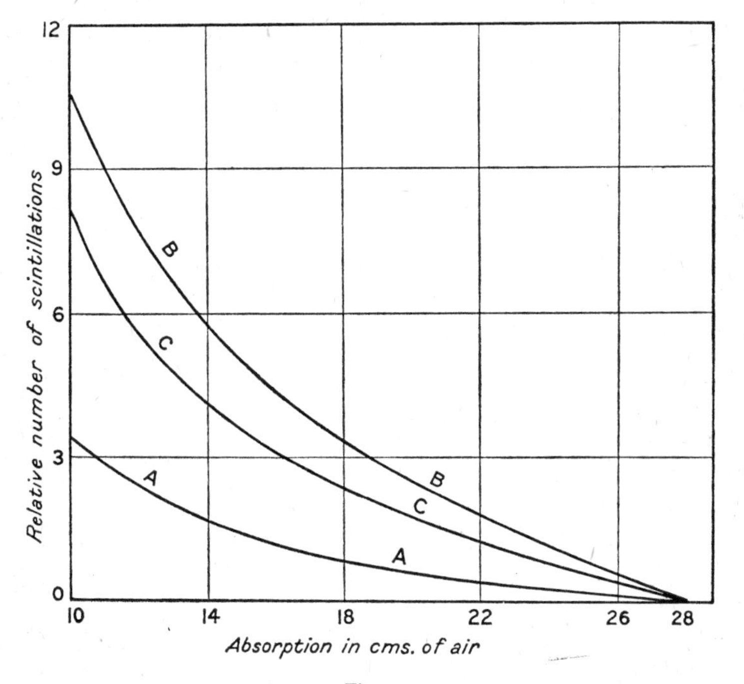

Fig. 1

to be about equal in brightness to H scintillations. A systematic series of observations was undertaken to account for the origin of these scintillations. In the first place we have seen that the passage of α particles through nitrogen and oxygen gives rise to numerous bright scintillations which have a range of about 9 cm. in air. These scintillations have about the range to be expected if they are due to swift N or O atoms, carrying unit charge, produced by collision with α particles. All experiments have consequently been made with an absorption greater than 9 cm. of air, so that these atoms are completely stopped before reaching the zinc sulphide screen.

It was found that these long-range scintillations could not be due to the presence of water vapour in the air; for the number was only slightly reduced by thoroughly drying the air. This is to be expected, since on the average the number of the additional scintillations due to air was equivalent to the number of H atoms produced by the mixture of hydrogen at 6 cm. pressure with oxygen. Since on the average the vapour pressure of water in air was not more than 1 cm., the effects of complete drying would not reduce the number by more than one sixth. Even when oxygen and carbon dioxide saturated with water vapour at 20° C. were introduced in place of dry air, the number of scintillations was much less than with dry air.

It is well known that the amount of hydrogen or gases containing hydrogen is normally very small in atmospheric air. No difference was observed whether air was taken directly from the room or from outside the laboratory or was stored for some days over water.

There was the possibility that the effect in air might be due to liberation of H atoms from the dust nuclei in the air. No appreciable difference, however, was observed when the dried air was filtered through long plugs of cotton-wool, or by storage over water for some days to remove dust nuclei.

Since the anomalous effect was observed in air, but not in oxygen, or carbon dioxide, it must be due either to nitrogen or to one of the other gases present in atmospheric air. The latter possibility was excluded by comparing the effects produced in air and in chemically prepared nitrogen. The nitrogen was obtained by the well-known method of adding ammonium chloride to sodium nitrite, and stored over water. It was carefully dried before admission to the apparatus. With pure nitrogen, the number of long-range scintillations under similar conditions was greater than in air. As a result of careful experiments, the ratio was found to be 1·25, the value to be expected if the scintillations are due to nitrogen.

The results so far obtained show that the long-range scintillations obtained from air must be ascribed to nitrogen, but it is important, in addition, to show that they are due to collision of α particles with atoms of nitrogen through the volume of the gas. In the first place, it was found that the number of the scintillations varied with the pressure of the air in the way to be expected if they resulted from collision of α particles along the column of gas. In addition, when an absorbing screen of gold or aluminium was placed close to the source, the range of the scintillations was found to be reduced by the amount to be expected if the range of the expelled atom was proportional to the range of the colliding α particles. These results show that the scintillations arise from the volume of the gas and are not due to some surface effect in the radioactive source.

In fig. 1 curve A the results of a typical experiment are given showing the variation in the number of natural scintillations with the amount of absorbing matter in their path measured in terms of centimetres of air for α particles. In these experiments carbon dioxide was introduced at a pressure calculated to give the same absorption of the α rays as ordinary air. In curve B the corresponding curve is given when air at N.T.P. is introduced in place of carbon dioxide. The difference curve C shows the corresponding variation of the number of scintillations arising from the nitrogen in the air. It was generally observed that the ratio of the nitrogen effect to the natural effect was somewhat greater for 19 cm. than for 12 cm. absorption.

In order to estimate the magnitude of the effect, the space between the source and screen was filled with carbon dioxide at diminished pressure and a known pressure of hydrogen was added. The pressure of the carbon dioxide and of hydrogen were adjusted so that the total absorption of α particles in the mixed gas should be equal to that of the air. In this way it was found that the curve of absorption of H atoms produced under these conditions was somewhat steeper than curve C of fig. 1. As a consequence, the amount of hydrogen mixed with carbon dioxide required to produce a number of scintillations equal to that of air, increased with the increase of absorption. For example, the effect in air was equal to about 4 cm. of hydrogen at 12 cm. absorption, and about 8 cm. at 19 cm. absorption. For a mean value of the absorption, the effect was equal to about 6 cm. of hydrogen. This increased absorption of H atoms under similar conditions indicated either that (1) the swift atoms from air had a somewhat greater range than the H atoms, or (2) that the atoms from air were projected more in the line of flight of the α particles.

While the maximum range of the scintillations from air using radium C as a source of α rays appeared to be about the same, viz. 28 cm., as for H atoms produced from hydrogen, it was difficult to fix the end of the range with certainty on account of the smallness of the number and the weakness of the scintillations. Some special experiments were made to test whether, under favourable conditions, any scintillations due to nitrogen could be observed beyond 28 cm. of air absorption. For this purpose a strong source (about 60 mg. Ra activity) was brought within 2·5 cm. of the zinc sulphide screen, the space between containing dry air. On still further reducing the distance, the screen became too bright to detect very feeble scintillations. No certain evidence of scintillations was found beyond a range of 28 cm. It would therefore appear that (2) above is the more probable explanation.

In a previous paper (III.) we have seen that the number of swift atoms of nitrogen or oxygen produced per unit path by collision with α particles is about the same as the corresponding number of H atoms in hydrogen. Since the number of long-range scintillations in air is equivalent to that produced under similar conditions in a column of hydrogen at 6 cm. pressure, we may consequently conclude that only one long-range atom is produced for every 12 close collisions giving rise to a swift nitrogen atom of maximum range 9 cm.

It is of interest to give data showing the number of long-range scintillations produced in nitrogen at atmospheric pressure under definite conditions. For a column of nitrogen 3·3 cm. long, and for a total absorption of 19 cm. of air from the source, the number due to nitrogen per milligram of activity is ·6 per minute on a screen of 3·14 sq. mm. area.

Both as regards range and brightness of scintillations, the

long-range atoms from nitrogen closely resemble H atoms, and in all probability are hydrogen atoms. In order, however, to settle this important point definitely, it is necessary to determine the deflexion of these atoms in a magnetic field. Some preliminary experiments have been made by a method similar to that employed in measuring the velocity of the H atom (see paper II.). The main difficulty is to obtain a sufficiently large deflexion of the stream of atoms and yet have a sufficient number of scintillations per minute for counting. The α rays from a strong source passed through dry air between two parallel horizontal plates 3 cm. long and 1·6 mm. apart, and the number of scintillations on the screen placed near the end of the plates was observed for different strengths of the magnetic field. Under these conditions, when the scintillations arise from the whole length of the column of air between the plates, the strongest magnetic field available reduced the number of scintillations by only 30 per cent. When the air was replaced by a mixture of carbon dioxide and hydrogen of the same stopping power for α rays, about an equal reduction was noted. As far as the experiment goes, this is an indication that the scintillations are due to H atoms; but the actual number of scintillations and the amount of reduction was too small to place much reliance on the result. In order to settle this question definitely, it will probably prove necessary to employ a solid nitrogen compound, free from hydrogen, as a source, and to use much stronger sources of α rays. In such experiments, it will be of importance to discriminate between the deflexions due to H atoms and possible atoms of atomic weight 2. From the calculations given in paper III., it is seen that a collision of an α particle with a free atom of mass 2 should give rise to an atom of range about 32 cm. in air, and of initial energy about ·89 of that of the H atom produced under similar conditions. The deflexion of the pencil of these rays in a magnetic field should be about ·6 of that shown by a corresponding pencil of H atoms.

Discussion of results

From the results so far obtained it is difficult to avoid the conclusion that the long-range atoms arising from collision of α particles with nitrogen are not nitrogen atoms but probably atoms of hydrogen, or atoms of mass 2. If this be the case, we must conclude that the nitrogen atom is disintegrated under the intense forces developed in a close collision with a swift α particle, and that the hydrogen atom which is liberated formed a constituent part of the nitrogen nucleus. We have drawn attention in paper III. to the rather surprising observation that the range of the nitrogen atoms in air is about the same as the oxygen atoms, although we should expect a difference of about 19 per cent. If in collisions which give rise to swift nitrogen atoms, the hydrogen is at the same time disrupted, such a difference might be accounted for, for the energy is then shared between two systems.

It is of interest to note, that while the majority of the light atoms, as is well known, have atomic weights represented by $4n$ or $4n + 3$ where n is a whole number, nitrogen is the only atom which is expressed by $4n + 2$. We should anticipate from radioactive data that the nitrogen nucleus consists of three helium nuclei each of atomic mass 4 and either two hydrogen nuclei or one of mass 2. If the H nuclei were outriders of the main system of mass 12, the number of close collisions with the bound H nuclei would be less than if the latter were free, for the α particle in a collision comes under the combined field of the H nucleus and of the central mass. Under such conditions, it is to be expected that the α particle would only occasionally approach close enough to the H nucleus to give it the maximum velocity, although in many cases it may give it sufficient energy to break its bond with the central mass. Such a point of view would explain why the number of swift H atoms from nitrogen is less than the corresponding number in free hydrogen and less also than the number of swift nitrogen atoms. The general results indicate that the H nuclei, which are released, are distant about twice the diameter of the electron (7×10^{-13} cm.) from the centre of the main atom. Without a knowledge of the laws of force at such small distances, it is difficult to estimate the energy required to free the H nucleus or to calculate the maximum velocity that can be given to the escaping H atom. It is not to be expected, *a priori*, that the velocity or range of the H atom released from the nitrogen atom should be identical with that due to a collision in free hydrogen.

Taking into account the great energy of motion of the α particle expelled from radium C, the close collision of such an α particle with a light atom seems to be the most likely agency to promote the disruption of the latter: for the forces on the nuclei arising from such collisions appear to be greater than can be produced by any other agency at present available. Considering the enormous intensity of the forces brought into play, it is not so much a matter of surprise that the nitrogen atom should suffer disintegration as that the α particle itself escapes disruption into its constituents. The results as a whole suggest that, if α particles—or similar projectiles—of still greater energy were available for experiment, we might expect to break down the nucleus structure of many of the lighter atoms.

I desire to express my thanks to Mr. William Kay for his invaluable assistance in counting scintillations.

University of Manchester,
April 1919.

Bibliography

THE PUBLICATIONS OF THE LATE LORD RUTHERFORD

1894

Magnetization of iron by high-frequency discharges. *Trans. N.Z. Inst.*, **27.** 481–513.

1895

Magnetic viscosity. *Trans. N.Z. Inst.*, **28.** 182–204.

1896

A magnetic detector of electrical waves and some of its applications. *Roy. Soc. Phil. Trans.*, **189.** 1–24.

A magnetic detector of electrical waves and some of its applications. Abstract. *Proc. Roy. Soc.*, **60.** 361. 184–186.

A magnetic detector of electrical waves. Abstract. *British Assn. for Adv. of Science, Report*, 724.

On the passage of electricity through gases exposed to Röntgen rays. (J. J. Thomson). *Phil. Mag.*, V. **42.** 392–407.

1897

On the electrification of gases exposed to Röntgen rays, and the absorption of Röntgen radiation by gases and vapours. *Phil. Mag.*, V. **43.** 241–255.

The velocity and rate of recombination of the ions of gases exposed to Röntgen radiation. *Phil. Mag.*, V. **44.** 422–440.

1898

The discharge of electrification by ultra-violet light. *Camb. Phil. Soc., Proc.*, **9.** 401–416.

1899

Uranium radiation and the electrical conduction produced by it. *Phil. Mag.*, V. **47.** 109–163.

Thorium and uranium radiation. (R. B. Owens). *Roy. Soc. of Canada, Trans.*, **2.** 5. 9–12.

1900

A radioactive substance emitted from thorium compounds. *Phil. Mag.*, V. **49.** 1–14.

Radioactivity produced in substances by the action of thorium compounds. *Phil. Mag.*, V. **49.** 161–192.

Über eine von Thoriumverbindungen emittierte radioaktive Substanz. *Phys. Zeit.*, **1.** 32. 347–348.

Energy of Röntgen and Becquerel rays and the energy required to produce an ion in gases. Abstract. (R. K. McClung), *Proc. Roy. Soc.*, **67.** 438. 245–250.

Über der Energie der Becquerel- und Röntgen-Strahlen und über die zur Erzeugung von Ionen in Gasen nötige Energie. *Phys. Zeit.*, **2.** 4. 53–55.

1901

Energy of Röntgen and Becquerel rays, and the energy required to produce an ion in gases. (R. K. McClung). *Roy. Soc., Phil. Trans.*, **196.** 25–59.

Einfluss der Temperatur auf die "Emanation" radioaktiver Substanzen. *Phys. Zeit.*, **2.** 29. 429–431.

The new gases from radium. (H. T. Brooks). *Roy. Soc. of Canada, Trans.*, **2.** 7. 21–25.

Discharge of electricity from glowing platinum. *Roy. Soc. of Canada Trans.*, **2.** 7. 27–33.

Emanations from radioactive substances. *Nature*, **64.** 157–158.

Dependence of the current through conducting gases on the direction of the electric field. *Phil. Mag.*, VI. **2.** 210–228.

Discharge of electricity from glowing platinum, and velocity of the ions. *Phys. Rev.*, **13.** 321–344.

Transmission of excited radioactivity. Abstract. *Amer. Phys. Soc., Bull.*, **2.** 37–43.

1902

Übertragung erregter Radioaktivität. *Phys. Zeit.*, **3.** 10. 210–214.

Erregte Radioaktivität und in der Atmosphäre hervorgerufene Ionisation. (S. J. Allen). *Phys. Zeit.*, **3.** 11. 225–230.

Versuche über erregte Radioaktivität. *Phys. Zeit.*, **3.** 12. 254–257.

The new gas from radium. (H. T. Brooks). *Chem. News*, **85.** 196–197.

The radioactivity of thorium compounds. I. An investigation of the radioactive emanation. (F. Soddy). *Chem. Soc. Journ.*, **81.** 321–350.

The existence of bodies smaller than atoms. Abstract. *Roy. Soc. of Canada, Trans.*, **2.** 8. 79–86.

Magnetische Ablenkbarkeit der Strahlen von radioaktiven Substanzen. (S. G. Grier). *Phys. Zeit.*, **3.** 17. 385–390.

Penetrating rays from radioactive substances. *Nature*, **66.** 318–319.

Comparison of the radiations from radioactive substances. (H. T. Brooks). *Phil. Mag.*, VI. **4.** 1–23.

The radioactivity of thorium compounds. II. The cause and nature of radioactivity. (F. Soddy). *Chem. Soc. Journ.*, **81.** 837–860.

Sehr durchdringende Strahlen von radioaktiven Substanzen. *Phys. Zeit.*, **3.** 22. 517–520.

Deviable rays of radioactive substances. (A. G. Grier). *Phil. Mag.*, VI. **4.** 315–330.

The cause and nature of radioactivity. Part I. (F. Soddy). *Phil. Mag.*, VI. **4.** 370–396.

The cause and nature of radioactivity. Part II. (F. Soddy). *Phil. Mag.*, VI. **4.** 569–585.

Excited radioactivity and ionization of the atmosphere. (S. J. Allen). *Phil. Mag.*, VI. **4.** 704–723.

On the condensation points of the thorium and radium emanations. (F. Soddy). *Chem. Soc. Proc.*, 219.

The radioactivity of thorium compounds. I. An investigation of the radioactive emanation. (F. Soddy). *Chem. News*, **85.** 271–272, 282–285, 293–295 and 304–308.

The cause and nature of radioactivity. Parts I and II. (F. Soddy). *Zeits. Phys. Chem.*, **42.** 81–109 and 174–192.

1903

Excited radioactivity and the method of its transmission. *Phil. Mag.*, VI. **5.** 95–117.

Die magnetische und elektrische Ablenkung der leicht absorbierbaren Radiumstrahlen. *Phys. Zeit.*, **4.** 8. 235–240.
The magnetic and electric deviation of the easily absorbed rays from radium. *Phil. Mag.*, VI. **5.** 177–187.
Penetrating radiation from the earth's surface. Abstract. (H. L. Cooke). *Phys. Rev.*, **16.** 183.
Radioactivity of ordinary materials. *Nature*, **67.** 511–512.
The radioactivity of uranium. (F. Soddy). *Phil. Mag.*, VI. **5.** 441–445.
A comparative study of the radioactivity of radium and thorium. (F. Soddy). *Phil. Mag.*, VI. **5.** 445–457.
Some remarks on radioactivity. *Phil. Mag.*, VI. **5.** 481–485.
Condensation of the radioactive emanations. (F. Soddy). *Phil. Mag.*, VI. **5.** 561–576.
Radioactive change. (F. Soddy). *Phil. Mag.*, VI. **5.** 576–591.
The amount of emanation and helium from radium. *Nature*, **68.** 366–367.
Heating effect of the radium emanation. (H. T. Barnes). *Nature*, **68.** 622.
Heating effect of the radium emanation. (H. T. Barnes). *Nature*, **69.** 126.
Radioactive processes. *Phys. Soc., Proc.*, **18.** 595–597 and 598–600.

1904

Radioactivity of radium and its concentration. *Nature*, **69.** 222.
Heating effect of the radium emanation. (H. T. Barnes). *Phil. Mag.*, VI. **7.** 202–219.
Nature of the gamma rays from radium. *Nature*, **69.** 436–437.
The succession of changes in radioactive bodies. Abstract. *Proc. Roy. Soc.*, **73.** 495. 493–496.
Slow transformation products of radium. *Phil. Mag.*, VI. **8.** 636–650.
Succession of changes in radioactive bodies. *Roy. Soc., Phil. Trans.*, **204.** 169–219.
Heating effect of the gamma rays of radium. (H. T. Barnes). *Nature*, **71.** 151–152.
Difference between radioactivity and chemical change. *Jahrbuch d. Radioaktivität u. Elektronik*, **1.** 103–127.
Radioactivity. (Cambridge University Press).
Disintegration of the radioactive elements. *Harper's Monthly Magazine*, **108.** 279–284.

The radiation and emanation of radium. *Sci. Amer. Sup.*, **58.** 24073–24074 and 24086–24088.

Does the radioactivity of radium depend upon its concentration? *Phys. Rev.*, **18.** 117–118.

Succession of changes in radioactive bodies. London, p. 50.

Das Zerfallen der radioactiven Elemente. *Fiz. Obezr. Varsava*, **5.** 202–213.

Heating effects of the radium emanation. (H. T. Barnes). *Phys. Rev.*, **18.** 118–119.

1905

Present problems of radioactivity. *Archives des Sciences*, **19.** 31–59.

Slow transformation products of radium. *Nature*, **71.** 341–342.

Charge carried by the alpha rays from radium. *Nature*, **71.** 413–414.

Positive charge of alpha rays. *Elect. Rev., N.Y.*, **46.** 490.

Heating effect of the gamma rays from radium. (H. T. Barnes). *Phil. Mag.*, VI. **9.** 621–628.

Note on the radioactivity of weak radium solutions. *Phil. Mag.*, VI. **9.** 711–712.

Anmerkung (zu der Arbeit von A. S. Eve. Die Eingenschaften geringer Radiummengen). *Phys. Zeit.*, **6.** 9. 269.

Relative proportion of radium and uranium in radioactive minerals. (B. B. Boltwood). *Amer. Journ. Sci.*, **20.** 55–56.

Proportion of radium and uranium in minerals. (B. B. Boltwood). *Chem. News*, **92.** 38–39.

Some properties of the alpha rays from radium. *Phil. Mag.*, VI. **10.** 163–176.

Charge carried by the alpha and beta rays of radium. *Phil. Mag.*, VI. **10.** 193–208.

Slow transformation products of radium. *Phil. Mag.*, VI. **10.** 290–306.

Heating effect of the radium emanation. *Rep. Austr. Assn., Dunedin*, **10.** 86–91.

Present problems in radioactivity. *Pop. Science Monthly*, **67.** 5–34.

Produits de transformation lente du radium. Trad. de l'angl. par L. Bloch. *Radium, Paris*, **2.** 355–361.

Slow transformation products of radium. *Trans. Intern. Elect. Congr. St. Louis*, 1904, **1.** 285–301.

Some properties of the α-rays from radium. *Roy. Soc. of Canada, Trans.*, II. 3–16 (Section III).

Der Unterschied zwischen radioaktiver und chemischer Verwandlung. *Fiz. Obezr., Varsava,* **6.** 20–40.

1906

Some properties of the alpha rays from radium. (Second Paper). *Phil. Mag.,* VI. **11.** 166–176.

Magnetic and electric deflection of the alpha rays of radium. Abstract. *Phys. Rev.,* **22.** 122–123.

Über einige Eigenschaften der Alpha-Strahlen des Radiums. *Phys. Zeit.,* **7.** 5. 137–143.

The retardation of the velocity of the alpha particles in passing through matter. *Phil. Mag.,* VI. **11.** 553–554.

Relative proportion of radium and uranium in radioactive minerals. (B. B. Boltwood). *Amer. Journ. Sci.,* **22.** 1–3.

Retardation of the alpha particle from radium in passing through matter. *Phil. Mag.,* VI. **12.** 134–146.

Distribution of the intensity of the radiation from radioactive sources. *Phil. Mag.,* VI. **12.** 152–158.

Absorption of radioactive emanations by charcoal. *Nature,* **74.** 634.

The recent radium controversy. *Nature,* **74.** 634–635.

The mass and velocity of the alpha particles expelled from radium and actinium. *Phil. Mag.,* VI. **12.** 348–371.

Mass of the alpha particles from thorium. (O. Hahn). *Phil. Mag.,* VI. **12.** 371–378.

Radioactive transformations. (Yale University Press; Constable & Co.)

Some properties of the α rays from radium. II. *Phys. Rev.,* **22.** 123–125.

Distribution de l'intensité du rayonnement des sources radioactives. *Radium, Paris,* **3.** 257–260.

Present problems of radioactivity. *Congress of Arts and Science, Universal Exposition, St. Louis,* 1904, **4.** 157–186.

1907

Production of radium from actinium. *Nature,* **75.** 270–271.

The velocity and energy of the alpha particles from radioactive substances. *Phil. Mag.,* VI. **13.** 110–117.

The origin of radium. *Nature,* **76.** 126.

The production and origin of radium. Abstract. *British Assn. for Adv. of Sci., Report,* 456.

The effect of high temperature on the activity of the products of radium. Abstract. (J. E. Petavel). *British Assn. for Adv. of Sci., Report*, 456–457.

Origin of radium. *Nature*, **76.** 661.

The production and origin of radium. *Manchester Lit. and Phil. Soc., Mem.*, IV. **52.** 5–7.

The production and origin of radium. *Phil. Mag.*, VI. **14.** 733–749.

Radioaktive Umwandlungen. *Wissenschaft*, Heft 21. 285.

Die Radioaktivität. Unter Mitwirkung des Verfassers ergänzte autoris. deutsche Ausg. von E. Aschkinass. Berlin, pp. 597.

Some cosmical aspects of radioactivity. *J. Roy. Astr. Soc., Canada*, **1.** 145–165.

Ueber Masse und Geschwindigkeit des von Radium und Aktinium ausgesandten α-Teilchens. *Jahrb. Radioakt.*, **4.** 1–6.

Vitesse et énergie des particules α des substances radioactives. Traduit de l'anglais par Léon Bloch. *Radium, Paris*, **4.** 84–87.

1908

A method of counting the number of alpha particles from radioactive matter. (H. Geiger). *Manchester Lit. and Phil. Soc., Mem.*, IV. **52.** 9. 1–3.

Recent advances in radioactivity. *Nature*, **77.** 422–426.

Spectrum of the radium emanation. (T. Royds). *Nature*, **78.** 220–221.

Experiments with the radium emanation. (1) The volume of the emanation. *Phil. Mag.*, VI. **16.** 300–312.

Spectrum of the radium emanation. (T. Royds). *Phil. Mag.*, VI. **16.** 313–317.

An electrical method of counting the number of alpha particles from radioactive substances. (H. Geiger). *Proc. Roy. Soc.*, A. **81.** 546. 141–161.

The charge and nature of the alpha particle. (H. Geiger). *Proc. Roy. Soc.*, A. **81.** 546. 162–173.

The nature of the alpha particles. *Nature*, **79.** 12–15.

The action of the radium emanation upon water. (T. Royds). *Phil. Mag.*, VI. **16.** 812–818.

Nature of the alpha particle. (T. Royds). *Manchester Lit. and Phil. Soc., Mem.*, IV. **53.** 1. 1–3.

Some properties of the radium emanation. *Manchester Lit. and Phil. Soc., Mem.*, IV. **53.** 2. 1–2.

Der Ursprung des Radiums (Bericht). *Jahrb. Radioakt.*, **5.** 153–166.
Die Ladung und Natur des α-Teilchens. (H. Geiger). *Jahrb. Radioakt.*, **5.** 408–423; and *Radium, Paris*, **6.** 265–271.
Une méthode électrique de numération des particules α émises par les substances radioactives. (H. Geiger). *Radium, Paris*, **5.** 257–264.
Spectra de l'émanation du radium. (T. Royds). *Radium, Paris*, **5.** 200–201.

1909

Nature of the alpha particle. (T. Royds). *Chem. News*, **99.** 49.
Eine elektrische Methode, die von radioaktiven Substanzen ausgesandten α-Teilchen zu zählen. (H. Geiger). *Phys. Zeit.*, **10.** 1. 1–6.
Die Ladung und Natur des α-Teilchens. (H. Geiger). *Phys. Zeit.*, **10.** 2. 42–46.
The boiling point of the radium emanation. *Nature*, **79.** 457–458.
The nature of the alpha particle from radioactive substances. (T. Royds). *Phil. Mag.*, VI. **17.** 281–286.
Recent advances in radioactivity. *Chem. News*, **99.** 171–174, 181–183.
Differences in the decay of the radium emanation. (Y. Tuomikoski). *Manchester Lit. and Phil. Soc., Mem.*, IV. **53.** 12. 1–2.
Condensation of the radium emanation. *Phil. Mag.*, VI. **17.** 723–729.
Atomic theory and the determination of atomic magnitudes. *British Ass. for Adv. of Science, Report*, 373–385.
The action of the alpha rays on glass. *Manchester Lit. and Phil. Soc., Mem.*, IV. **54.** 5. 1.
Production of helium by radium. (B. B. Boltwood). *Manchester Lit. and Phil. Soc., Mem.*, IV. **54.** 6. 1–2.
Die Atom-Theorie in der Physik. *Natw. Rdsch.*, **24.** 481–485, 496–501.
Die neuesten Fortschritte der Atomistik. *Phys. Zeits.*, **10.** 762–771.
Opening address to Section A of the British Association at Winnipeg, 1909. *Nature*, **81.** 257–263.
Nature des particules et des substances radioactives. (T. Royds). *Radium, Paris*, **6.** 47–50.

The nature of the α-Particle from radioactive substances. (T. Royds). *Jahrb. Radioakt.*, **6.** 1–7.

1910

Action of the alpha rays on glass. *Phil. Mag.*, VI. **19.** 192–194.

Properties of polonium. *Nature*, **82.** 491–492.

Theory of the luminosity produced in certain substances by alpha rays. *Proc. Roy. Soc.*, A, **83.** 566. 561–572.

Radium standards and nomenclature. *Nature*, **84.** 430–431.

The number of alpha particles emitted by uranium and thorium and by uranium minerals. (H. Geiger). *Phil. Mag.*, VI. **20.** 691–698.

The probability variations in the distribution of alpha particles. (H. Geiger). *Phil. Mag.*, VI. **20.** 698–704.

Existieren die Atome, Molekeln und Elektronen? *Umschau*, **14.** 341–344, 369–372.

1911

The scattering of the alpha and beta rays and the structure of the atom. *Manchester Lit. and Phil. Soc., Mem.*, IV. **55.** 18–20.

Untersuchungen über die Radiumemanation. II. Die Umwandlungsgeschwindigkeit. *K. Akad. Wiss., Vienna, Sitzungsberichte*, **120.** 2a. 303–312.

Die Erzeugung von Helium durch Radium. (B. B. Boltwood). *K. Akad. Wiss., Vienna, Sitzungsberichte*, **120.** 2a. 313–336.

Radioactivity of thorium. *Röntgen Soc., Journ.*, **7.** 23–30.

The scattering of alpha and beta particles by matter and the structure of the atom. *Phil. Mag.*, VI. **21.** 669–688.

Production of helium from radium. (B. B. Boltwood). *Phil. Mag.*, VI. **22.** 586–604.

Transformation and nomenclature of the radioactive emanations. (H. Geiger). *Phil. Mag.*, VI. **22.** 621–629.

An international standard of radium. Akad. Verlagsgesellschaft, Leipzig.

The transformation of radium. *J. Soc. Chem. Indust.*, **30.** 659–662.

1912

Balance method for comparison of quantities of radium. (J. Chadwick). *Phys. Soc., Proc.*, **24.** 141–151, 156–157.

Balance method for comparison of quantities of radium. (J. Chadwick). *Le Radium*, **9.** 195–200.

The origin of beta and gamma rays from radioactive substances. *Phil. Mag.*, VI. **24.** 453–462.

Photographic registration of alpha particles. (H. Geiger). *Phil. Mag.*, VI. **24.** 618–623.

Origin of beta and gamma rays from radioactive substances. *Le Radium*, **9.** 337–341.

Wärme-Entwicklung durch Radium und Radiumemanation. (H. Robinson). *K. Akad. Wiss., Vienna, Sitzungsberichte*, **121.** 2a. 1491–1516.

On the energy of the groups of beta rays from radium. *Phil. Mag.*, VI. **24.** 893–894.

Sur l'origine des rayons β et γ des substances radioactives. *Radium, Paris*, **9.** 399.

1913

A new International Physical Institute. *Nature*, **90.** 545–546.

Heating effect of radium and its emanation. (H. Robinson) *Phil. Mag.*, VI. **25.** 312–330.

The age of pleochroic haloes. (J. Joly). *Phil. Mag.*, VI. **25.** 644–657.

The analysis of the gamma rays from radium B and radium C. (H. Richardson). *Phil. Mag.*, VI. **25.** 722–734.

Analysis of the gamma rays from radium D and radium E. (H. Richardson). *Phil. Mag.*, VI. **26.** 324–332.

The reflection of gamma rays from crystals. (E. N. da C. Andrade). *Nature*, **92.** 267.

Scattering of alpha particles by gases. (J. M. Nuttall). *Phil. Mag.*, VI. **26.** 702–712.

The analysis of the beta rays from radium B and radium C. (H. Robinson). *Phil. Mag.*, VI. **26.** 717–729.

Über die Masse und die Geschwindigkeiten der von den radioaktiven Substanzen ausgesendeten Alpha Teilchen. (H. Robinson). *K. Akad. Wiss., Vienna, Sitzungsberichte*, **122.** 2a. 1855–1884.

The British radium standard. *Nature*, **92.** 402–403.

Structure of the atom. *Nature*, **92.** 423.

Analysis of the gamma rays of the thorium and actinium products. (H. Richardson). *Phil. Mag.*, VI. **26.** 937–948.

Radioactive substances and their radiations. (Cambridge University Press).

1914

The structure of the atom. *Phil. Mag.*, VI. **27.** 488–498.

The wavelength of the soft gamma rays from radium B. (E. N. da C. Andrade). *Phil. Mag.*, VI. **27.** 854–868.

The spectrum of the penetrating gamma rays from radium B and radium C. (E. N. da C. Andrade). *Phil. Mag.*, VI. **28.** 263–273.

Spectrum of the beta rays excited by gamma rays. (H. Robinson and W. F. Rawlinson). *Phil. Mag.*, VI. **28.** 281–286.

Discussion on the structure of atoms and molecules. Abstract. *British Ass. for Adv. of Science, Report*, 293–294 and 301.

The connexion between the beta and gamma ray spectrum. *Phil. Mag.*, VI. **28.** 305–319.

Radium constants on the International Standard. *Phil. Mag.*, VI. **28.** 320–327.

The mass and velocities of the alpha particles from radioactive substances. (H. Robinson). *Phil. Mag.*, VI. **28.** 552–572.

1915

Origin of the spectra given by beta and gamma rays of radium. *Manchester Lit. and Phil. Soc., Mem.*, IV. **59.** 17–19.

Radiations from exploding atoms. *Nature*, **95.** 494–498.

Maximum frequency of the X-rays from a Coolidge tube for different voltages. (J. Barnes and H. Richardson). *Phil. Mag.*, VI. **30.** 339–360.

Efficiency of the production of X-rays from a Coolidge tube. (J. Barnes). *Phil. Mag.*, VI. **30.** 361–367.

The constitution of matter and the evolution of the elements. *Smithsonian Report for* 1915, 167–202.

Radiations from exploding atoms. *Engineering*, **99.** 657–659.

Radiations from exploding atoms. *Electrician*, **75.** 363–364.

1916

Long-range alpha particles from thorium. (A. B. Wood). *Phil. Mag.*, VI. **31.** 379–386.

X-ray spectra of the elements. *Engineering*, **102.** 320.

1917

Penetrating power of the X-radiation from a Coolidge tube. *Phil. Mag.*, VI. **34.** 153–162.

1918

X-rays. *Röntgen Soc., Journ.*, **14.** 75–86.

1919

Collision of alpha particles with light atoms. I. Hydrogen. *Phil. Mag.*, VI. **37.** 537–561.

Collision of alpha particles with light atoms. II. Velocity of the hydrogen atoms. *Phil. Mag.*, VI. **37.** 562–571.

Collision of alpha particles with light atoms. III. Nitrogen and oxygen atoms. *Phil. Mag.*, VI. **37.** 571–580.

Collision of alpha particles with light atoms. IV. An anomalous effect in nitrogen. *Phil. Mag.*, VI. **37.** 581–587.

Radium and the electron. *Nature*, **104.** 226–230.

Radioactivity and gravitation. (A. H. Compton). *Nature*, **104.** 412.

Collision of α-particles with light atoms. *Nature*, **103.** 415–418.

1920

Nuclear constitution of atoms. *Proc. Roy. Soc.*, A. **97.** 686. 374–400.

Building-up of atoms. *Engineering*, **110.** 382.

Nuclear constitution of atoms. *Nature*, **105.** 500–501.

1921

On the collision of alpha particles with hydrogen atoms. *Phil. Mag.*, VI. **41.** 307–308.

The disintegration of elements by alpha particles. (J. Chadwick). *Nature*, **107.** 41.

Electricity and matter. *Engineering*, **111.** 296–297, 345–347 and 379–381.

The mass of the long range particles from thorium C. *Phil. Mag.*, VI. **41.** 570–574.

The artificial disintegration of light elements. (J. Chadwick). *Phil. Mag.*, VI. **42.** 809–825.

Radium and the Electron. (*Smithsonian Institution, Annual Report*, 1919).

Stability of atoms. *Proc. Phys. Soc.*, **33.** 389–394.

1922

Artificial disintegration of the elements. *Chem. Soc., Journ.*, **121.** 400–415.

Radioactivity. *Engineering*, **113.** 299–300, 331–332, 365–366, 386–387, 414–415, 464–466.

Disintegration of elements. *Nature*, **109.** 418.
Radioactivity. *Electrician*, **88.** 411–413, 501–504.
Artificial disintegration of the elements. *Nature*, **109.** 584–586, 614–617.
Identification of a missing element. *Nature*, **109.** 781.
Electricity and matter. *Inst. Elec. Eng., Journ.*, **60.** 613–618.
Electricity and matter. *Nature*, **110.** 182–185.
The disintegration of elements by alpha particles. (J. Chadwick). *Phil. Mag.*, VI. **44.** 417–432.

1923

Atomic projectiles and their properties. *Engineering*, **115.** 242–243, 264–266, 306–308, 338–340, 358–359, 798–800.
Atomic projectiles and their properties. *Electrician*, **90.** 366–367. **91.** 60–61, 120–121, 144–145.
Life-history of an alpha particle. *Engineering*, **115.** 769–770.
Capture and loss of electrons by alpha particles. *Camb. Phil. Soc., Proc.*, **21.** 504–510.
Life-history of an alpha particle. *Nature*, **112.** 305–312.
The life of an alpha particle. *Electrician*, **91.** 194–195.
The electrical structure of matter. *British Ass. for Adv. of Science, Report*, **1.** 24.
The electrical structure of matter. *Nature*, **112.** 409–419.
The electrical structure of matter. *Science* (N.S.), **58.** 209–221.

1924

The capture and loss of electrons by alpha particles. *Phil. Mag.*, VI. **47.** 277–303.
The bombardment of elements by alpha particles. (J. Chadwick). *Nature*, **113.** 457.
Properties of gases in high and low vacua. *Engineering*, **117.** 330, 365–366, 387, 429.
The nucleus of the atom. *Engineering*, **117.** 458–459.
Further experiments on the artificial disintegration of elements. (J. Chadwick). *Phys. Soc., Proc.*, **36.** 417–422.
On the origin and nature of the long-range particles observed with sources of radium C. (J. Chadwick). *Phil. Mag.*, VI. **48.** 509–526.
Early days of radioactivity. *Frank. Inst., Journ.*, **198.** 281–290.
Natural and artificial disintegration of the elements. *Frank. Inst., Journ.*, **198.** 725–744.

Die elektrische Struktur der Materie. *Naturwissensch.*, **12.** 1–14.
Die elektrische Struktur der Materie. *Strahlentherapie*, **16.** 883–913.

1925

The stability of atoms. *Disc.*, **6.** 402–403.
The stability of atoms. *Roy. Soc. Arts, Journ.*, **73.** 389–402.
Disintegration of atomic nuclei. *Nature*, **115.** 493–494.
Studies of atomic nuclei. *Engineering*, **119.** 437–438.
Moseley's work on X-rays. *Nature*, **116.** 316–317.
Scattering of alpha particles by atomic nuclei and the law of force. (J. Chadwick). *Phil. Mag.*, VI. **50.** 889–913.
The natural X-ray spectrum of radium B. (W. A. Wooster). *Camb. Phil. Soc., Proc.*, **22.** 834–837.
Electrical Structure of Matter. (*Smithsonian Institution, Annual Report*, 1924).
Studies of atomic nuclei. *Science*, **62.** 209–211.

1926

The rare gases of the atmosphere. *Engineering*, **121.** 353–354, 388–390, 438, 458–459.
Discussion on the electrical state of the upper atmosphere. *Proc. Roy. Soc.*, A, **111.** 757. 1–3.
Electric waves and their propagation. *Nature*, **118.** 809–811.

1927

Anniversary address by the President of the Royal Society, November, 1926. *Proc. Roy. Soc.* A, **113.** 765. 481–495.
Alpha rays and atomic structure. *Engineering*, **123.** 375–376, 409–410, 460–461, 492–493.
Atomic nuclei and their transformations. *Phys. Soc., Proc.*, **39.** 359–372.
Structure of the radioactive atom and origin of the alpha rays. *Phil. Mag.*, VII. **4.** 580–605.
The scattering of alpha particles by helium. (J. Chadwick). *Phil. Mag.*, VII. **4.** 605–620.
Study and research in physics. *Nature*, **120.** 657–659.
Scientific aspects of intense magnetic fields and high voltages. *Nature*, **120.** 809–811.
Structure of radioactive atoms and the origin of the α-rays. *Atti Congr. Intern. dei Fisica Como.* **1.** 55–64.

1928

Anniversary address by the President of the Royal Society, November, 1927. *Proc. Roy. Soc.*, A, **117.** 777. 300–316.
Professor Bertram B. Boltwood. *Nature*, **121.** 64–65.
Transformation of matter. *Engineering*, **125.** 315–316, 360, 387.
Production and properties of high-frequency radiation. *Nature*, **122.** 883–886.

1929

Anniversary address by the President of the Royal Society, November, 1928. *Proc. Roy. Soc.*, A, **122.** 789. 1–23.
Origin of actinium and age of the earth. *Nature*, **123.** 313–314.
Molecular motions in rarefied gases. *Engineering*, **127.** 319–321, 347–348, 381, 449–450.
Energy relations in artificial disintegrations. (J. Chadwick). *Camb. Phil. Soc., Proc.*, **25.** 186–192.
Penetrating radiations. *Engineer*, **147.** 413.
Opening discussion on the structure of atomic nuclei. *Proc. Roy. Soc.*, A, **123.** 792. 373–382.
Recent reactions between theory and experiment. *Nature*, **124.** 878–880.
M. Planck. *Naturwissensch.*, **17.** 483.

1930

Anniversary address by the President of the Royal Society, November, 1929. *Proc. Roy. Soc.*, A, **126.** 801. 184–203.
Atomic nuclei and their structure. *Engineering*, **129.** 371–372, 397–398, 437–438, 470–471.
A new method of analysis of groups of alpha rays. (I) The alpha rays from radium C, thorium C, and actinium C. (F. A. B. Ward and C. E. Wynn-Williams). *Proc. Roy. Soc.*, A, **129.** 809. 211–234.
Intense magnetic fields and low temperature research. *Nature*, **126.** 884–885.
Radiations from Radioactive Substances. (James Chadwick and C. D. Ellis). (Cambridge University Press).
The transmutation of matter. *Engineering*, **129.** 549–550.

1931

Anniversary address by the President of the Royal Society, December, 1930. *Proc. Roy. Soc.*, A, **130.** 813. 239–259.

Analysis of the long-range alpha particles from Radium C. (F. A. B. Ward and W. Lewis). *Proc. Roy. Soc.*, A, **131.** 818. 684–703.
Helium and its properties. Abstract. *Nature*, **128.** 137–138.
Discussion on ultra-penetrating rays. *Proc. Roy. Soc.*, A, **132.** 819. 337–340.
The origin of the gamma rays. (C. D. Ellis). *Proc. Roy. Soc.*, A, **132.** 820. 667–688.
Analysis of the alpha particles emitted from thorium C and actinium C. (C. E. Wynn-Williams and W. B. Lewis). *Proc. Roy. Soc.*, A, **133.** 822. 351–366.
α-Teilchen grosser Reichweite und die Entstehung der γ-Strahlen. *Göttinger Nachr.*, 1931, 248–251, Nr. 2.

1932

Origin of the gamma rays. *Nature*, **129.** 457–458.
The gamma rays from actinium emanation and their origin. (B. V. Bowden). *Proc. Roy. Soc.*, A, **136.** 829. 407–412.
Opening address on the structure of atomic nuclei. *Proc. Roy. Soc.*, A, **136.** 830. 735–744.
Atomic projectiles and their applications. Abstract. *Nature*, **130.** 730–731.
Erinnerungen an die Frühzeit der Radioaktivität. *Zeits. f. Elektrochem.*, **38.** 476–480.

1933

Recent results upon the transmutation of the elements. Abstract. *Nature*, **131.** 388–389.
Analysis of alpha rays by an annular magnetic field. (C. E. Wynn-Williams, W. B. Lewis, and B. V. Bowden). *Proc. Roy. Soc.*, A, **139.** 839. 617–637.
The transmutation of the elements. *Disc.*, **14.** 105–108.
Experiments on the transmutation of elements by protons. (M. L. E. Oliphant). *Proc. Roy. Soc.*, A, **141.** 843. 259–281.
Atomic transmutation. *The Times*, London (September 12th).
Makers of science. *Nature*, **132.** 367–369.
The transmutation of lithium by protons and by ions of the heavy isotope of hydrogen. (M. L. E. Oliphant and B. B. Kinsey). *Proc. Roy. Soc.*, A, **141.** 845. 722–733.
A review of a quarter of a century's work on atomic transmutation. Abstract. *British Ass. for Adv. of Science, Report*, 431–432.

Analysis of the long-range alpha particles from radium C by the magnetic focusing method. (W. B. Lewis and B. V. Bowden). *Proc. Roy. Soc.*, A, **142.** 846. 347–361.

Artificial Transmutation of the Elements. (Oxford University Press).

Heavy hydrogen. *Nature*, **132.** 955–956.

Observations by Lord Rutherford on 'Interaction of hard γ-rays with atomic nuclei' by C. Y. Chao and T. T. Kung. *Nature*, **132.** 709.

1934

The transmutation of the atom. *Scientific Monthly*, **38.** 15–23.

Bombardment of the heavy isotopes of hydrogen by alpha particles. (A. E. Kempton). *Proc. Roy. Soc.*, A, **143.** 850. 724–730.

Transmutation effects observed with heavy hydrogen. (M. L. Oliphant and P. Harteck). *Nature*, **133.** 413.

The new hydrogen. *Nature*, **133.** 481–484.

Opening address on heavy hydrogen. *Proc. Roy. Soc.*, A, **144.** 851. 1–5.

Transmutation effects observed with heavy hydrogen. (M. L. Oliphant and P. Harteck). *Proc. Roy. Soc.*, A, **144.** 853. 692–703.

The new hydrogen. *Scientia*, **55.** 341–349.

The periodic law and its interpretation. *Chem. Soc., Journ.*, **1.** 635–642.

Madame Curie. *Nature*, **134.** 90–91.

Report of the Academic Assistance Council. *The Times*, London. (November 16th).

Opening survey on disintegration and synthesis of nuclei and elementary particles. International Conference of Physics, London. Vol. I, *Nuclear Physics*, 4–16 and 162. (Physical Society).

The new hydrogen. *Proc. Roy. Inst.*, **28.** 277–289.

The new hydrogen. *Science* (N.S.), **80.** 21–25.

The transmutations of matter. *Engineering*, **137.** 420–422.

1935

Radioactivity: old and new. *Nature*, **135.** 289–292.

The accurate determination of the energy released in certain nuclear transformations. (M. L. E. Oliphant and A. E. Kempton). *Proc. Roy. Soc.*, A, **149.** 866. 406–416.

Electromagnetic radiations. *Engineering*, **139.** 314–316, 341–342, 357–358, 434–436.

Madame Curie. *Slavonic Rev.*, **13.** 673–676.
Atomic physics. *Nature,* **135.** 683–685.
Some nuclear transformations of beryllium and boron, and the masses of the light elements. (M. L. E. Oliphant and A. E. Kempton). *Proc. Roy. Soc.*, A, **150.** 869. 241–258.

1936

The transformation of energy (The Watt Anniversary Lecture for 1936). *Papers of the Greenock Philosophical Society.*
The transformation of energy. *Nature,* **137.** 135–137.
Protection of science and learning. *New Statesman and Nation,* **11.** 453.
Radioactivity and atomic theory. *Chem. Soc., Journ.*, **1.** 508–516.
Society for the protection of science and learning. *Science,* **83.** 372.
Science in development. *Nature,* **138.** 865–869.
The electric arc and its application. *Proc. Roy. Inst.*, **29.** 256–259.
Radioaktivität und Atomtheorie. *Naturwissensch.*, **24.** 673–680.

1937

The transmutation of heavy elements. Abstract. *Nature,* **139.** 540.
The search for the isotopes of hydrogen and helium of mass 3. *Nature,* **140.** 303–305.
The transmutation of heavy elements. *Proc. Roy. Inst.*, **29.** 4. 630–635.
The Newer Alchemy. (Cambridge University Press).

1938

Presidential address prepared for the Jubilee Meeting of the Indian Science Congress. Abstract. *Nature,* **141.** 1–2.
Transmutation of matter. (Part of presidential address prepared for the Jubilee Meeting of the Indian Science Congress). *Nature,* **141.** 58–61.

PAPERS PUBLISHED FROM THE PHYSICAL LABORATORIES, UNIVERSITY OF MANCHESTER, 1907–19

A complete bibliography of Rutherford's publications during his life is given elsewhere in this volume. Papers published by other members of the Laboratories during the period 1907–19 *are listed below under the names of individual authors, with the names of any co-authors shown in brackets. In two cases (N. Bohr and H. G. J. Moseley) a few important related papers, published from other institutions, have also been included.*

E. N. da C. Andrade

1913

Reflection of gamma rays from crystals. (E. Rutherford). *Nature*, **92.** 267.

1914

The wavelength of the soft gamma rays from radium B. (E. Rutherford). *Phil. Mag.*, VI. **27.** 854–868.
The spectrum of the penetrating gamma rays from radium B and radium C. (E. Rutherford). *Phil. Mag.*, VI. **28.** 263–273.
Flow in metals under large constant pressures. *Proc. Roy. Soc.*, A. **90.** 329–342.

G. N. Antonoff

1910

Radium D and its products of transformation. *Phil. Mag.*, VI. **19.** 825–839.

1911

The disintegration products of uranium. *Phil. Mag.*, VI. **22.** 419–432.
Absorption spectrum of selenium vapour. (E. J. Evans). *Astrophys. Journ.*, **34.** 277–287.

J. Barnes

1915

Maximum frequency of the X-rays from a Coolidge tube for different voltages. (E. Rutherford and H. Richardson). *Phil. Mag.*, VI. **30.** 339–360.

Efficiency of the production of the X-rays from a Coolidge tube. (E. Rutherford). *Phil. Mag.*, VI. **30.** 361–367.

The high frequency spectrum of Tungsten. *Phil. Mag.*, VI. **30.** 368–370.

Continuous spectra of gases. *Nature*, **95.** 451.

H. Bateman

1909

The reflexion of light at an ideal plane mirror moving with a uniform velocity of translation. *Phil. Mag.*, VI. **18.** 890–895.

1910

The solution of the integral equation connecting the velocity of propagation of an earthquake-wave in the interior of the earth with the times which the disturbance takes to travel to the different stations on the earth's surface. *Phil. Mag.*, VI. **19.** 576.

The relation between electro-magnetism and geometry. *Phil. Mag.*, VI. **20.** 623–628.

On the probability distribution of α-particles. *Phil. Mag.* VI. **20.** 704.

Solution of a system of differential equations occurring in the theory of radioactive transformations. *Proc. Cambridge Phil. Soc.*, **15.** 423–427.

U. Behn

1907

Ratio of specific heats for helium by Kundt's tube. (H. Geiger). *Deutsch. Phys. Gesell.*, **9.** 22. 657–666.

1908

On the polymorphic changes of ammonium nitrate. *Proc. Roy. Soc.*, A. **80.** 444–457.

H. F. Biggs

1916

On the energy of the secondary beta rays produced by partly absorbed gamma rays. *Phil. Mag.*, VI. **31.** 361–367.

N. Bohr

1913

Spectra of helium and hydrogen. *Nature*, **92.** 231–233.

On the theory of the decrease of velocity of moving electrified particles on passing through matter. *Phil. Mag.*, VI. **25.** 10–31.

On the constitution of atoms and molecules. *Phil. Mag.*, VI. **26.** 1–25.

On the constitution of atoms and molecules. II. Systems containing only a single nucleus. *Phil. Mag.*, VI. **26.** 476–502.

On the constitution of atoms and molecules. III. Systems containing several nuclei. *Phil. Mag.*, VI. **26.** 857–875.

1914

On the effect of electric-magnetic fields on spectral lines. *Phil. Mag.*, VI. **27.** 506–524.

Atomic models and Röntgen-ray spectra. (H. G. J. Moseley). *Nature*, **92.** 553—554.

1915

On the series spectrum of hydrogen and the structure of the atom. *Phil. Mag.*, VI. **29.** 332–335.

Spectra of hydrogen and helium. *Nature*, **95.** 6–7.

On the quantum theory of radiation and the structure of the atom. *Phil. Mag.*, VI. **30.** 394–415.

On the decrease of velocity of swiftly moving electrified particles in passing through matter. *Phil. Mag.*, VI. **30.** 581–612.

B. B. Boltwood

1909–1910

Production of helium by radium. (E. Rutherford). *Manchester Lit. and Phil. Soc. Mem.*, **54.** 6. 1–2.

1911

Production of helium from radium. (E. Rutherford). *Phil. Mag.*, VI. **22.** 586–604.

Die Erzeugung von Helium durch Radium. (E. Rutherford). *K. Akad. Wiss., Vienna, Sitzungsberichte*, **120.** 2a. 313–336.

Report on the separation of ionium and actinium from certain residues and on the production of helium by ionium. *Proc. Roy. Soc.*, A. **85.** 77–81.

PAPERS PUBLISHED FROM THE PHYSICAL LABORATORIES

W. A. Borodowski

1910

Absorption of β-rays from radium by solutions. *Phil. Mag.*, VI. **19.** 605–619.

R. W. Boyle

1911

The behavior of radium emanation at low temperatures. *Phil. Mag.*, VI. **21.** 722–732.

The solubility of radium emanation. Application of Henry's law at low partial pressures. *Phil. Mag.*, VI. **22.** 840–854.

J. Chadwick

1912

Balance method for comparison of quantities of radium. (E. Rutherford). *Proc. Phys. Soc.*, **24.** 141–151 and 156–157.

Balance method for comparison of quantities of radium. (E. Rutherford). *Le Radium*, **9.** 195–200.

Absorption of γ-rays by gases and light substances. *Proc. Phys. Soc.*, **24.** 152–156 and 156–157.

The γ-rays excited by the β-rays of radium. *Phil. Mag.*, VI. **24.** 594–600.

1913

The excitation of γ-rays by α-rays. *Phil. Mag.*, VI. **25.** 193–197.

The excitation of γ-rays by the α-rays of ionium and radiothorium. (A. S. Russell). *Proc. Roy. Soc.*, A. **88.** 217–229.

1914

The γ-rays of polonium, radium, and radioactinium. (A. S. Russell). *Phil. Mag.*, VI. **27.** 112–125.

Distribution in intensity in the magnetic spectrum of the β-rays of radium (B+C). *Deutsch. Phys. Gesell.*, **168.** 383–391.

C. Croxson

1916

Structure of the spectrum line λ4685. (E. J. Evans). *Nature*, **97.** 56–57.

Preliminary note on the Stark effect of the 4686 spectrum line. (E. J. Evans). *Phil. Mag.*, VI. **32.** 327–329.

C. G. DARWIN

1912

A theory of the absorption and scattering of the α-rays. *Phil. Mag.*, VI. **23.** 901–920.
The transformations of the active deposit of thorium. (E. Marsden). *Proc. Roy. Soc.*, A. **87.** 17–29.
Effect of diurnal rotation on the upper atmosphere. *Phil. Mag.*, VI. **23.** 664–668.
Simultaneous action of magnetism and gravitation upon ionized gases. *Comptes Rendus*, **155.** 1145–1146.

1913

On some orbits of an electron. *Phil. Mag.*, VI. **25.** 201—210.
The reflection of the X-rays. (H. G. J. Moseley). *Phil. Mag.*, VI, **26.** 210–232.
The reflection of the X-rays. (H. G. J. Moseley). *Nature*, **90.** 594.

1914

Radiation pressure. *Nature*, **92.** 585.
The theory of X-ray reflection. I. *Phil. Mag.*, VI. **27.** 315–333.
Collision of α-particles with light atoms. *Phil. Mag.*, VI. **27.** 499–506.
The theory of X-ray reflection. II. *Phil. Mag.*, VI. **27.** 675–690.

W. G. DUFFIELD

1908

The effect of pressure upon arc spectra. No. 1. Iron. *Roy. Soc. Phil. Trans.* A. **208.** 111–162.
The effect of pressure upon arc spectra. No. 1. Iron. *Proc. Roy. Soc.*, A. **79.** 597–599.
Spectrum near poles of an iron arc. *Astrophys. Journ.*, **27.** 260–271.
Emission spectrum of silver heated in a carbon-tube furnace in air. (R. Rossi). *Astrophys. Journ.*, **28.** 371–378.
The effect of pressure upon arc spectra. No. 2. Copper λ4000–λ4600. *Proc. Roy. Soc.*, A. **81.** 378–380.

1910

The effect of pressure upon arc spectra. No. 3. Silver; No. 4. Gold. *Proc. Roy. Soc.*, A. **84.** 118–123.

W. Dziewulski

1912

Kerr effect. *Phys. Zeit.*, **13.** 642–649.
Determination of solar motion. *Acad. Sci. Cracovie, Bull.*, **7a.** 811–832.

E. J. Evans

1909

Arc spectrum of iron. *Astrophys. Journ.*, **29.** 157–159.
Arc spectrum of titanium. *Astrophys. Journ.*, **29.** 160–163.

1910

Absorption spectrum of iodine vapour at high temperatures. *Astrophys. Journ.*, **32.** 1–16.
The deflexion by a magnetic field of radium B on recoil from radium A. (W. Makower). *Phil. Mag.*, VI. **20.** 882–886.

1911

Absorption spectrum of selenium vapour. (G. N. Antonoff). *Astrophys. Journ.*, **34.** 277–287.

1912

Absorption spectrum of tellurium vapour. *Astrophys. Journ.*, **36.** 228–238.

1913

Spectra of helium and hydrogen. *Nature*, **92.** 5.

1915

The spectra of helium and hydrogen. *Phil. Mag.*, VI. **29.** 284–297.

1916

Some observations on the absorption spectra of the vapour of inorganic salts. *Phil. Mag.*, VI. **31.** 55–62.
Structure of the spectrum line λ4685. (C. Croxson). *Nature*, **97.** 56–57.

Preliminary note on the Stark effect of the 4686 spectrum line. (C. Croxson). *Phil. Mag.*, VI, **32.** 327–329.

K. Fajans

1911

Radioactive products of short life. (H. G. J. Moseley). *Phil. Mag.*, VI. **22.** 629–638.

1912

The growth of radium C from radium B. (W. Makower). *Phil. Mag.*, VI. **23.** 292–302.

Disintegration of radium C. *Phys. Zeit.*, **13.** 699–705.

D. C. H. Florance

1910

Primary and secondary γ-rays. *Phil. Mag.*, VI. **20.** 921–938.

1913

A study of the ionization produced by β- and γ-rays at high pressures. *Phil. Mag.*, VI. **25.** 172–183.

1914

Secondary γ radiation. *Phil. Mag.*, VI. **27.** 225–244.

Secondary γ radiation. *Phil. Mag.*, VI. **28.** 363–367.

A. D. Fokker

1914

Mean energy of a rotating electric molecule in a radiation field. *Ann. d. Physik*, **43.** 5. 810–820.

Brownian movements in radiation field. *Phys. Zeit.*, **15.** 96–98.

H. Geiger

1907

Ratio of specific heats for helium by Kundt's tube. (U. Behn). *Deutsch. Phys. Gesell.*, **9.** 22. 657–666.

1908

The irregularities in the radiation from radioactive bodies. *Phil. Mag.*, **15.** 539–547.

An electrical method of counting the number of α-particles from radioactive substances. (E. Rutherford). *Proc. Roy. Soc.*, A. **81.** 546. 141–161.

A method of counting the number of alpha particles from radioactive matter. (E. Rutherford). *Manchester Lit. and Phil. Soc. Mem.*, IV. **52.** 9. 1–3.

The charge and nature of the alpha particle. (E. Rutherford). *Proc. Roy. Soc.*, A. **81.** 546. 162–173.

On the scattering of the alpha particles by matter. *Proc. Roy. Soc.*, A. **81.** 174–177.

Die Ladung und Natur des α-Teilchens. (E. Rutherford). *Jahrb. Radioakt.*, **5.** 408–423, and *Radium, Paris*, **6.** 265–271.

Une méthode électrique de numération des particules α émises par les substances radioactives. (E. Rutherford). *Radium, Paris*, **5.** 257–264.

1909

Eine elektrische Methode, die von radioaktiven Substanzen ausgesandten α-Teilchen zu zählen. (E. Rutherford). *Phys. Zeits.*, **10.** 1. 1–6.

Die Ladung und Natur des α-Teilchens. (E. Rutherford). *Phys. Zeit.*, **10.** 2. 42–46.

The ionization produced by an alpha particle. Part I. *Proc. Roy. Soc.*, A. **82.** 486–495.

On a diffuse reflection of the alpha particles. (E. Marsden). *Proc. Roy. Soc.*, A. **82.** 495–500.

1910

The number of alpha particles emitted by uranium and thorium and by uranium minerals. (E. Rutherford). *Phil. Mag.*, VI. **20.** 691–698.

The probability variations in the distribution of alpha particles. (E. Rutherford). *Phil. Mag.*, VI. **20.** 698–704.

The scattering of the alpha particles by matter. *Proc. Roy. Soc.*, A. **83.** 492–504.

The ionization produced by an alpha particle. Part II. Connection between ionization and absorption. *Proc. Roy. Soc.*, A. **83.** 505–515.

The number of alpha particles emitted by the emanations of actinium and thorium. (E. Marsden). *Phys. Zeit.*, **11.** 7–11.

1911

Note on the scattering of alpha particles. *Proc. Roy. Soc.*, A. **86.** 235–240.

The transformation of the actinium emanation. *Phil. Mag.*, VI. **22.** 201–204.

The ranges of the alpha particles from various radioactive substances and a relation between range and period of transformation. (J. M. Nuttall). *Phil. Mag.*, VI. **22.** 613–621.

On the relative numbers of ions produced by the β-particles from the various radioactive substances. (A. F. Kovarik). *Phil. Mag.*, VI. **22.** 604–613.

Transformation and nomenclature of the radioactive emanations. (E. Rutherford). *Phil. Mag.*, VI. **22.** 621–629.

1912

The ranges of the alpha particles from uranium. (J. M. Nuttall). *Phil. Mag.*, VI. **23.** 439–445.

Photographic registration of alpha particles. (E. Rutherford). *Phil. Mag.*, VI. **24.** 618–623.

The ranges of the alpha particles from the thorium and actinium products. (J. M. Nuttall). *Phil. Mag.*, VI. **24.** 647–654.

1913

The laws of deflexion of alpha particles through large angles. (E. Marsden). *Phil. Mag.*, VI. **25.** 604–623.

J. A. Gray

1910

The heterogeneity of the β-particles from a thick layer of radium E. (W. Wilson). *Phil. Mag.*, VI. **20.** 870–875.

The distribution of velocity of the β-particles from a radioactive substance. *Proc. Roy. Soc.*, A. **84.** 136–141.

1911

Secondary γ-rays produced by β-rays. *Proc. Roy. Soc.*, A. **85.** 131–139.

The nature of the γ-rays excited by β-rays. *Proc. Roy. Soc.*, A. **86.** 513–529.

1912

A note on the absorption of β-rays. *Proc. Roy. Soc.*, A. **87.** 487–489.

The similarity in nature of X- and primary γ-rays. *Proc. Roy. Soc.*, A. **87.** 489–501.

H. C. Greenwood

1909

An approximate determination of the boiling points of metals. *Proc. Roy. Soc.*, A. **82.** 396–408.

The influence of pressure on the boiling points of metals. *Proc. Roy. Soc.*, A. **83.** 483–491.

W. M. Gregory

1911

Electrical state of the upper atmosphere. (W. Makower, A. J. Makower, H. Robinson). *Quart. J. R. Met. Soc.*, **37.** 341–349.

Electrical state of the upper atmosphere. (W. Makower, A. J. Makower, H. Robinson). *Electrician*, **67.** 742–743.

W. A. Harwood

1910

Upper air temperatures outside and inside balloons. *Nature*, **82.** 366.

G. A. Hemsalech

1917

On the relative behaviour of the light radiations emitted by iron vapour under the influence of thermal and chemical actions in flames. *Phil. Mag.*, VI. **33.** 1–18.

The origin of the line spectrum emitted by iron vapour in the explosion region of the air-coal gas flame. *Phil. Mag.*, VI. **33.** 221–242.

Note on the production of coloured flames of high luminosity for demonstration and experimental purposes. *Phil. Mag.*, VI. **33.** 243–245.

Grouping of lines in spectrum of iron. *Comptes Rendus*, **163.** 757–759.

1918

A comparative study of the flame and furnace spectra of iron. *Phil. Mag.*, VI. **36.** 209–230.

The origin of the line spectrum emitted by iron vapour in an electric tube. Resistance furnace at temperatures above 2500° C. *Phil. Mag.*, VI. **26.** 281–296.

G. von Hevesy

1911

Solubility of actinium emanation in liquids and charcoal. *Phys. Zeit.*, **12.** 1214–1224.

Detection of actinium in minerals. *Phys. Zeit.*, **12.** 1213–1214.

1912

Radioactive methods in electro-chemistry. *Phys. Zeit.*, **13.** 715–719.

Connection between the chemical characteristics of radioelements and the series of radioactive transformations. *Phys. Zeit.*, **13.** 672–673.

The electro-chemistry of radioactive bodies. *Phil. Mag.*, VI. **23.** 628–646.

The potential of tantalum. (R. E. Slade). *Zeit. Elektrochem.*, **18.** 1001–1002.

1913

The valency of the radioelements. *Phil. Mag.*, **25.** 390–414.

The diffusion of uranium. (L. von Putnoky). *Phil. Mag.*, VI. **25.** 415–418.

Valency of the radioactive elements. *Phys. Zeit.*, **14.** 49–62.

The diffusion of uranium. (L. von Putnoky). *Phys. Zeit.*, **14.** 63–65.

1914

The diffusion and valency of the radioelements. *Phil. Mag.*, VI. **27.** 586–601.

M. Ishino

1916

Velocity of secondary kathode rays emitted by gases under the action of high-speed kathode rays. *Phil. Mag.*, VI. **32.** 202–222.

1917

The scattering and the absorption of the gamma rays. *Phil. Mag.*, VI. **33.** 129–146.

S. J. KALENDYK

1914

Conductivity of salt vapours. *Proc. Roy. Soc.*, A. **90.** 634–647

S. KINOSHITA

1908

Condensation of the actinium and thorium emanations. *Phil. Mag.*, VI. **16.** 121–131.

1909

The photographic action of the alpha particles emitted from radioactive substances. *Proc. Roy. Soc.*, A. **83.** 432–453.

A. F. KOVARIK

1910

Absorption and reflection of the beta particles by matter. *Phil. Mag.*, VI. **20.** 849–866.

On the reflection of homogeneous beta particles of different velocities. (W. Wilson). *Phil. Mag.*, VI. **20.** 866–870.

1911

On the relative number of ions produced by the beta particles from the various radioactive substances. (H. Geiger). *Phil. Mag.*, VI. **22.** 604–613.

Mobility of the positive and negative ions in gases at high pressures. *Proc. Roy. Soc.*, A. **86.** 154–162.

Half period of actinium C. *Phys. Zeit.*, **12.** 83.

W. C. LANTSBERRY

1915

The passage of alpha particles through hydrogen. II. (E. Marsden). *Phil. Mag.*, VI. **30.** 240–243.

S. Lees

1914

Note on the analysis of energy distribution for natural radiation. *Phil. Mag.*, VI. **28.** 794–798.

Miss May Sybil Leslie

1911

Molecular weights of thorium emanation. *Comptes Rendus*, **153.** 328–330.

Thorium and its disintegration products. *Le Radium*, **8.** 356–363.

1912

A comparison of the coefficients of diffusion of thorium and actinium emanations with a note on their periods of transformation. *Phil. Mag.*, VI. **24.** 637–647.

W. Makower

1907

Note on the rate of decay of the active deposit from radium. (W. Wilson). *Phil. Mag.*, VI. **14.** 404–408. *Phys. Soc.*, May 24, 1907.

1908

Number and absorption of the beta particles emitted by radium. *Elec. Eng.*, **4.** 392, 392–393. Read before the British Ass. at Dublin, Sept. 4, 1908.

Decay of radium B and radium C at high temperatures. (S. Russ). *Phys. Zeit.*, **9.** 250–251.

1909

Volatility of radium A and radium C. *Manchester Lit. and Phil. Soc., Mem.*, **53.** 7. 1–8.

On the number and the absorption by matter of the beta particles emitted by radium. *Phil. Mag.*, VI. **17.** 171–180.

Radiation of the active deposit from radium. (S. Russ). *Nature*, **79.** 340.

The expulsion of radioactive matter in the radium transformations. (S. Russ). *Proc. Roy. Soc.*, A. **82.** 205–224.

The electrical state of the upper atmosphere. (M. White and E. Marsden). *K. Akad. Wiss., Vienna, Sitzungsberichte*, **118.** 2a. 629–701.

PAPERS PUBLISHED FROM THE PHYSICAL LABORATORIES

1910

The recoil of radium C from radium B. (S. Russ). *Phil. Mag.*, VI. **19.** 100–115.

The recoil of radium B from radium A. (S. Russ). *Nature*, **83.** 460.

The deflection by an electrostatic field of radium B on recoil from radium A. (S. Russ). *Phil. Mag.*, VI. **20.** 875–882.

The deflection by a magnetic field of radium B on recoil from radium A. (E. J. Evans). *Phil. Mag.*, VI. **20.** 882–886.

1911

Scattering during radioactive recoil. (S. Russ). *Manchester Lit. and Phil. Soc., Mem.*, **55.** 2. 1–4.

Electrical state of the upper atmosphere. (A. J. Makower, W. M. Gregory, H. Robinson). *Quart. J. R. Met. Soc.*, **37.** 341–349.

Electrical state of the upper atmosphere. (A. J. Makower, W. M. Gregory, H. Robinson). *Electrician*, **67.** 742–743.

1912

The growth of radium C from radium B. (K. Fajans). *Phil. Mag.*, VI. **23.** 292–302.

γ-Radiation from radium B. (H. G. J. Moseley). *Phil. Mag.*, VI. **23.** 302–310.

1913

Some experiments to detect β-rays from radium A. (S. Russ). *Phys. Soc. Proc.*, **25.** 253–255, 255.

1914

Passage of alpha particles through photographic films. (H. P. Walmsley). *Phys. Soc. Proc.*, **26.** 261–263.

1915

The magnetic deflection of the recoil stream from radium A. (H. P. Walmsley). *Phil. Mag.*, VI. **29.** 253–258.

The velocity of the alpha particle from radium A. (N. Tunstall). *Phil. Mag.*, VI. **29.** 259–260.

The recoil of radium D from radium C. (A. B. Wood). *Phil. Mag.*, VI. **30.** 811–815.

1916

The straggling of alpha particles. *Phil. Mag.*, VI. **32.** 222–226.

The efficiency of recoil of radium D from radium C. *Phil. Mag.*, VI. **32.** 226–229.

E. Marsden

1909

On a diffuse reflection of the alpha particles. (H. Geiger). *Proc. Roy. Soc.*, A. **82.** 495–500.

The electrical state of the upper atmosphere. (W. Makower and Miss M. White). *K. Akad. Wiss. Vienna, Sitzungsberichte*, **118.** 2a. 629–701.

1910

The number of alpha particles emitted by the emanations of actinium and thorium. (H. Geiger). *Phys. Zeit.*, **11.** 7–11.

1912

The transformations of the active deposits of thorium. (C. G. Darwin). *Proc. Roy. Soc.*, A. **87.** 17–29.

1913

The retardation of alpha particles by metals. (H. Richardson). *Phil. Mag.*, VI. **25.** 184–193.

The decrease in velocity of alpha particles in passing through matter. (T. S. Taylor). *Proc. Roy. Soc.*, A. **88.** 443–454.

Branch products in actinium C. (R. H. Wilson). *Nature*, **92.** 29.

The laws of deflexion of alpha particles through large angles. (H. Geiger). *Phil. Mag.*, VI. **25.** 604–623.

Some experiments with the active deposit of thorium. (R. H. Wilson). *Phil. Mag.*, VI. **26.** 354–361.

A method for the determination of the molecular weights of the radioactive emanations with an application to actinium emanation. (A. B. Wood). *Phil. Mag.*, VI, **26.** 948–952.

1914

The transformations in the active deposit of actinium. (P. B. Perkins). *Phil. Mag.*, VI. **27.** 690–703.

The passing of alpha particles through hydrogen. *Phil. Mag.*, VI. **27.** 824–830.

The transformations of actinium C. (R. W. Varder). *Phil. Mag.*, VI. **28.** 818–821.

1915

The passage of alpha particles through hydrogen. II. (W. C. Lantsberry). *Phil. Mag.*, VI. **30.** 240–243.

H. G. J. Moseley

1911

Radioactive products of short life. (K. Fajans). *Phil. Mag.*, VI. **22.** 629–638.

1912

γ-Radiation from radium B. (W. Makower). *Phil. Mag.*, VI. **23.** 302–310.

The number of β-particles emitted in the transformation of radium. *Proc. Roy. Soc.*, A. **87.** 230–255.

1913

The attainment of high potentials by the use of radium. *Proc. Roy. Soc.*, A. **88.** 471–476.

The reflection of the X-rays. (C. G. Darwin). *Phil. Mag.*, VI. **26.** 210–232.

The reflection of the X-rays. (C. G. Darwin). *Nature*, **90.** 594.

The high frequency spectra of the elements. I. *Phil. Mag.*, VI. **26.** 1024–1034.

1914

The high frequency spectra of the elements. II. *Phil. Mag.*, VI. **27.** 703–713.

The number of ions produced by the β and γ radiations from radium. (H. Robinson). *Phil. Mag.*, VI. **28.** 327–337.

Atomic models and Röntgen ray spectra. (N. Bohr). *Nature*, **92.** 553–554.

E. Newberry

1915

The reduction of metallic oxides with hydrogen at high pressures. (J. N. Pring) *Proc. Roy. Soc.*, A. **92.** 276–285.

J. M. Nuttall

1911

The ranges of the alpha particles from various radioactive substances and a relation between range and period of transformation. (H. Geiger). *Phil. Mag.*, VI. **22.** 613–621.

1912

The ranges of the alpha particles from uranium. (H. Geiger). *Phil. Mag.*, VI. **23.** 439–445.

The ranges of the alpha particles from the thorium and actinium products. (H. Geiger). *Phil. Mag.*, VI. **24.** 647–654.

1913

Scattering of alpha particles by gases. (E. Rutherford). *Phil. Mag.*, VI. **26.** 702–712.

S. Oba

1914

The absorption of gamma rays. *Phil. Mag.*, VI. **27.** 601–607.

A. Parker

1912

The ionization produced by carbon at high temperatures. (J. N. Pring) *Phil. Mag.*, VI. **23.** 192–200.

P. B. Perkins

1914

A determination of the periods of transformation of thorium, actinium emanations. *Phil. Mag.*, VI. **27.** 720–731.

The transformations in the active deposit of actinium. (E. Marsden). *Phil. Mag.*, VI. **27.** 690–703.

J. N. Pring

1906

Direct union of carbon and hydrogen at high temperatures. (R. S. Hutton). *J. Chem. Soc.*, **89.** 1591–1601.

1910

Direct union of carbon and hydrogen at high temperatures. II. *J. Chem. Soc.*, **97.** 498–511.

1911

Syntheses of hydrocarbons at high temperatures. (D. M. Fairlie). *J. Chem. Soc.*, **99.** 1796–1811.

1912

Influence of physical condition of the metals on kathode over voltage. (J. R. Curzon). *Trans. Faraday Soc.*, **7.** 237–243, 243–244.

The ionization produced by carbon at high temperatures. (A. Parker). *Phil. Mag.*, VI. **23.** 192–200.

The methane equilibrium. (D. M. Fairlie). *J. Chem. Soc.*, **101.** 91–103.

1913

The origin of thermal ionization from carbon. *Proc. Roy. Soc.*, A. **89.** 344–360.

Some factors determining the kathode over voltage. *Zeit. Elektrochem.*, **19.** 255–262.

1914

The occurrence of ozone in the upper atmosphere. *Proc. Roy. Soc.*, A. **90.** 204–219.

1916

The reduction of metallic oxides with hydrogen at high pressures. (E. Newberry) *Proc. Roy. Soc.*, A. **92.** 276–285.

L. von Putnoky

1913

The diffusion of uranium. (G. von Hevesy). *Phil. Mag.*, VI. **25.** 415–418.

The diffusion of uranium. (G. von Hevesy). *Phys. Zeit.*, **14.** 63–65.

S. Ratner

1916

Mobility of the negative ion. *Phil. Mag.*, VI. **32.** 441–461.

1917

The distribution of the active deposit of radium in an electric field. *Phil. Mag.*, VI. **33.** 429–448.

1918

On some properties of the active deposit of radium. *Phil. Mag.*, VI. **36.** 397–405.

W. F. Rawlinson

1914

A note on the X-ray spectrum of nickel. *Phil. Mag.*, VI. **28.** 274–277.

The magnetic spectrum of the beta rays excited in metals by soft X-rays. (H. Robinson). *Phil. Mag.*, VI. **28.** 277–281.

Spectrum of the beta rays excited by gamma rays. (E. Rutherford and H. Robinson). *Phil. Mag.*, VI. **28.** 281–286.

1915

The decrease in velocity of beta particles in passing through matter. *Phil. Mag.*, VI. **30.** 627–632.

H. Richardson

1913

The retardation of alpha particles by metals. (E. Marsden). *Phil. Mag.*, VI. **25.** 184–193.

The analysis of the gamma rays from radium B and radium C. (E. Rutherford). *Phil. Mag.*, VI. **25.** 722–734.

Analysis of the gamma rays from radium D and radium E. (E. Rutherford). *Phil. Mag.*, VI. **26.** 324–332.

Analysis of the gamma rays of the thorium and actinium products. (E. Rutherford). *Phil. Mag.*, VI. **26.** 937–948.

1914

Analysis of the gamma rays from the uranium products. *Phil. Mag.*, VI. **27.** 252–256.

The excitation of gamma rays by beta rays. *Proc. Roy. Soc.*, A. **90.** 521–531.

The absorption in lead of the gamma rays emitted by radium B and radium C. *Proc. Roy. Soc.*, A. **91.** 396–404.

1915

Maximum frequency of the X-rays from a Coolidge tube for different voltages. (E. Rutherford and J. Barnes). *Phil. Mag.*, VI. **30.** 339–360.

H. Robinson

1911

The electrical state of the upper atmosphere. (W. Makower, A. J. Makower, W. M. Gregory). *Quart. J. R. met. Soc.*, **37.** 341–349.

The electrical state of the upper atmosphere. (W. Makower, A. J. Makower, W. M. Gregory). *Electrician*, **67.** 742–743.

1912

Wärme-Entwicklung durch Radium und Radiumemanation. (E. Rutherford). *K. Akad. Wiss., Vienna, Sitzungsberichte*, **121.** 2a. 1491–1516.

1913

Heating effect of radium and its emanation. (E. Rutherford). *Phil. Mag.*, VI. **30.** 312–330.

Über die Masse und die Geschwindigkeiten der von den radioaktiven Substanzen ausgesendeten Alpha Teilchen. (E. Rutherford). *K. Akad. Wiss., Vienna, Sitzungsberichte*, **122.** 2a. 1855–1884.

The analysis of the beta rays from radium B and radium C. (E. Rutherford). *Phil. Mag.*, VI. **26.** 717–729.

1914

The magnetic spectrum of the beta rays excited in metals by soft X-rays. (W. F. Rawlinson). *Phil. Mag.*, VI. **28.** 277–281.

Spectrum of the beta rays excited by gamma rays. (E. Rutherford, W. F. Rawlinson). *Phil. Mag.*, VI. **28.** 281–286.

The number of ions produced by the beta and gamma radiations from radium. (H. G. J. Moseley). *Phil. Mag.*, VI. **28.** 327–337.

The mass and velocities of the alpha particle from radioactive substances. (E. Rutherford). *Phil. Mag.*, VI. **28.** 552–572.

R. Rossi

1908

Emission spectrum of silver heated in a carbon tube furnace in air. (W. G. Duffield). *Astrophys. Journ.*, **28.** 371–378.

1909

The effect of pressure on the band spectra of the fluorides of the metals of the alkaline earths. *Proc. Roy. Soc.*, A. **82.** 518–523.

The effect of pressure upon arc spectra—titanium. *Proc. Roy. Soc.*, A. **83.** 414–420.

1911

On the pressure displacement of spectral lines. *Phil. Mag.*, VI. **21.** 499–501.

On a relation between the atomic volumes and the spectra of elements. *Phil. Mag.*, VI. **22.** 922–925.

Arc spectrum of vanadium under pressure. *Astrophys. Journ.*, **34.** 21–25.

Widening of hydrogen lines by high pressure. *Astrophys. Journ.*, **34.** 299.

1912

An investigation of the spectrum of ionium. (A. S. Russell). *Proc. Roy. Soc.*, A. **87.** 478–484.

Pole lines in arc spectrum. *Astrophys. Journ.*, **35.** 279–285.

1913

Series of lines in the spectrum of neon. *Phil. Mag.*, VI. **26.** 981–984.

T. Royds

1908

Spectrum of the radium emanation. (E. Rutherford). *Nature*, **78.** 220–221.

Spectrum of the radium emanation. (E. Rutherford). *Phil. Mag.*, VI. **16.** 313–317.

Spectra de l'emanation du radium. (E. Rutherford). *Radium, Paris,* **5.** 200–201.

The action of the radium emanation upon water. (E. Rutherford). *Phil. Mag.*, VI. **16.** 812–818.

Nature of the alpha particle. (E. Rutherford). *Manchester Lit. and Phil. Soc., Mem,.* **53.** 1. 1–3.

The constitution of the electric spark. *Roy. Soc. Phil. Trans.*, A. **208.** 333–347.

1909

Nature of the alpha particle. (E. Rutherford). *Chem. News,* **99.** 49.

The nature of the alpha particle from radioactive substances. (E. Rutherford). *Phil. Mag.*, VI. **17.** 281–286.

Nature des particules et des substances radioactives. (E. Rutherford). *Radium, Paris,* **6.** 47–50.

The nature of the alpha particle from radioactive substances. (E. Rutherford). *Jahrb. Radioakt.*, **6.** 1–7.

The grating spectrum of radium emanation. *Phil. Mag.*, VI, **17.** 202–204.

A comparison of the radium emanation spectra by different observers. *Proc. Roy. Soc.*, A. **82.** 22–25.

Further experiments on the constitution of the electric spark. *Phil. Mag.*, VI. **19.** 285–290.

S. Russ

1908

The distribution in electric fields of the active deposits of radium, thorium and actinium. *Phil. Mag.*, VI. **15.** 601–614.

On the electrical charge of the active deposit of actinium. *Phil. Mag.*, VI. **15.** 737–745.

Decay of radium A and radium C at high temperatures. (W. Makower). *Phys. Zeit.*, **9.** 250–251.

1909

The diffusion of actinium and thorium emanations. *Phil. Mag.*, VI. **17.** 412–422.

The expulsion of radioactive matter in the radium transformations. (W. Makower). *Proc. Roy. Soc.*, A. **82.** 205–224.

Radiation of the active deposit from radium. (W. Makower). *Nature,* **79.** 340.

1910

Radioactive recoil. *Manchester Lit. and Phil. Soc. Mem.*, **54.** 2. 1–12.

The recoil of radium C from radium B. (W. Makower). *Phil. Mag.*, VI. **19.** 100–115.

The recoil of radium B from radium A. (W. Makower). *Nature*, **83.** 460.

The deflection by an electrostatic field of radium B on recoil from radium A. (W. Makower). *Phil. Mag.*, VI. **20.** 875–882.

1911

Scattering during radioactive recoil. (W. Makower). *Manchester Lit. and Phil. Soc. Mem.*, **55.** 2. 1–4.

1913

Some experiments to detect β-rays from radium A. (W. Makower). *Phys. Soc. Proc.*, **25.** 253–255, 255.

A. S. Russell

1911

The effect of temperature upon radioactive disintegration. *Proc. Roy. Soc.*, A. **86.** 240–253.

1912

The volatility of radium C. *Phil. Mag.*, VI. **24.** 134–137.

Measurements of specific heats at low temperatures. *Phys. Zeit.*, **13.** 59–64.

Radium content of uranium minerals. (W. Marckwald). *Jahrb. Radioakt.*, **8.** 457–470.

An investigation of the spectrum of ionium. (R. Rossi). *Proc. Roy. Soc.*, A. **87.** 478–484.

1913

The penetrating power of the gamma rays from radium C. *Proc. Roy. Soc.*, A. **88.** 75–82.

The excitation of gamma rays by the alpha rays of ionium and radiothorium. (J. Chadwick). *Proc. Roy. Soc.*, A. **88.** 217–229.

Period system and the radio elements. *Chem. News*, **107.** 49–52.

1914

The gamma rays of polonium, radium and radioactinium. (J. Chadwick). *Phil. Mag.*, VI. **27.** 112–125.

R. R. SAHNI

1915

The photographic action of alpha, beta and gamma rays. *Phil. Mag.*, VI. **29.** 836–841.

1917

The scattering of alpha particles by gases. *Phil. Mag.*, VI. **33.** 290–295.

H. SCHRADER

1912

On the existence of chemical compounds of short lived radioactive elements. *Phil. Mag.*, VI. **24.** 125–134.

R. E. SLADE

1912

The potential of tantalum. (G. von Hevesy) *Zeit. Elektrochem.*, **18.** 1001–1002.

H. STANSFIELD

1908

The echelon spectroscope. *Nature*, **77.** 198, 222.
The mercury green line. *Nature*, **78.** 8.

1909

The echelon spectroscope, its secondary action and the structure of the green mercury line. *Phil. Mag.*, VI. **18.** 371–396.

1912

Changes in diffraction spectra produced by aberration and the aberration of an echelon grating. (H. P. Walmsley). *Phil. Mag.*, VI. **23.** 25–35.

Miss Jadwiga Szmidt

1914

On the distribution of energy in the different types of gamma rays emitted from certain radioactive substances. *Phil. Mag.*, VI. **28.** 527–539.

1915

Note on the excitation of gamma rays by beta rays. *Phil. Mag.*, VI. **30.** 220–224.

T. S. Taylor

1912

Number of ions produced by an alpha particle from polonium. *Phil. Mag.*, VI. **23.** 670–676.

Ionization curve for alpha rays from polonium in mercury vapour. *Phil. Mag.*, VI. **24.** 296–301.

1913

The range and ionization of the alpha particle in simple gases. *Phil. Mag.*, VI. **26.** 402–410.

The decrease in velocity of alpha particles in passing through matter. (E. Marsden). *Proc. Roy. Soc.*, A. **88.** 443–454.

N. Tunstall

1915

The velocity of the alpha particle from radium A. (W. Makower). *Phil. Mag.*, VI. **29.** 259–260.

Y. Tuomikowski

1909

Differences in the decay of radium emanation. (E. Rutherford). *Manchester Lit. and Phil. Soc. Mem.*, **53.** 12. 1–2.

Absorption of gamma rays from radium by lead. *Phys. Zeit.*, **10.** 372–374.

R. W. VARDER

1914

The transformations of actinium C. (E. Marsden). *Phil. Mag.*, VI. **28.** 818–821.

1915

The absorption of homogeneous beta rays. *Phil. Mag.*, VI. **29.** 725–733.

H. P. WALMSLEY

1912

Changes in diffraction spectra produced by aberration and the aberration of an echelon grating. (H. Stansfield). *Phil. Mag.*, VI. **23.** 25–35.

1913

The distribution of the active deposit of actinium in electric fields. *Phil. Mag.*, VI. **26.** 381–401.

1914

The distribution of the active deposit of radium in electric fields. *Phil. Mag.*, VI. **28.** 539–552.

The passage of alpha particles through photographic films. *Proc. Phys. Soc.*, **26.** 261–263. (W. Makower).

1915

The magnetic deflection of the recoil stream from radium A. (W. Makower). *Phil. Mag.*, VI. **29.** 253–258.

MISS MARGARET WHITE

1909

The electrical state of the upper atmosphere. (W. Makower, E. Marsden). *K. Akad. Wiss., Vienna, Sitzungsberichte*, **118.** 2a. 629–701.

R. H. WILSON

1913

Some experiments with the active deposit of thorium. (E. Marsden). *Phil. Mag.*, VI. **26.** 354–361.

Branch products in actinium C. (E. Marsden). *Nature*, **92.** 29.

W. Wilson

1907

Note on the rate of decay of the active deposit from radium. (W. Makower). *Phil. Mag.*, VI. **14.** 404–408. Phys. Soc., May 24th, 1907.

Photoelectric effect and conductivity. *Ann. Physik.*, **23.** 1. 107–130.

1909

On the absorption of homogeneous beta rays by matter and on the variations of the absorption of the rays with velocity. *Proc. Roy. Soc.*, A. **82.** 612–628.

The effect of pressure on the natural ionization in a closed vessel, and on the ionization produced by the gamma rays. *Phil. Mag.*, VI. **17.** 321–325.

1910

On the reflection of homogeneous beta particles of different velocities. (A. F. Kovarik). *Phil. Mag.*, VI, **20.** 866–870.

The heterogeneity of the beta particles from a thick layer of radium E. (J. A. Gray). *Phil. Mag.*, VI. **20.** 870–875.

The decrease of velocity of the beta particles on passing through matter. *Proc. Roy. Soc.*, A. **84.** 141–150.

1911

The variation of ionization with velocity for the beta particles. *Proc. Roy. Soc.*, A. **85.** 240–248.

The effect of temperature on the absorption coefficient of iron for gamma rays. *Phil. Mag.*, VI. **21.** 532–534.

The discharge of positive electricity from hot bodies. *Phil. Mag.*, VI. **21.** 634–640.

A. B. Wood

1913

The range of the recoil atoms from thorium C and actinium C. *Phil. Mag.*, VI. **26.** 1–55.

A method for the determination of the molecular weights of the radioactive emanation with an application to actinium emanation. (E. Marsden). *Phil. Mag.*, VI. **26.** 948–952.

1914

Volatilization of extremely thin radioactive deposits. *Proc. Roy. Soc.*, A. **91**, 543–560.
Volatility of thorium D. *Phil. Mag.*, VI. **28.** 808–818.
Volatility of thorium active deposit. *Proc. Phys. Soc.*, **26.** 248–260.

1915

The recoil of radium D from radium C. (W. Makower). *Phil. Mag.*, VI. **30.** 811–815.
Velocities of the alpha particles from thorium active deposit. *Phil. Mag.*, VI. **30.** 702–710.
Photographic effect of recoil atoms. (A. T. Stevens). *Proc. Phys. Soc.*, **27.** 189–192.

1916

Long range alpha particles from thorium. (E. Rutherford). *Phil. Mag.*, VI. **31.** 379–386.

Postscript

In 1919 Rutherford was appointed Cavendish Professor of Experimental Physics in the University of Cambridge. The following light-hearted song, written shortly after Rutherford's arrival in Cambridge, formed part of the 'Post-Prandial Proceedings of the Cavendish Society'. It provides a suitable postscript to this volume.

AN ALPHA RAY

Air 'A Jovial Monk'

1. An alpha ray was I, contented with my lot;
From Radium C I was set free
And outwards I was shot.
My speed I quickly reckoned,
As I flew through space,
Ten thousand miles per second
Is not a trifling pace!
For an alpha ray
Goes a good long way
In a short time t,
As you easily see;
Though I don't know why
My speed's so high,
Or why I bear a charge $2e$.

2. And in my wild career, as swiftly on I flew,
A rarefied gas wouldn't let me pass,
But I pushed my way right through.
I had some lively tussles
To make it ionize,
But I set the small corpuscles
A-buzzing round like flies.

For an alpha ray
Hasn't time to stay
While a trifling mass
Of expanded gas,
That stands in awe,
Of Maxwell's law,
Obstructs the road when I want to pass.

3. An electroscope looked on, as I made that gas conduct;
Beneath the field the gas did yield
And the leaf was greatly 'bucked'.
But in my exultation
I lost my senses clean,
And I made a scintillation
As I struck a zinc blende screen
For an alpha ray
Makes a weird display
With fluorescence green
On a zinc blende screen,
When the room's quite dark,
You see a spark
That marks the spot where I have been.

4. But now I've settled down, and move about quite slow;
For I alas, am helium gas
Since I got that dreadful blow.
But though I'm feeling sickly
Still no one now denies,
That I ran that race so quickly,
I've won a Nobel Prize.
For an alpha ray
Is a thing to pay
And a Nobel Prize,
One cannot despise,
And Rutherford
Has greatly scored,
As all the world now recognize.

A. A. Robb.

This book was composed in 11 on 12 point
'Monotype' Baskerville by Adlard and Son Ltd
and printed by them at The Bartholomew Press
Dorking, Surrey, on white wove paper made by
C. Townsend, Hook and Company Ltd.
Facsimile figures in original papers
by Reproduction Drawings Ltd
Line and half-tone blocks by
the Century Engraving Co.
The book was bound by
Newdigate Press Ltd.